COMPUTER TECHNOLOGY

COMPUTER TECHNOLOGY

O.R. Lawrence
Electronics and Computer Technology
Instructor
West Ferris Secondary School
North Bay, Ontario

McGraw-Hill Ryerson Limited
Toronto   Montreal   New York   Auckland
Bogotá   Cairo   Guatemala   Hamburg
Johannesburg   Lisbon   London   Madrid
Mexico   New Delhi   Panama   Paris   San Juan
São Paulo   Singapore   Sydney   Tokyo

Computer Technology

ISBN 0-07-548711-X

2 3 4 5 6 7 8 9 10 THB 3 2 1 0 9 8 7 6 5 4

Printed and bound in Canada

Canadian Cataloguing in Publication Data

Lawrence, O.R. (Orville Robert), date
Computer technology

For use in schools.
Includes index.
ISBN 0-07-548711-X

1. Computers – Circuits.   2. Logic circuits.
I. Title

TK7888.4.L38 1984   621.3819'535
C84-098227-5

In memory of my parents,
Louisa and Nelson Lawrence.

Dedicated to Steven and Kevin

CONTENTS

PREFACE

No branch of science has changed as rapidly as electronics. Since the invention of the transistor in 1948 there has been steady development in the field. First, the transistor replaced the vacuum tube; then the integrated circuit replaced groups of transistors; now, the microprocessor has to a large extent replaced single-function integrated circuits.

This rapid change, which is still going on, has put heavy demands on both teachers and students. Never before has there been an area of study that experienced this kind of revolution. At the same time, the new technology has brought with it tremendous opportunities, providing students with exciting career possibilities. Also, it allows teachers to present interesting and up-to-date courses in an expanding field.

This text is designed to make the study of computer technology as interesting and practical as possible. An effort has been made to make clear the relevance of the material in each chapter to actual computer systems. Block diagrams at the beginning of each chapter present an overview of the basic sections of a computer. The particular sections of the system discussed in the chapters are shown in colour. Thus the reader can quickly see the way various circuits work together to perform logical functions.

Outlines for over 50 experiments are included in the book. These experiments call for components that are readily available and encourage hands-on experience with basic logic circuits. Appendix A gives pinout assignments and data sheets for all the chips used in the Experiments. These provide all the basic information required to properly use ICs.

I am indebted to many of my recent students who have helped classroom-test both the experiments and the text. As usual, they have been open and honest critics.

I wish also to thank Gilles Gaudet of École Secondaire Algonquin for reviewing some of the material and for his advice and encouragement.

I am pleased as well to acknowledge the help and cooperation extended to me by McGraw-Hill Ryerson sponsoring editor Don Lipsett. His skill and patience have helped to create a clearer text.

I especially wish to thank my wife Barbara for her help in typing the original manuscript.

Orville Robert Lawrence
North Bay, Ontario 1983

INTRODUCTION

For hundreds of years machines have been used to do arithmetic and other tasks. In 1621 William Oughtred developed a calculating device called the slide rule. He based his design on Napier's logarithms, which had been published about six years previously. Then in 1642, Blaise Pascal, at the age of 19, invented an adding machine. His basic design was so practical that it was used in electromechanical calculators until they were made obsolete in recent years by electronic calculators.

Between 1671 and 1691, Gottfried Wilhelm von Leibnitz improved on Pascal's adding machine and finally produced one that would extract roots as well as do all four basic arithmetic functions.

In 1725, a Frenchman named Basile Bouchon developed a method of controlling the needles in weaving machines by means of punched paper tape. About 75 years later, another Frenchman, Joseph Marie Jacquard, used binary-coded cards for controlling looms.

In 1833, Charles Babbage used Jacquard's binary card system to develop the first real computer. (He called it an "analytical engine.") His machine was never perfected, but it served as a model for further developments.

Twenty-one years after Babbage invented his binary calculator, George Boole developed a logic presented in mathematical form. His work formed the foundation for the logical method and shorthand called Boolean algebra.

In 1938, Claude Shannon used Boolean algebra to express electrical-circuit conditions. His theories and methods were used by designers at the University of Pennsylvania to construct ENIAC, the first electronic computer. ENIAC was put into service in 1945. This huge, power-hungry machine, which had over 19-000 vacuum tubes and could do more than 5000 additions per second, was a tremendous

step forward from Babbage's primitive design.

Nevertheless, the invention of the transistor in 1948 made the tubes, relays, and high power consumption of ENIAC obsolete. The second-generation computers of the 1950s were smaller and more reliable.

Medium-scale integration (MSI) techniques were developed in the early 1960s. In this period, Burroughs Corporation produced a computer that could execute 200 million instructions per second.

Besides having tremendous speed, modern computers can store huge amounts of data. And new designs are making greater speed and larger storage available in smaller and smaller devices.

The microtechnology of the 1970s and 1980s has made chip designs possible whereby tens of thousands of transistors can be placed in an

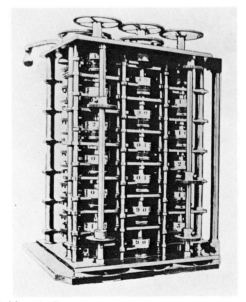

Babbage's Computer
Courtesy of IBM

xi

area less than four millimetres square. This scale of fabrication has made it possible to integrate on one chip all the components necessary for a computer. Such a chip is called a microprocessor.

Microprocessor
Courtesy of IBM

COMPUTER TECHNOLOGY

CHAPTER 1
Binary Numbers

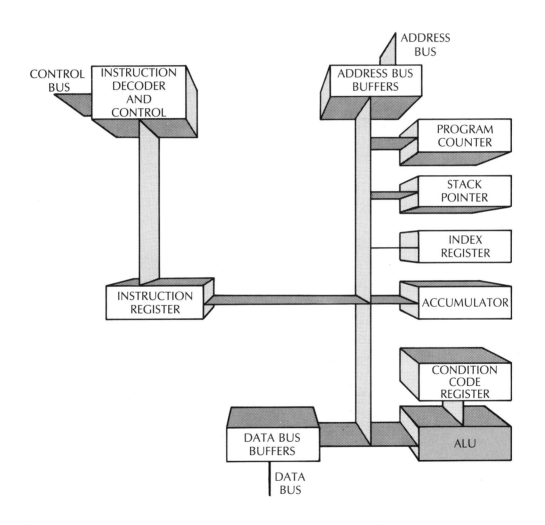

■ INTRODUCTION ■

In this chapter we will study the *binary number system*. All digital computer circuits use binary numbers in some form. It is important to master this system if we are to understand how the circuits function.

The binary number system is much simpler than our familiar decimal system. In the latter, ten digits are used, zero through nine; in the former, only two digits are used, *zero* and *one*. Electronic circuits can easily and accurately deal with this two-digit number system.

The four basic arithmetic operations — addition, subtraction, multiplication, and division — can be reduced to two: addition and subtraction. Multiplication can be thought of as repeated addition and division as repeated subtraction. This fact makes it possible to handle these operations by means of rather simple electronic circuits. And when binary numbers are used, "electronic arithmetic" is easily performed.

1.1 The Binary Number System

In transposing a number from the familiar decimal system into the binary system, one must keep in mind two things which have important meaning in numbers: the position of each digit, and the placement of the zero. For example, recall that in the decimal system the number 105 is arranged this way:

Hundreds	Tens	Units
1	0	5

Thus, in 105 and 500 the digit 5 has different meanings. In the first it stands for 5 units; in the second it stands for 5 hundreds. The value of a digit is affected by its position, each position standing for a different power of ten. That is why the decimal system is often called the *base ten system*:

	Hundreds	Tens	Units
Digit	1	0	5
Meaning	1×10^2	0×10^1	5×10^0
Value	100	00	5

The numbers 10^2, 10^1, 10^0 represent the numbers by which the digits are multiplied — their *place value*.

The binary system is organized in exactly this way, except that place value depends on the powers of *two*. Thus, it is also referred to as the *base two system*. The binary progression is as follows:

$$\cdots \quad 2^5 \quad 2^4 \quad 2^3 \quad 2^2 \quad 2^1 \quad 2^0$$
$$\cdots \quad 32 \quad 16 \quad 8 \quad 4 \quad 2 \quad 1$$

In this system, for example, the number 10110 has the value 22 in decimal. The binary number 10110 stands for:

$$
\begin{aligned}
1 \times 16 &= 16 \\
0 \times 8 &= 0 \\
1 \times 4 &= 4 \\
1 \times 2 &= 2 \\
0 \times 1 &= \underline{0} \\
&\ 22
\end{aligned}
$$

Similarly binary 111101 = 61 as follows:

$$
\begin{aligned}
1 \times 32 &= 32 \\
1 \times 16 &= 16 \\
1 \times 8 &= 8 \\
1 \times 4 &= 4 \\
0 \times 2 &= 0 \\
1 \times 1 &= \underline{1} \\
&\ 61
\end{aligned}
$$

We will deal with binary numbers in more detail later in this chapter, where we learn how to handle fractional values and basic arithmetic operations in binary. At this point it is important merely to see that there are just two digits to be concerned with in the binary number system and that any number can be expressed using zeros and ones. This aspect of binary numbers makes them ideally suited for computer circuits.

Here we should also note that number systems can be based on many other numbers than two and ten. For example, in the next chapter we will look at systems based on eight and on sixteen. When there is a possibility of ambiguity, the number system of a set of digits is often indicated by a subscript:

10110_{10} is a number in the base ten system and means "ten thousand, one hundred ten"

10110_2 is a number in the base two system and means (converted to base ten) "twenty-two"

256_8 is a number in the base eight system (see Chapter 2)

$3E9B_{16}$ is a number in the base sixteen system (see Chapter 2)

The base of a system is also called its *radix*.

1.2   Why Binary?

In the basic components of electronic circuits only two conditions are possible: in a conductor, current can be flowing or not flowing; a lamp can be lit or not lit; a transistor can conduct or be cut off; a capacitor can be charged or neutral. These characteristics make the binary system a "natural" for computers. For example, a conducting transistor or a charged capacitor can be used to represent a binary one digit, and the opposite state can represent a binary zero; a closed switch or the presence of a voltage can be used to represent a binary one digit, and the opposite state can represent a binary zero.

Computers are arranged to respond to these circuit and component states and produce conditions that can stand for numbers. The conditions might simply be the "on" state of the number-shaped lights of a pocket calculator.

Figure 1.1 illustrates how a simple circuit could be used to display binary numbers by means of a row of lamps (on = 1, off = 0). If S_3 is closed, binary 001 is displayed; if both S_2 and S_3 are closed, binary 011 is displayed. This simple circuit can be used to represent the numbers from zero to seven in binary. (Decimal 7 = binary 111.)

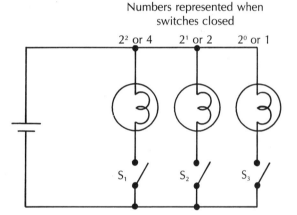

Figure 1.1 Binary Lamp Display

1.3   Binary Number Fractions

In the base ten (decimal) system, a place value of 10^{-1} tells us to divide the digit by ten once; a place value of 10^{-2} tells us to divide the digit by ten twice (or simply to divide by 100).

Example 1

In the decimal number 0.83, the "8" means:

$$8 \times 10^{-1} = \frac{8}{10} = 0.8$$

and the "3" means:

$$3 \times 10^{-2} = \frac{3}{100} = 0.03$$

This procedure can be applied to the binary system. Thus, $2^{-1} = {}^1/_2$ or 0.5 and $2^{-2} = {}^1/_4$ or 0.25. The table below shows a partial list of values for positive and negative powers of two.

2^6	64
2^5	32
2^4	16
2^3	8
2^2	4
2^1	2
2^0	1

2^{-1}	0.5
2^{-2}	0.25
2^{-3}	0.125
2^{-4}	0.062 5
2^{-5}	0.031 25
2^{-6}	0.015 625

Conversion

The binary values given in the table allow us to convert easily from binary to decimal or vice versa for values equal to or greater than one. But for fractional values conversion can become a tedious process, so two simplifying methods will be given in the next sections.

It should be noted that some fractional conversions are straightforward. The decimal number 0.75, for example, is equal to 0.5 + 0.25 or $2^{-1} + 2^{-2}$ and so would be represented in binary as 0.11. Decimal 14.25 would be represented by binary 1110.01. Going the other way, the binary number 0.0011 would be represented in decimal as 0.1875. To see this, first break the binary number down into its components:

Binary Digit	0 .	0	0	1	1
Place Value	2^0	2^{-1}	2^{-2}	2^{-3}	2^{-4}

Decimal Equivalent	1	0.5	0.25	0.125	0.0625

Then calculate the values of the digits and add these values:

$$
\begin{aligned}
0 \times 1 &= 0 \\
0 \times 0.5 &= 0 \\
0 \times 0.25 &= 0 \\
1 \times 0.125 &= 0.125 \\
1 \times 0.0625 &= \underline{0.0625} \\
&\ 0.1875
\end{aligned}
$$

The two methods for less straightforward conversions follow.

Base Ten to Base Two

To convert a decimal fraction to binary, first multiply the fraction by two. If the product has an integer part, the first significant binary fractional digit is 1; otherwise, it is 0. We next multiply the *fractional* part of the first product by two to obtain the next significant digit; and so on until the fractional part of the product is zero or until we have reached a suitable accuracy.

Example 2

0.8125 = 0.1101 is obtained as follows:

$$
\begin{aligned}
0.8125 \times 2 &= 1.6250 \quad \text{Most sig. digit} \\
0.6250 \times 2 &= 1.2500 \\
0.2500 \times 2 &= 0.5000 \\
0.5000 \times 2 &= 1.0000 \quad \text{Least sig. digit}
\end{aligned}
$$

Example 3

0.7893 = 0.1100101 (approx.) is obtained as follows:

$$
\begin{aligned}
0.7893 \times 2 &= 1.5786 \quad \text{Most sig. digit} \\
0.5786 \times 2 &= 1.1572 \\
0.1572 \times 2 &= 0.3144 \\
0.3144 \times 2 &= 0.6288 \\
0.6288 \times 2 &= 1.2576 \\
0.2576 \times 2 &= 0.5152
\end{aligned}
$$

$0.5152 \times 2 = \overset{\frown}{1}.0304$ Least sig. digit

Etc. to desired accuracy

Base Two to Base Ten

When converting binary fractions to decimal form, repeated division is used.

The rightmost or least significant digit (LSD) of the binary number is divided by two and added to the next least significant digit. The result is then itself divided by two and added to the next digit, and this result is treated in the same way; the process is continued until the zero ahead of the binary point is involved in the result. This last result is the desired decimal form of the binary fraction.

Example 4

Binary point

↓

$0.010\overset{/}{1} = 0.3125$ is obtained as follows:

LSD ↘

$\dfrac{1}{2} + 0 = 0.5$

$\dfrac{0.5}{2} + 1 = 1.25$

$\dfrac{1.25}{2} + 0 = 0.625$

$\dfrac{0.625}{2} + 0 = 0.3125$ Zero ahead of the binary point

1.4   Binary Operations

Addition

The rules for binary addition are basically the same as those for decimal addition. When the sum of corresponding digits exceeds one, the column must start again at zero, and a carry of one is taken to the next higher column. The rules for adding columns are as follows:

Addition Rules

Digits Added	Sum	Carry
0 + 0 =	0	0
0 + 1 =	1	0
1 + 0 =	1	0
1 + 1 =	0	1

Example 5

```
 1111      Check    15
+ 111             +  7
10110              22
```

As usual, we start the addition with the least significant digit.

If the carries for the above addition are to be shown, it is written as follows:

```
   1111
+   111
   1111    Carries
  10110
```

Example 6

```
   11010.0010    Check    26.1250
+  110111.0001          + 55.0625
   11111   Carries       81.1875
 1010001.0011
```

Subtraction

Binary subtraction can be done in two basic ways. The first method is called *direct binary subtraction* or the *borrow method*; the second is called the *complement method*.

Borrow Method

This method is similar to subtraction in the decimal system. We borrow from the next higher column in order to subtract a higher number from a smaller number.

Example 7

```
  4 (1)3
  5    4 (1)2
- 2    5    3
  2    8    9
```

Here we borrow from the 4 to make the 2 a twelve and then borrow from the 5 to make the remaining 3 a thirteen. This leaves the 5 with a value of 4.

We are really subtracting $200 + 50 + 3$ from $500 + 40 + 2$. If we subtract in stages we get:

```
  500        40          2
- 200      - 50        - 3
  300      - 10        - 1
```

Adding the three differences gives 289. But this procedure involves negative values, while the borrow method eliminates them.

```
  4          (1)3
  500         40         (1)2
- 200       - 50        - 3
  200         80          9    = 289
```

The borrow method of binary subtraction involves the following rules:

Subtraction Rules

Digits Subtracted	Difference	Borrow
$0 - 0 =$	0	0
$1 - 1 =$	0	0
$1 - 0 =$	1	0
$0 - 1 =$	1	1

Here we borrow a one from the next higher column, just as we do in decimal.

Example 8

```
  101            5
- 010          - 2
  011            3
```

When we show the borrowing it becomes:

```
  0
  1 (1)0   1
- 0   1   0
  0   1   1
```

It is helpful to think of the binary result $10 - 1 = 1$ in terms of its decimal equivalent. We are really subtracting 1 from 2, since binary $10 = 2$.

Example 9

```
  1001           9
- 0110         - 6
  0011           3
```

In this example there is no 1 in the next higher column. Therefore, borrowing must be done twice just as in decimal subtraction. When the necessary borrowing is shown the minuend is altered.

```
  1001    Minuend before borrowing
- 0110    Subtrahend
  0011    Difference
```

```
  0   1 (1)0   1    Minuend after borrowing
- 0   1   1   0    Subtrahend
  0   0   1   1    Difference
```

Example 10

```
  10001          17
- 01110        - 14
  00011           3
```

The logic of this method of borrowing is the same as that which underlies borrowing in decimal subtraction.

Example 11

```
  1000    Minuend         8
- 0001                  - 1
  0111                    7
```

When we borrow we get:

```
  0   1   1 (1)0   Minuend
- 0   0   0   1
  0   1   1   1
```

Notice that the minuend after borrowing has the same value it had before borrowing. That is, $1000 = 8$ and $0\,1\,1\,{}^1 0 = 8$. The ${}^1 0$ in the 2^0 column has a value of 2 as a result of the borrow. In order to maintain the value of the number, the zeros in the 2^1 and 2^2 columns must be changed to ones as a result of the borrow from the 2^3 column.

Again, this is exactly the same reasoning that applies to borrowing in decimal subtraction. This is shown in the next example.

Example 12

Borrowing in Decimal Subtraction

$$
\begin{array}{r}
1000 \\
-\quad 5 \\
\hline
995
\end{array}
$$

In order to subtract 5 from the 10^0 column we must borrow to make the 0 a 10. We cannot borrow from the 10^1 or 10^2 column so we borrow from the 10^3 column. This reduces the 1000 by 10 making it 990. After borrowing, the minuend is, in effect, written as $990 + 10$. Therefore, its value is still 1000.

Complement Method

The complement method of binary subtraction is the one that best suits computer circuits. This is because it uses the processes of *complementation* and *addition*, and addition is the basic operation performed by such circuits. Multiplication is performed by repeated addition, and division is done by repeated subtraction, which, as we shall see, is done by a form of addition.

First, let us understand the meaning of a complement. *The arithmetic complement of a number is the difference between that number and the next higher power of the base used.*

Example 13

The complement of 8 in the base ten (decimal) system is 2:

$$8 = 8 \times 10^0$$
Next higher power $= 10^1 = 10$
$$10 - 8 = 2$$

Example 14

The complement of 85 is 15 (base ten):

$$85 = (8 \times 10^1) + (5 \times 10^0)$$
Next higher power $= 10^2 = 100$
$$100 - 85 = 15$$

In our common decimal system we can subtract conventionally or we can use the *ten's complement method*. Subtraction by the ten's complement method is done by *adding the complement of the subtrahend to the minuend, and then dropping the digit representing the higher power.*

Example 15

Conventional Method

$$
\begin{array}{rl}
850 & \text{Minuend} \\
-\ 225 & \text{Subtrahend} \\
\hline
625 & \text{Difference}
\end{array}
$$

Ten's Complement Method

$$
\begin{array}{rl}
1000 & \\
-\ 225 & \\
\hline
775 & \text{Complement of subtrahend} \\
850 & \text{Minuend} \\
+\ 775 & \\
\hline
1625 & \\
-\ 1000 & \text{Dropping digit of higher power} \\
\hline
625 & \text{Difference}
\end{array}
$$

To repeat: when we use the complement system to get the difference — 625 in this example — we do it by addition of the complement rather than by subtraction of the number itself.

Some might object to the complement method because, as shown in the example, we had to subtract twice. However, note that the second subtraction was performed merely by dropping the 1 in 1625. In binary, the first subtraction is also simple. When we apply binary to computers, we will see better the advantages of the complement method.

Before dealing with binary subtraction, let us look at a slight simplification of the ten's complement method. We can avoid the problem of borrowing if in calculating the complement we can arrange to subtract the subtrahend from a series of nines rather than zeros. The nine's complement thus obtained can be converted to the ten's complement by simply adding one. This is called the *nine's complement method*.

Example 16

Conventional Method

```
   850
 - 225
   625
```

Nine's Complement Method

First we take the nine's complement and add one to arrive at the ten's complement:

```
   999
 - 225
   774   Nine's complement of 225
 +   1
   775   Ten's complement of 225
```

Then we use the ten's complement as before to find the difference:

```
     850
 +   775
    1625
 -  1000
     625
```

When subtracting in binary by means of the complement method we use equivalents of the nine's and ten's complements. The equivalent of the nine's complement in binary is the *one's complement*; the equivalent of the ten's complement is the *two's complement*.

One's Complement

The one's complement of a binary number is obtained by changing all zeros to ones and all ones to zeros.

Example 17

```
110010   Binary number
001101   One's complement of number
```

Computers change binary numbers into their one's complements by means of simple inverter circuits, which will be examined in Chapter 4.

To subtract one binary number from another we add the one's complement of the subtrahend to the minuend. In each case, prior to complementation, zeros are added to the leftmost side of subtrahend until it contains the same number of digits as the minuend.

Example 18

Conventional Method

```
   1001              9
 - 0101            - 5
   0100              4
```

One's Complement Method

```
   1001   9, uncomplemented
 + 1010   One's complement of 5
  10011
   ↑
  Carry bit
```

```
   0011
 +    1   Carry bit
   0100
```

The binary 1 carry bit is known as an *end-around carry*, as it is brought down to the first column and added to the rest of the number. It indicates that the result of the calculation is positive.

In the case where there is no 1 carry bit, the result is negative and is in its one's complement form, as shown in the next example.

Example 19

```
  010                    2
−  101                 −  5
   ?                   −  3
```

```
  010
+ 010     One's complement of 5
  0100
  ↑
  Carry bit
```

The result in this example appears to be wrong, as it yields a value of 4 instead of − 3. However, when there is no binary one end-around carry the result given is the complement of the answer.

The complement of 100 is 011, which has a value of 3. Further, the absence of a binary one end-around carry tells us that the answer is negative. Thus we have the required result of − 3.

Two's Complement

The two's complement system of subtracting is used extensively in computers. It has the advantage that no end-around carry is required.

To change a binary number into its two's complement, first all the zeros are changed to ones and all the ones to zeros; then one is added to the result. (In other words, add one to the one's complement.) If there is a carry it is ignored.

Example 20

```
  1101     Binary number

  0010     One's complement
+    1
  0011     Two's complement
```

The next example shows how to subtract using the two's complement.

Example 21

Conventional Method

```
  101                     5
−  010     Subtrahend   −  2
  011                     3
```

Two's Complement Method

```
  101     One's compl. of subtrahend
+   1
  110     Two's compl. of subtrahend
```

```
  101     5, uncomplemented
+ 110     Two's compl. of subtrahend
  1011
  ↑
  Carry bit
```

After the carry bit is dropped we have our required answer of positive 3. The 1 carry bit tells us that the result is positive. If the answer had been negative it would have been accompanied by a 0 carry bit and would have been in its *two's complement form*.

Example 22

```
  010                    2
−  101                 −  5
   ?                   −  3
```

Convert 101 into its two's complement 011 (= 010 + 001) and add it to 010.

```
  010
+ 011
  0101
  ↑
  Carry bit
```

The 0 carry bit shows that the answer is negative and in its two's complement form. To convert the result into its equivalent decimal value, the two's complement procedure is reversed. In this case we subtract 1 from 101 and take the complement.

```
  101    Two's complement of 3
−   1
  100    One's complement of answer
```

The complement then is 011, thus the value of 3. It is known to be negative because of the 0 carry bit.

Another way to convert the binary number from its two's complement form to its true form is by complementing and adding one. This method avoids subtraction and is known as *recomplementation*.

Example 23

```
  101    Two's complement of 3

  010    Complement
+   1
  011    3, uncomplemented
```

Example 24

```
  0110            6
− 1000          − 8
    ?           − 2

  0110    6, uncomplemented
+ 1000    Two's complement of 8
 01110    Two's complement
 ↑
 Carry bit
```

(Note that the two's complement of 8 is coincidentally the same as binary 8.)

Reversing the procedure to find the true value:

```
  1110
−    1
  1101    One's compl. of ans. (unsigned)

  0010    Answer (unsigned)
  2       Answer, decimal form (unsigned)
```

Since the carry was zero, the result is − 2.

− 2 Answer

As noted, this reversing step can also be done by recomplementing.

Multiplication

It was mentioned earlier that multiplication is normally done in computers by a form of repeated addition. However, here we will briefly examine a method of binary multiplication similar to that used for hand calculation in the base ten system.

The method involves the following rules:

Multiplication Rules

Digits Multiplied	Product
0 × 0 =	0
0 × 1 =	0
1 × 0 =	0
1 × 1 =	1

Since these rules are identical to those of decimal multiplication, it is logical that the rest of the procedure is the same for binary.

Example 25

```
  1110            14
×  101          ×  5
    ?             70
```

Thus 1110 × 101 must equal 1000110.

```
    1110
×    101
    1110
   0000
  1110
 1000110
```

Division

Division can be thought of as a process of repeated subtraction and, like multiplication, can be done by computers with a form of adder circuit.

As we would expect, the same rules apply for division as for multiplication, since division is the inverse of multiplication. And the following example will indicate that binary division is done in exactly the same way as decimal division.

Example 26

$11101.1 \div 101$ $\qquad$ $29.5 \div 5 = 5.9$

```
        101.111...
101)11101.100...
    101
    0100
     000
    1001
     101
    1001
     101
    1000
     101
     011    Remainder
```

$101.111... = 5.875$

If we continue the division we will arrive at the exact answer, 5.9.

1.5 Signed Numbers

Computers must be able to distinguish between positive and negative numbers. This is accomplished by using a *sign bit*. The sign bit generally occupies the position of the leftmost or *most significant bit* (MSB).

To understand better the idea of "most significant" bits, we must note here that the number of bits a computer is able to store in its *register* or memory and deal with at a time is limited. Computers have built-in "word lengths," which are determined by computer design and cost, and affect the speed of the system. In any stored "word," the most significant bit occupies the leftmost position in the register, and the least significant bit the rightmost.

When a negative number is stored, the leftmost position is used for the sign bit. When the sign bit is a zero, the number stored is positive; if it is a one, the number stored is negative. Note that sign bits are not part of the numbers they are attached to.

N.B.: The sign bit is not to be confused with the *carry bit*. The carry bit occurs when two numbers are subtracted by the one's or the two's complement method; it is part of the mechanics of binary subtraction, whether done by humans or by computers. Besides indicating the sign of the answer it tells us its form. The sign bit, on the other hand, merely indicates for a computer whether a number is positive or negative, regardless of its form.

Example 27

Value: +6
Word length: 5 bits

Example 28

Value: −5
Word length: 5 bits

The binary numbers in these examples are presented in their true form; however, computers can store them in any one of several forms.

Example 29

Decimal Number Stored

−10

True Binary Form

```
1    1010
↑    ⌣⌣
Sign  Magnitude
```

One's Complement Form

1   0101

↑   ⌣
Sign Magnitude

Two's Complement Form

1   0110

↑   ⌣
Sign Magnitude

The computer generally handles negative numbers in their two's complement form, while positive numbers are represented in simple unsigned binary. *Thus, a negative number is represented in binary as the number you add to a positive number of the same magnitude to get zero.* For example, if we are restricted to "4-bit binary," positive 5 is 0101 and negative 5 is 1011. When we add them together we get 0000 (with a one carry, which does not appear because we are limited to four bits). This applies to all possible pairs of numbers in 4-bit binary.

4-Bit Binary Representation	Unsigned Value	Two's Complement Value
0000	0	0
0001	1	1
0010	2	2
0011	3	3
0100	4	4
0101	5	5
0110	6	6
0111	7	7
1000	8	−8
1001	9	−7
1010	10	−6
1011	11	−5
1100	12	−4
1101	13	−3
1110	14	−2
1111	15	−1

Regardless of the number of bits we are re-

stricted to, we can change the sign of such numbers by complementation.

Example 30

$+3 = 0011$

Two's Complement

$$\begin{array}{r} 1100 \\ + \quad 1 \\ \hline 1101 \end{array} = -3$$

Example 31

$-6 = 1010$

Two's Complement

$$\begin{array}{r} 0101 \\ + \quad 1 \\ \hline 0110 \end{array} = +6$$

Signed-Number Rules

The two's complement system makes signed-number arithmetic easy: the rules are the same as for decimal numbers.

1. Adding two positive numbers produces a positive sum; adding two negative numbers produces a negative sum.
2. To add numbers with different signs, find their difference and give it the sign of the larger number.
3. When subtracting, change the sign of the subtrahend and add it to the minuend, applying rules 1 and 2.

Remember: Sign bits are not part of the numbers. They are only used to indicate their signs.

The following examples illustrate the above rules. (Note that 5-bit words are used.)

Example 32

Addition of Two Positive Numbers

(+5)	00101	Uncomplemented
+ (+4)	+ 00100	Uncomplemented
(+9)	01001	Uncomplemented

These binary numbers are all stored in their true form as they are all positive.

Example 33

Addition of Two Negative Numbers

```
  (−5)          11011    Two's compl.
+ (−4)        + 11100    Two's compl.
  (−9)         10111    Two's compl.
                ↑
              Sign bit
```

10111 = negative 1001

The computer would hold or store the sum in its two's complement form, converting it only if it were called up for display.

Example 34

Addition of Numbers with Different Signs, I

```
  (−5)          11011    Two's compl.
+ (+4)        + 00100    Uncomplemented
  (−1)         11111    Two's compl.
                ↑
              Sign bit
```

11111 = negative 0001

Example 35

Addition of Numbers with Different Signs, II

```
  (+5)          00101    Uncomplemented
+ (−4)        + 11100    Two's compl.
  (+1)         00001    Uncomplemented
                ↑
              Sign bit
```

Example 36

Subtraction

```
  (+5)          00101    Uncomplemented
− (+4)        − 11100    Two's compl.
  (+1)         00001    Uncomplemented
                ↑
              Sign bit
```

Because we are subtracting the +4 we change its sign and add it to the +5. This means we take the two's complement of +4 and add it to +5.

Example 37

Subtraction of Two Positive Numbers

```
  (+4)          00100    Uncomplemented
− (+5)        − 11011    Two's compl.
  (−1)         11111    Two's compl.
                ↑
              Sign bit
```

11111 = negative 0001

Example 38

Subtraction of Negative Number from Positive

```
  (+4)          00100    Uncomplemented
− (−5)        − 00101    Uncomplemented
  (+9)         01001    Uncomplemented
                ↑
              Sign bit
```

Example 39

Subtraction of Positive Number from Negative

```
  (−5)          11011    Two's compl.
− (+4)        − 11100    Two's compl.
  (−9)         10111    Two's compl.
                ↑
              Sign bit
```

10111 = negative 1001

As we can see from the examples, computers can handle all the signed-number operations by addition: multiplication and division are performed by repeated addition and repeated subtraction — the repeated subtraction being done by two's complement addition.

Questions

1. Explain how binary numbers differ from decimal ·numbers.
2. What is meant by the *power* of a number?
3. Why is the binary system used in computers?
4. Express the following decimal numbers in binary: 35, 16, 84, 7, 3.25, 8.15
5. Express the following binary numbers in decimal: 110, 10100, 11.01, 10111.01, 1.001
6. Add, showing the carries.

1011	11110	10.101	0.011
+ 101	+ 1111	+ 1.001	+ 0.111

7. Subtract, using the borrow method.

1011	101	10011	10.01
− 111	− 011	− 01011	− 01.10

8. Subtract, using the two's complement method.

1011	1011	1010	0110
− 0101	− 0111	− 1011	− 1000

9. Define *number complement*.
10. What is the advantage of doing subtraction by complementation and addition?
11. How do computers identify positive and negative numbers?
12. How does a sign bit differ from a carry bit?
13. Write the following numbers in 4-bit binary.

    $+3, -3, +7, -7, -4, -9$

14. Add the following signed numbers in two's complement binary.

(-6)	(-7)
$+(+3)$	$+(-8)$

15. Subtract the following signed numbers in two's complement binary.

$(+7)$	$(+3)$	$(+4)$	(-5)
$-(+6)$	$-(+6)$	$-(-8)$	$-(+7)$

CHAPTER 2

Number Systems and Binary Coding

It was explained in Chapter 1 that computer circuits are binary devices — that is, their elements record only one of two conditions. This characteristic of electrical circuitry makes binary numbers a necessity; however, binary can be used in more than one way.

In doing calculations, for example, we may either convert the numbers entirely to binary or *take digits one by one and give their binary equivalents*. In the latter case we end up with a kind of mixture of number systems.

Suppose we are starting in the base ten system. We can then express the number 27 entirely in binary:

11011

or digit by digit in binary:

010 111

If we do this last, a space is inserted between the digits as shown. Notice that the above number is still basically in the base ten system and that we have merely *coded its digits in binary*.

Binary coding, of course, can be used for any number system, not only base ten. In fact, for many applications it is better to use some other number system. In this chapter we will look at two in common use, the octal (base 8) and the hexadecimal (base 16). We will also look at the ASCII code, which enables computers to recognize and handle letters, punctuation, special instructions, and mathematical symbols as well as numbers by assigning them *arbitrary* binary codes.

2.1 Octal Numbers

Our common decimal number system uses ten digits, 0 to 9. These are used in different combinations to represent all possible numbers. If these ten digits were to be converted to binary equivalents, four binary digits would be needed:

Decimal Digit	Binary Code
0	0000
1	0001
2	0010
3	0011
4	0100
5	0101
6	0110
7	0111
8	1000
9	1001

We can see that six combinations of 0 and 1 were not used: 1010, 1011, 1100, 1101, 1110, and 1111. Thus, these combinations are wasted in a system with a base of ten. However, with an eight-digit or *octal* number system, all possible combinations are used, and only three binary digits are needed.

Octal Digit	Binary Code
0	000
1	001
2	010
3	011
4	100
5	101
6	110
7	111

There are no wasted binary codes in this system. That is, all 3-bit binary combinations are used to represent the eight octal digits.

Each digit in an octal number corresponds to a power of 8. The following table for some positive and negative powers of eight will be found useful.

8^4	4096
8^3	512
8^2	64
8^1	8
8^0	1

8^{-1}	8^{-2}	8^{-3}	8^{-4}	8^{-5}
$\dfrac{1}{8}$	$\dfrac{1}{64}$	$\dfrac{1}{512}$	$\dfrac{1}{4096}$	$\dfrac{1}{32\,768}$

Of course, digital circuits use the binary number system, not octal; however, octal is a convenient way of recording values stored in binary registers. It is not our purpose to emphasize the octal number system, but in this chapter we will examine conversions and basic arithmetic operations.

Conversion

Octal to Decimal

In converting from octal to decimal, each digit is multiplied by its corresponding power of eight and the resulting products are added.

Example 1

Express the octal number 246 in decimal.

$$246_8 = (2 \times 8^2) + (4 \times 8^1) + (6 \times 8^0)$$
$$= 128 + 32 + 6$$
$$= 166_{10}$$

Example 2

$$1267.4_8 = (1 \times 8^3) + (2 \times 8^2) + (6 \times 8^1)$$
$$+ (7 \times 8^0) + (4 \times 8^{-1})$$
$$= 512 + 128 + 48 + 7 + 0.5$$
$$= 695.5_{10}$$

Decimal to Octal

Decimal-to-octal conversion of whole numbers can be done simply. Divide the decimal number by 8, noting the remainder; then divide the quotient by 8, again noting the remainder. Continue in this manner until the quotient is 0. The remainders in reverse order give the octal equivalent.

Example 3

Express the decimal number 252 in octal.

	Quotient	Remainder
$\frac{252}{8} =$	31	4
$\frac{31}{8} =$	3	7
$\frac{3}{8} =$	0	3

The octal number is 374. This can be checked by following the octal-to-decimal procedure:

$$374_8 = (3 \times 8^2) + (7 \times 8^1) + (4 \times 8^0)$$
$$= 192 + 56 + 4$$
$$= 252_{10}$$

To convert a decimal fraction to octal, divide the number by 1/8 (that is, multiply by 8) and note the whole-number part of the product. Then multiply the fractional part of the product by 8, again noting the whole-number part of the product. The noted numbers, taken in the order they were obtained, make up the octal number.

Example 4

Express the decimal number 0.19 in octal.

$$\frac{0.19}{1/8} = \begin{array}{l} 0.19 \times 8 = {}^1.52 \\ 0.52 \times 8 = {}^4.16 \\ 0.16 \times 8 = {}^1.28 \\ 0.28 \times 8 = {}^2.24 \\ 0.24 \times 8 = {}^1.92 \\ 0.92 \times 8 = {}^7.36 \\ 0.36 \times 8 = {}^2.88 \end{array}$$
Etc. to desired accuracy

The octal number is about 0.1412172. If more accuracy were desired we could continue the operation.

Again, we can check by converting back to decimal numbers, rounding off first if we wish. Rounding to four places, the octal number is 0.1412, and:

$$0.1412_8 = \left(1 \times \frac{1}{8^1}\right) + \left(4 \times \frac{1}{8^2}\right)$$
$$+ \left(1 \times \frac{1}{8^3}\right) + \left(2 \times \frac{1}{8^4}\right)$$
$$= \frac{1}{8} + \frac{4}{64} + \frac{1}{512} + \frac{2}{4096}$$
$$= 0.125 + 0.0625 + 0.001\,953$$
$$+ 0.000\,488$$
$$= 0.189\,941 \text{ or about } 0.19$$

Binary Coding

Any octal digit can easily be written in 3-digit binary form. This makes binary coding of octal numbers easy. For example, octal 23 in its binary-coded form is:

010 011

It should be remembered that this conversion is done on a digit-by-digit basis: a set of three binary digits is used to replace each of the octal digits. *The sets of three binary digits are not intended to be read as a continuous binary number.*

Example 5

| 607 | Octal number |
| 110 000 111 | Binary code |

Example 6

| 4.56 | Octal number |
| 100.101 110 | Binary code |

Converting in the opposite direction is similar. We simply group the binary digits in threes, working both ways from the binary point, and replace the groups with their octal-digit meanings.

Example 7

| 011.010 | Binary-coded octal |
| 3.2 | Octal number |

Important: Though, as we have said, binary-coded numbers are not read as continuous binary numbers, in the special case of binary-coded octals the meaning is the same whether they are grouped into octal or read continuously as binary. Therefore 011.010 (as coded octal) is the same as 11.01 (pure binary) and we can check the above conversion as follows:

Check

Binary $11.01 = 3.25_{10}$
Octal $3.2 = (3 \times 8^0) + (2 \times 8^{-1})$
$$= 3 + \left(2 \times \frac{1}{8}\right)$$
$$= 3 + 0.25$$
$$= 3.25_{10}$$

Operations

Octal Addition

The rules for octal addition are:

1. Add the columns; if the sum is equal to or greater than 8, the base is subtracted the number of times necessary to reduce the column result to a value less than 8.
2. The number of times the base is subtracted is indicated as a carry and is added to the next column before the next addition is done.
3. If the result of any column is less than 8 there is no subtraction and no carry.

Example 8

Add octal 35, 63.

1	1		Carries
	3	5	
+	6	3	
(1)	(10)	(8)	Decimal sum
	− 8	− 8	Subtracting base
1	2	0	Octal sum

Check

Octal 35 = decimal 29
Octal 63 = decimal 51
Octal 120 = decimal 80

Example 9

Add octal 13, 27, 52.

1	1		Carries
	1	3	
	2	7	
+	5	2	
(1)	(9)	(12)	Decimal sum
	− 8	− 8	Subtracting base
1	1	4	Octal sum

Check

Octal	13 =	decimal 11
	27 =	33
	52 =	42
	114 =	76

Octal Subtraction

Octal number subtraction, too, is similar to the decimal operation.

Example 10

Subtract octal 16 from octal 43.

```
    3
  4 (1)3   Minuend
− 1    6   Subtrahend
  2    5
```

In the first column it is necessary to borrow 1 from the 4, making it a 3. The 3 in the minuend becomes one-three, and the 6 in the subtrahend is subtracted from it. The difference is 5, since "13" in octal means eleven. The second column is handled the same way. Of course, the answer is in octal and must be converted to decimal.

Example 11

Subtract octal 1717 from octal 2172.

```
  1        6
  2 (1)1   7 (1)2
- 1   7    1    7
  _____
      2    5    3
```

Check

$$2172_8 = 1146_{10}$$
$$-1717_8 = -975_{10}$$
$$\overline{253_8} = \overline{171_{10}}$$

In addition and subtraction, as an alternative to the octal arithmetic, one may convert the octal digits to binary-coded octal, do the addition or subtraction in binary, and then convert back to octal.

Example 12

```
   47              100 111
+  36           +  011 110
  ____            _____
  105_8           1 000 101
```

$$1\,000\,101 = 105$$

Octal Multiplication

To multiply in the decimal number system a multiplication table is needed. The same is true of the octal number system.

Octal Multiplication Table

	0	1	2	3	4	5	6	7
0	0	0	0	0	0	0	0	0
1	0	1	2	3	4	5	6	7
2	0	2	4	6	10	12	14	16
3	0	3	6	11	14	17	22	25
4	0	4	10	14	20	24	30	34
5	0	5	12	17	24	31	36	43
6	0	6	14	22	30	36	44	52
7	0	7	16	25	34	43	52	61

Thus, $5 \times 6 = 36$ in octal, which of course means $(3 \times 8^1) + (6 \times 8^0) = 24 + 6 = 30_{10}$. The table is used the same way as in decimal;

any addition required in the process is done using the rules for octal addition.

Example 13

```
  177    Multiplicand
× 27     Multiplier
_____
 1371    Partial product
  376    Partial product
_____
 5351    Product
```

As in decimal we start with the rightmost digit of the multiplier:

$7 \times 7 = 61$		Carry 6
$7 \times 7 = 61$, and $61 + 6 = 67$		Carry 6
$7 \times 1 = 7$, and $7 + 6 = 15$		

Continuing with the next digit:

$2 \times 7 = 16$		Carry 1
$2 \times 7 = 16$, and $16 + 1 = 17$		Carry 1
$2 \times 1 = 2$, and $2 + 1 = 3$		

The first partial product is 1371. The second is 376. These are added as in decimal, but according to the rules of octal addition:

```
    1     1                   Carries
    1     3    7    1
+   3     7    6
  _____
  (4)  (10)  (13)  (1)        Decimal sum
       - 8   - 8   - 0        Subtracting base
  _____
    5     3    5    1         Octal sum
```

Example 14

```
    532
  × 371
  _____
    532
   4566
  2016
  _____
  250212
```

Octal Division

Octal division, like decimal division, involves just multiplication and subtraction; but, of course, these must be done according to the octal rules.

Example 15

$62_8 \div 2_8 = ?$

$$
\begin{array}{r}
31 \\
2\overline{)62} \\
\underline{6} \\
02 \\
\underline{2} \\
0
\end{array}
$$

Check

$31_8 = 25_{10}$

$$\frac{62_8}{2_8} = \frac{50_{10}}{2_{10}} = 25_{10}$$

Example 16

$1714_8 \div 22_8 = ?$

$$
\begin{array}{r}
66 \\
22\overline{)1714} \\
\underline{154} \\
154 \\
\underline{154}
\end{array}
$$

Check

$66_8 = 54_{10}$

$$\frac{1714_8}{22_8} = \frac{972_{10}}{18_{10}} = 54_{10}$$

A Note on Octal

The student should remember that in order for a computer to be able to use the octal system, all digits must be coded in 3-bit binary.

In many applications, however, it is more efficient to code numbers in *four* bits. In the next section, we will study a number system devised for 4-bit coding: the hexadecimal or base sixteen system.

2.2 Hexadecimal Numbers

Computers are often designed with word lengths of 8, 16, or 32 bits. If we could put binary data into 4-bit groups, instead of 3-bit groups as was done in octal, it would be to our advantage. Hexadecimal numbers are ideally suited for this.

Besides lending themselves to 4-bit binary coding, hexadecimal numbers have the advantage of making it possible to write large numbers with only a few digits. This can be handy for manual "memory addressing." Some microcomputers can store 65 536 numbers, each at a different location in the register, and each location must be identified by a number just like a house on a street. If we use zero as one of the *addresses*, decimal 0 through 65 535 are needed. In binary, this is 0000000000000000 to 1111111111111111; in hexadecimal, it can be written 0000 to FFFF.

Hexadecimal numbers, as the name indicates, are based on sixteen and so use 16 distinct digits. The symbols used for these digits are the ten decimal symbols 0 to 9 and the six letters A, B, C, D, E, F. Four binary bits are just sufficient to represent all the hexadecimal digits.

Hexadecimal Digit	Decimal Meaning	Binary Code
0	0	0000
1	1	0001
2	2	0010
3	3	0011
4	4	0100
5	5	0101
6	6	0110
7	7	0111
8	8	1000
9	9	1001
A	10	1010
B	11	1011

C	12	1100
D	13	1101
E	14	1110
F	15	1111

Place value in hexadecimal numbers is organized as usual:

$$\ldots 16^3 \; 16^2 \; 16^1 \; 16^0 \; 16^{-1} \; 16^{-2} \; 16^{-3} \ldots$$

$$16^3 \;\; = 4096$$
$$16^2 \;\; = 256$$
$$16^1 \;\; = 16$$
$$16^0 \;\; = 1$$
$$16^{-1} = 0.0625$$
$$16^{-2} = 0.003\,906\,2$$
$$16^{-3} = 0.000\,244\,14$$

Recall that:

$$16^{-1} = \frac{1}{16}$$

$$16^{-2} = \frac{1}{16^2} = \frac{1}{256}$$

and so on.

Conversion

Hexadecimal to Decimal

When converting from hexadecimal to decimal, the same methods are used as for binary and octal.

Example 17

Express the hexadecimal number 2A4F.8 in decimal.

8×16^{-1}	$= 8 \times 0.0625$	$=$	0.5
$F \times 16^0$	$= 15 \times 1$	$=$	15.0
4×16^1	$= 4 \times 16$	$=$	64.0
$A \times 16^2$	$= 10 \times 256$	$=$	2 560.0
2×16^3	$= 2 \times 4096$	$=$	8 192.0

$$10\,831.5_{10}$$

Example 18

Express the hexadecimal number 3AC2 in decimal.

2×16^0	$= 2 \times 1$	$=$	2
$C \times 16^1$	$= 12 \times 16$	$=$	192
$A \times 16^2$	$= 10 \times 256$	$=$	2 560
3×16^3	$= 3 \times 4096$	$=$	12 288

$$15\,042_{10}$$

Decimal to Hexadecimal

The procedure for conversion from decimal to hexadecimal is basically the same as that for conversion from decimal to octal or any other base.

Example 19

Express the decimal number 1324 in hexadecimal.

	Quotient	Remainder in Decimal	Remainder in Hexadecimal
$\dfrac{1324}{16} =$	82	12	C
$\dfrac{82}{16} =$	5	2	2
$\dfrac{5}{16} =$	0	5	5

$$1324_{10} = 52C_{16}$$

Check

52C

$C \times 16^0$	$= 12 \times 1$	$=$	12
2×16^1	$= 2 \times 16$	$=$	32
5×16^2	$= 5 \times 256$	$=$	1280

$$1324$$

Example 20

Express the decimal number 38.25 in hexadecimal.

As in decimal-to-octal, conversion of numbers involving fractions is more tedious. First, the 38 must be converted to its hexadecimal equivalent. Then the fractional part is converted.

		Quotient	Remainder
$\dfrac{38}{16}$	=	2	6
$\dfrac{2}{16}$	=	0	2

Thus $38_{10} = 26_{16}$.

Now we must determine the hexadecimal equivalent of 0.25. Recall that:

$$16^{-1} = \frac{1}{16} = 0.0625_{10}.$$

Therefore, to find the hexadecimal value after the decimal point, 0.25 is simply divided by 0.0625 to get 4. Hence the hexadecimal equivalent of 0.25_{10} is 0.4_{16}.

Thus $38.25_{10} = 26.4_{16}$. The procedure is the same as that described earlier for the octal system.

Operations

Hexadecimal Addition

The same method of addition is used in hexadecimal as in octal.

Example 21

Add hexadecimal 7AF, 579.

	1	1		Carries
	7	A	F	
+	5	7	9	
(13)	(18)	(24)		Decimal sum
	-16	-16		Subtracting base
D	2	8		Hexadecimal sum

As we can see in the example, in adding columns we mentally convert hexadecimal digits to decimal and add in decimal. In the

first column, $F + 9 = 24$. Since 24 is greater than F (i.e., 15) we subtract the radix (16) from 24 and carry a one to the next column. The next column is added, including the carry, and the process repeated.

Check

To check the above addition, we first convert the answer to base ten:

$D28_{16} = ?$

$$\begin{aligned}
8 \times 16^0 &= 8 \times 1 &= 8 \\
2 \times 16^1 &= 2 \times 16 &= 32 \\
D \times 16^2 &= 13 \times 256 &= \underline{3328} \\
& & 3368_{10}
\end{aligned}$$

Then we convert each of the numbers being added:

$7AF = ?$

$$\begin{aligned}
F \times 16^0 &= 15 \times 1 &= 15 \\
A \times 16^1 &= 10 \times 16 &= 160 \\
7 \times 16^2 &= 7 \times 256 &= \underline{1792} \\
& & 1967_{10}
\end{aligned}$$

$579_{16} = ?$

$$\begin{aligned}
9 \times 16^0 &= 9 \times 1 &= 9 \\
7 \times 16^1 &= 7 \times 16 &= 112 \\
5 \times 16^2 &= 5 \times 256 &= \underline{1280} \\
& & 1401_{10}
\end{aligned}$$

Finally, we see if our result holds in the base ten system:

$1967 + 1401 = 3368$

Hexadecimal Subtraction

Subtraction in hexadecimal follows the same rules as in octal.

Example 22

Subtract hexadecimal 85E from hexadecimal C37.

B (1)2
$\cancel{C}$ $\cancel{3}$ (1)7   Minuend
− 8   5   E   Subtrahend
3   D   9

In the first column we are subtracting E (14) from 7. To do this we must borrow 1 from the 3 in the second column of the minuend. The 7 now becomes one-seven or 23. 23 minus 14 equals 9.

In the second column we are subtracting 5 from 2 (the 3 became 2 when we borrowed in the first step), so we must borrow 1 from C in the third column, which then becomes B. Hexadecimal 5 is now subtracted from one-two (18), yielding 13 or hexadecimal D.

In the third column, 8 is subtracted from B or 11, giving 3.

Check

Converting the answer to base ten:

$39D = 985_{10}$

Converting C37 to base ten:

$7 \times 16^0 = 7 \times 1 = 7$
$3 \times 16^1 = 3 \times 16 = 48$
$C \times 16^2 = 12 \times 256 = \underline{3072}$
3127_{10}

Converting 85E to base ten:

$E \times 16^0 = 14 \times 1 = 14$
$5 \times 16^1 = 5 \times 16 = 80$
$8 \times 16^2 = 8 \times 256 = \underline{2048}$
2142_{10}

Checking the result in base ten:

$3127 - 2142 = 985$

Hexadecimal Multiplication

Hexadecimal multiplication is a rather lengthy procedure, as there are 256 entries in the multiplication table. The easiest way to find products is to follow these steps:

1. Convert the numbers to decimal.
2. Multiply in decimal.
3. Convert the answer to hexadecimal.

Hexadecimal Division

The procedure for hexadecimal division is the same as for multiplication.

Binary Coding and Hexadecimal Conversion

Binary to Hexadecimal

In the section on octal numbers, it was noted that binary-coded octals are special in that they can be read continuously as pure binaries without any change in their value. The same is true for binary-coded hexadecimals.[1] (See earlier in this section for 4-bit codes of hexadecimal digits.)

This means that any pure binary number can easily be changed to its hexadecimal equivalent. Just think of it as a code for a hexadecimal.

For example, converting the binary number 1101100110110011 by the obvious method would involve finding the binary values for all binary weightings 2^0 through 2^{15}. But the binary number can be converted to hexadecimal much more directly. To do this, group the binary digits in *fours* starting at the binary point. Then replace the groups with their equivalent hexadecimal digits. These form the hexadecimal number.

Example 23

1101100110110011	Binary number
1101 1001 1011 0011	Groups of 4
D 9 B 3	Hex. equiv.
D9B3	Hex. number

---

1. To explain this, note that 8 and 16 are both powers of 2.

Binary to Hexadecimal to Decimal

This characteristic of the hexadecimal system also gives us an easy way to figure out the value of a long binary number. First convert to hexadecimal digits as above, and then convert to decimal.

Example 24

Express the binary number 110011 in decimal.

0011 0011   Groups of 4
 3   3   Hexadecimal equivalents

$33_{16} = (3 \times 16^1) + (3 \times 16^0)$
$\qquad = 48 + 3$
$\qquad = 51_{10}$ Decimal value

Example 25

Express the binary number 111011111001.11101 in decimal.

1110 1111 1001.1110 1000   Groups of 4
 E   F   9 . E   8   Hex. equiv.

$EF9.E8 = (14 \times 16^2) + (15 \times 16^1) + (9 \times 16^0)$
$\qquad\qquad + (14 \times 16^{-1}) + (8 \times 16^{-2})$
$\qquad = 3584 + 240 + 9 + 0.875$
$\qquad\quad + 0.031\,25$
$\qquad = 3\,833.906\,25_{10}$ Decimal value

Hexadecimal to Binary

This conversion is done in reverse order.

Example 26

Express the hexadecimal number ABC in binary.

 A   B   C   Hexadecimal digits
1010 1011 1100   Binary-coded hex.
 101010111100   Pure binary

Example 27

Express the hexadecimal number 3.7 in binary.

 3 . 7   Hexadecimal digits
0011.0111   Binary-coded hex.
 11.0111   Pure binary

Check

$3.7_{16} = (3 \times 16^0) + (7 \times 16^{-1})$
$\qquad = 3 + (7 \times 0.0625)$
$\qquad = 3 + 0.4375$
$\qquad = 3.4375_{10}$

$$11.0111_2 = 3 + \left(0 \times \frac{1}{2}\right) + \left(1 \times \frac{1}{4}\right)$$
$$+ \left(1 \times \frac{1}{8}\right) + \left(1 \times \frac{1}{16}\right)$$
$$= 3 + 0 + 0.25 + 0.125$$
$$+ 0.0625$$
$$= 3.4375_{10}$$

2.3 Coding Alphanumerics

Though computers deal with information by means of binary, octal, and hexadecimal numbers, they must also be able to handle numbers, letters, punctuation, special instructions, and mathematical symbols. Therefore a way is needed to convert all of these characters into a code usable by computers. Many codes have been developed for this purpose, but attempts have been made at standardization, resulting in the ASCII (American Standard Code for Information Interchange).

In ASCII all of the chosen alphanumerics are

translated into a 7-bit binary code. For example, the numeral 5 becomes 011 0101; the letter B becomes 100 0010; the comma becomes 010 1100. Note that, unlike the binary codes discussed earlier, the ASCII code is arbitrary (except for the last part of the numeral codes).

Appendix C gives the complete code.

2.4 Parity Bits

When electrical signals are transmitted from one point to another, they are susceptible to interference — we are all familiar with the "noise" pulses that get mixed with television signals and degrade the picture, and radio noise picked up during an electrical storm. Digital signals are no exception.

Interference of this kind can cause many problems for binary-data transmission. We have explained that binary digits are transmitted through pulses of voltage and current — the presence of a pulse can represent a binary 1 and the absence of a pulse a 0. But if an interference signal happens to create a noise pulse, the pulse could be read as binary 1 in a series that should not contain it. Safeguards must be devised to prevent computers from responding to error pulses. This is where parity bits come into the picture.

Example 28

1001 = 9 Binary number sent
1101 = 13 Number received
↑
Noise pulse

A parity bit is a binary digit — 0 or 1 — added to a binary word or code so as to make it have an odd or even number of binary 1 digits. The end results of the odd and even parity systems are the same.

Assume an odd parity system applied to the ASCII code. If the letter A is to be transmitted, binary 100 0001 is generated in the computer. Notice that there is an even number of 1 digits in this 7-bit code. Thus, a 1 parity bit would be added to the word to make the number odd. The equal sign (=) is coded 011 1101, which contains an odd number of binary ones. Thus a 0 parity bit would be added before transmitting the code in order to maintain the odd number of binary ones in the word.

In this way every "word" received by a terminal should have an odd number of binary ones in it. If it does not, the computer will "know" that an error pulse has crept into the transmission.

How the transmitting computer generates and adds the parity bits to the codes, and how the receiving computer checks for parity, will be explained when we consider logic circuits.

Questions

1. How do octal numbers differ from binary numbers?
2. How are octal numbers useful in computer systems?
3. Define *base eight number system*.
4. Express the following octal numbers in decimal: 242, 125, 67, 30, 12.4, 13.02
5. Express the following decimal numbers in octal: 220, 39, 22.19
6. Add the following octal numbers.

$$\begin{array}{cccc} 34 & 35 & 12 \\ +\ 66 & +\ 62 & 26 \\ & & +\ 54 \end{array}$$

7. Subtract the following octal numbers.

$$\begin{array}{cc} 36 & 216 \\ -\ 15 & -\ 135 \end{array}$$

8. Explain how hexadecimal numbers are suited to 4-bit binary words.
9. Explain the meaning of 16^{-2} and 16^3.
10. Express the following hexadecimal numbers in decimal: 2A4, 36B, 3BC4, 4F.A
11. Express the following decimal numbers in hexadecimal: 37, 681, 23.25
12. Subtract the following hexadecimal numbers.

$$\begin{array}{cc} C34 & 85E \\ -\ 62A & -\ 31F \end{array}$$

13. Convert the following hexadecimal numbers to binary-coded form: AB2, 2A, 9A
14. Explain the purpose of the ASCII code.
15. Explain odd and even parity. Why are parity systems used?

Experiments

Experiment 2.1

Object

To show the operation of a 7447 binary-to-decimal decoder.

Circuit

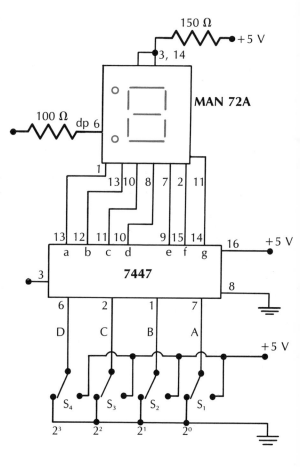

Figure E2.1

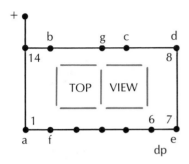

Figure E2.1 (cont.)

Steps

1. Connect the circuit. *Note:* If a 6-V source is used, connect the positive via a 180-Ω resistor instead of a 150-Ω resistor.
2. Ground ABCD inputs. Observe display.
3. Insert binary numbers 1 to 9 in sequence and observe display.
4. Set input to binary 1. Ground pin 3. Observe display.
5. Ground pin 6 of MAN 72A via 100 Ω and observe display.
6. What is the purpose of pin 6?

Experiment 2.2

Object

To show how a 7805 regulator is used to drop a DC input of 9 to 12 V to a steady 5 V.

Circuit

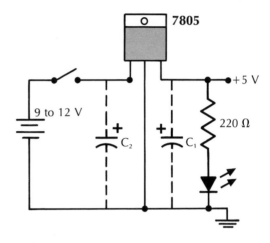

Notes: Add heat sink for currents over 100 mA. C_1: 1.0 μF high quality (tantalum). C_2: 2500 μF.

Figure E2.2

Steps

1. Connect the circuit to a 12-V source. Measure the DC output voltage.
2. Connect the circuit to a 9-V source. Measure the DC output voltage.
3. Why is the heat sink required for load currents over 100 mA?

CHAPTER 3

Circuit Elements

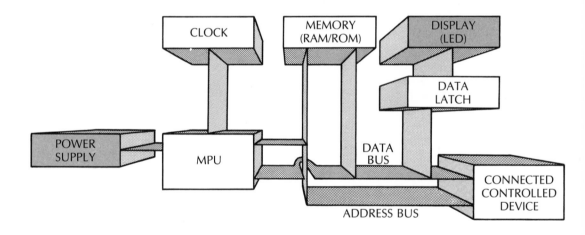

COMPUTER SYSTEM

■ INTRODUCTION ■

In this chapter we will examine the main electronic components used in computer circuits. Students who have a background in electronics will recognize that the level of discussion in this chapter is mainly qualitative or descriptive. This can be done because most computer circuits function as simple switching devices. As a result, a detailed and quantitative or mathematical treatment of these basic components will be avoided.

The chapter will cover the following points: the need for resistance in circuits, the unidirectional properties of junction diodes, the conduction properties of junction diodes, the conduction properties of junction and field-effect transistors, and the light-emitting properties of LEDs (light-emitting diodes).

3.1   Resistive Circuits

There are many kinds of circuits and one of the simplest and most common is the resistive circuit. A familiarity with basic DC and AC circuit theory is assumed here, and we will review circuit fundamentals only briefly.

A circuit must have at least these three parts: a *source* of energy, a conducting *path*, and a *load*.

The source may consist of a battery, an AC or DC generator, or any one of a wide variety of other devices. In any case, it produces a difference of *potential* or *voltage* that sets electrons in motion in the circuit. When a source is said to have a difference of potential at its terminals this implies that electrons will move between these terminals if a circuit is connected to them. In the case of a battery, electrons will flow from its negative terminal through the circuit and into its positive terminal. This completes the circuit. The difference of potential (voltage) is thought of as the electric field of force that causes current to flow through the circuit.

The conducting path is required to permit the easy transfer of charge (electrons) from the source to the load and from the load back to the source.

Before we continue our discussion we must recall the characteristics of charge as it pertains to current flow. Current flow refers to the drift of electrons in a circuit. Electrons, of course, are tiny, negatively charged particles that orbit about the nucleus of atoms. In certain materials, such as copper and aluminum, some of these orbiting electrons can be made to drift from one atom to another. This happens when a voltage is applied across the material. The voltage across a circuit causes many electrons to drift or flow around the circuit much as a pump would cause water to flow around a closed or complete path.

The conducting path allows for the easy movement of electrons. Even a small applied potential can cause a large flow of electrons. In order to control the number of electrons moving per unit time, a load or control element must be placed in the path. A common control element is the *resistor*.

Resistors can be made from many substances. Some of these are carbon, tungsten, nickel-chromium alloys, and impure silicon. Unlike the materials in other parts of the conducting path, the materials of resistors do not allow the easy movement of electrons from atom to atom. Atoms in resistive materials hold their electrons more strongly than do atoms in conductors. Because of this, considerable voltage is required to cause significant numbers of electrons to flow.

Because of this hold that atoms in resistive materials have on their outer electrons, there is a significant release of energy each time an electron breaks away from the parent atom.

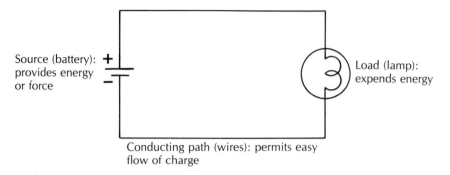

Figure 3.1 Circuit Elements

When electrons are moved in large numbers, thermal energy (heat) is generated in the resistor. In the case of the filament of a lamp, which can be thought of as a resistor, both heat and light are produced.

These three parts — source, path, and load — work together to cause a controlled flow of current around a circuit. (See Figure 3.1.)

Another characteristic of such a basic circuit is that the flow at any point is the same as at all other points. For example, if a battery were connected to a single lamp and x electrons per second flowed out of the negative terminal of the battery, x electrons per second would be found to flow at all other points. This means that this same number of electrons would be measured in the resistor (lamp filament), in the conductor, and also within the battery. We can consider moving electrons in a circuit to be like links of a moving chain. When one moves all of them move.

Some students object to this concept because it appears that we get something for nothing if the battery (or any source) gets back as many electrons as it sends out. But the point to remember is that the electrons that return to the source have lost their energy. In the case of the lamp circuit, this loss is in the form of heat and light as the electrons flow through the resistance of the lamp filament. However, these electrons can now be "rejuvenated" by the source and once again do work in flowing around the circuit.

In addition to a general understanding of a resistive circuit, it is important to acquire familiarity with basic circuit measurements and know how to select component values for basic circuits. For example, assume that a flow of 100 mA is required in a resistive circuit which is connected to a 10-V source. What resistance would be required? The answer is given by Ohm's Law:

$$R = \frac{V}{I}$$
$$= \frac{10}{0.1} = 100 \ \Omega$$

Notice that the basic units are used in the formula: V is expressed in volts (V), I in amperes (A), and R in ohms (Ω).

Now assume that a 1.5-kΩ resistor is used in a circuit and is selected to permit a current flow of 10 mA. We would require, then, a source voltage of 15 V.

$$V = IR$$
$$= 0.01 \times 1500$$
$$= 15 \ V$$

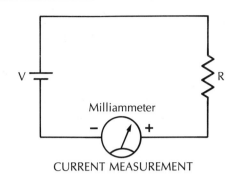

CURRENT MEASUREMENT

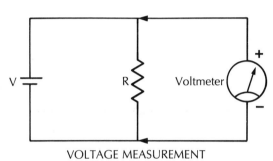

VOLTAGE MEASUREMENT

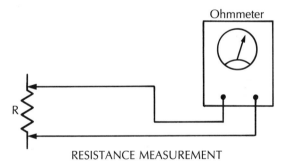

RESISTANCE MEASUREMENT

Figure 3.2 Measurement Methods

And finally, if we have a 10-kΩ resistor connected to a 1.5-V source, we can determine its current flow by calculation:

$$I = \frac{V}{R}$$
$$= \frac{1.5}{10\ 000}$$
$$= 0.000\ 15\ A$$
$$= 0.15\ mA$$
$$\text{or } 150\ \mu A\ \text{(microamperes)}$$

Testing

It is also important to know how to test a resistive circuit, because it can look normal and still not function electrically.

For example, carbon resistors can burn out and yet lack any exterior indications that this has happened. The source voltage would be present across the resistor but there would be no current flow through it. One way to test for this condition is physically to separate one end of the resistor from the circuit and insert a milliammeter to measure the current flow; if the resistor is burnt out (or open), of course, there would be no flow recorded on the meter. We could also test the resistor with an ohmmeter measurement once it is separated from the circuit. Remember that the resistance measurement must be done with the circuit voltage removed so that only the ohmmeter is present as a source for the resistor. (It is assumed that the reader is familiar with basic measurement procedures. If a review is required, the experiments at the end of this chapter will be helpful.) Figure 3.2 shows how to insert meters properly for the measurement of voltage (*V*), current (*I*), and resistance (*R*).

Students often make mistakes when testing resistive circuits because they forget that a resistance reading across a resistor in a circuit can be affected by other resistors in the same circuit. Figure 3.3 illustrates this point. If both

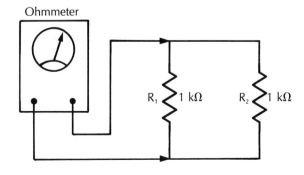

Figure 3.3 Resistance Measurement

resistors in Figure 3.3 are good, the ohmmeter reads about 500 Ω because it is driving current through the two resistors in parallel. In this case the resistor to be tested must be disconnected at one end.

To complete a review of basic resistive circuits, the reader should become familiar with the resistor colour code. The colour code is included in Appendix B. It would also be helpful to review parallel and series circuit theory for resistive circuits.

3.2 Diodes and Power Supplies

Diode Action

Diodes are commonly used in computer circuits. These components allow current to flow in only one direction in the circuit. We can think of a diode as a polarity-sensitive switch.

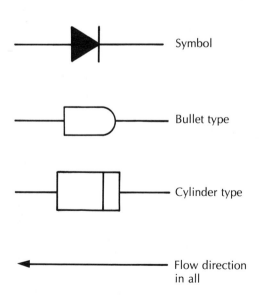

Symbol

Bullet type

Cylinder type

Flow direction in all

Figure 3.4 Solid State Diode

That is, it is sensitive to positive and negative polarities. When one polarity is applied to it, current will flow in the circuit; if the polarity of the source is reversed, no current will flow. (See Figure 3.4.)

The behaviour of the junction diode in simple circuits is illustrated in Figure 3.5. We see

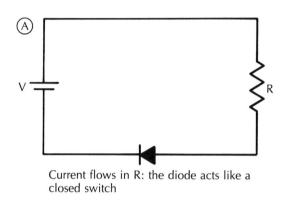

Current flows in R: the diode acts like a closed switch

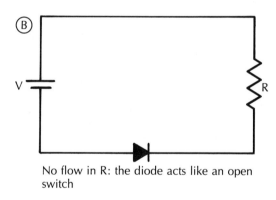

No flow in R: the diode acts like an open switch

Figure 3.5 The Diode as a Polarity-Sensitive Switch

from the figure that the diode will conduct when it is connected such that electrons enter at the "line" end. When electrons are directed to the "arrowhead" end they cannot get through. It is important to note that a diode can be used either to block or to allow current flow between points of similar charge. Figure 3.6 illustrates this.

In part A of the figure, we are considering the condition between the +6-V and +9-V points in the circuit. If a circuit were connected between these points current would flow due to the difference of potential of 3 V. Since the +9 point is 3 V more positive than the +6 point, it acts like the positive terminal while the +6 point acts like the negative terminal. Electrons would leave the +6 terminal and flow to the higher +9 terminal. Of course, there would be a similar flow between the

−9-V and −6-V terminals of the battery. This is because any current must be the same in all parts of a circuit.

In part B of the figure, current flows from the −9-V terminal to the −6-V terminal. The latter acts as though it were positive, because it is less negative than the −9-V terminal.

Rule: Electrons always attempt to move to a point of higher positive or less negative charge.

If we examine parts C, D, E, and F of the figure we can now see why current does or

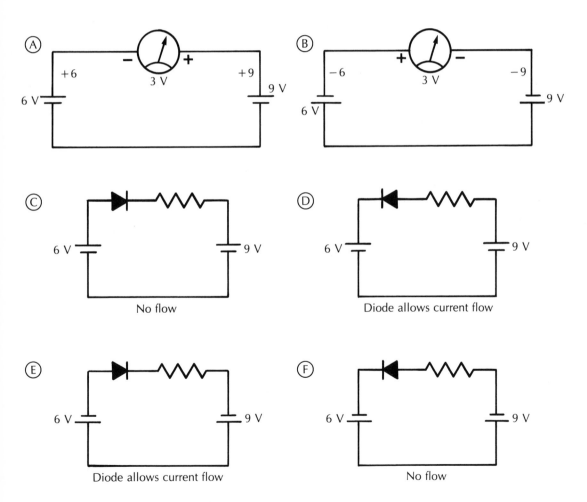

Figure 3.6 Diode Action between Points of Similar Charge

does not flow in these situations. It is due to the polarity sensitivity of the inserted diode. In C there can be no flow because electrons want to move from the +6 to the +9 point and the diode is inserted in a way that prevents flow from left to right. Current flow is permitted in E because electrons want to move from the −9-V to the −6-V point and the diode is properly inserted to allow this flow.

Junctions

How do diodes allow electrons to flow through them in only one direction? Junction diodes, of a sort, were used for over fifty years before an adequate explanation of their behaviour was advanced.

The answer lies in the way atoms are bonded together in semiconductor crystals. We will not attempt to deal with semiconductor properties and PN junctions in great detail here. Only the basic points will be discussed.

Most junction diodes are made from silicon, which is the basic building block of transistors of all types and of integrated circuits.

Silicon

Silicon is a common element in nature. When purified, it has a dark, glossy, metallic appearance.

In pure silicon crystals, the silicon atoms form a lattice-like structure in which they share some of their outer electrons. This phenomenon is called *covalent bonding*. When the atoms thus hang onto these outer electrons, the crystal acts as a good insulator. This is in contrast to a material like copper, in which the atoms do not bond in this way and many of the electrons are free to move about in the solid, making it an excellent electrical conductor.

Silicon has an atomic number of 14. Therefore, it normally has 14 electrons distributed

around it. The electrons are considered to be distributed in three orbits or main energy levels around the nucleus of the atom. The first orbit contains two electrons; the second contains four pairs of electrons; and the outermost contains the remaining four.

The two inner orbits or energy levels are described as "filled." They are highly stable. This means that a relatively large amount of energy would be needed to remove one of these electrons from its orbit. But in an isolated silicon atom, the outer orbit is not stable, because of its electron content. To be stable, it would have to have eight electrons in its outer orbit, rather than the four it does have. If eight electrons were present, they would be organized into a two-level orbit or energy distribution. A pair of electrons would occupy one part of the outer orbit called a subshell and the other three pairs would occupy the next subshell or outermost part of the outer orbit. An ideal and stable outer orbit would have eight electrons, two in one subshell or energy level and six in another.

This ideal outer orbit distribution would satisfy the strange demands of the two subshells of this outer orbit. However, the silicon atom would be "unhappy" with the total loading of electrons around it. This is because the silicon atom has 14 protons in its nucleus, and requires an equal number of electrons in order to balance its overall charge. Apparently the two ideal conditions, for the atom as a whole and for the outer subshell, cannot be simultaneously met.

In a pure silicon crystal, the demands of the outer subshell of an atom are met by its sharing electrons with adjacent atoms. Every outer subshell in every silicon atom in the material is looking for four more electrons. Consider one silicon atom surrounded in the crystal by four adjacent silicon atoms. At any instant, it can share one electron from each of the four atoms and "have" the four additional electrons

Ⓐ

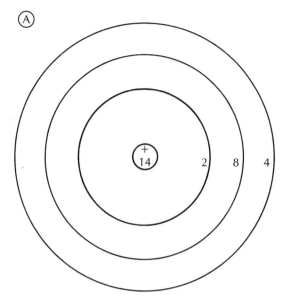

Silicon atom: electron distribution model

Ⓑ

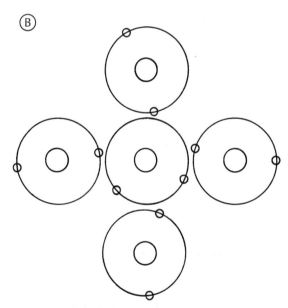

Outer subshell electrons for five silicon atoms

Figure 3.7 Silicon Bonding

its outer subshell seeks. The phenomenon of sharing permits an outer subshell to be satisfied without upsetting the overall balance of charge in the silicon atoms. Figure 3.7 illustrates silicon bonding. (If available, atom models should be used to show the three-dimensional nature of the crystal.)

Covalent bonding creates extremely stable subshells in the pure silicon crystal. The electrons are held tightly in place, and such silicon has the properties of an insulator.

Doping

Pure silicon alone is of little interest, for it simply acts as an insulator. Its value comes from the fact that it can be modified or *doped* so that it has certain conducting properties. It has been found that silicon conducts fairly readily if small quantities of other substances are added. For example, if the right amount of arsenic is added to a pure silicon crystal, the silicon conducts.

N-Type Silicon

N-type silicon is pure silicon that has been doped (treated) with a pentavalent impurity such as arsenic. Arsenic has an atomic number of 33. Its 33 electrons are arranged in four principal orbits or energy levels. The outer orbit contains five electrons in two subshells, two in one and three in the other.

When an arsenic atom is substituted for a silicon atom in a section of the crystal, its outer subshell will "see" and share an electron from the four surrounding silicon atoms. This means that the outer subshell of the arsenic atom now "sees" seven electrons in it (the original three plus four from the silicon atoms). But this subshell, you will recall, is satisfied with only six electrons. Thus, the "extra" electron is not tightly held in this section of the crystal; it can be moved in the crystal with very little applied energy.

It is true that the arsenic atom requires all of its electrons and would produce an attracting force if one of them were to leave the atom. However, the other important factor is the demand of the outer subshell, which considers one of the electrons present to be excess baggage. The play between these two forces creates a situation wherein one electron in the vicinity of every arsenic atom is reasonably free to move in the crystal.

Thus, when pure silicon is doped with arsenic atoms, the atoms enter the crystal structure and replace normal silicon atoms, causing the crystal to become a conductor.

It may seem that this is all wasted effort if we have only achieved conductivity in the silicon crystal. We must continue our discussion to see how these properties can result in diode action.

P-Type Silicon

P-type silicon is pure silicon that has been doped with a trivalent impurity such as indium. The atom of indium has three electrons in its outer orbit. This means that its outer subshell has only one electron in a subshell that would be stable with six electrons. When this atom appears in a pure silicon crystal in place of one of the silicon atoms, its outer subshell "sees" the four electrons from the four adjacent silicon atoms. This presents the outer subshell of the indium atom with only five electrons in a subshell that would be stable with six. The effect of this is such that the silicon crystal, once again, becomes a conductor. Conduction in this case is slightly different than for the arsenic impurity, as the following explanation will show.

The incomplete subshell of each indium atom has an attraction for electrons. It is true that the indium atom does not want additional electrons; but the subshell does. So again there are two forces at work in the crystal.

The unfilled subshell which attracts electrons, behaving like a positive charge, is called a *hole*. It takes very little energy to cause electrons to enter these holes. Even bonded electrons in filled, outer silicon subshells adjacent to the impurity atoms can be attracted into these areas of the crystal. Thus, if an electric force is applied to a crystal of P-type silicon, it will conduct, because there is an easy avenue for charge movement through the structure of the crystal.

N-TYPE SILICON

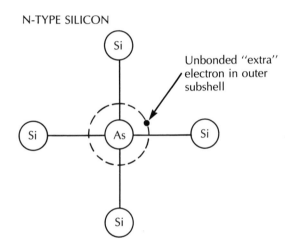

P-TYPE SILICON

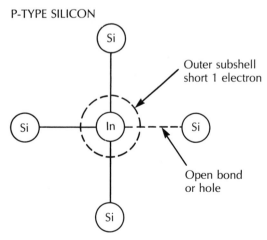

Figure 3.8 Doped Silicon

Figure 3.8 illustrates how the two types of doped silicon relate to the electron content of the outer subshells of the atoms in the crystal.

PN Junctions

Our discussion has shown how the doping of pure silicon with impurities such as arsenic and indium changes the crystal from an insulator to a conductor. Now we will see that when these two types of silicon are formed into what is called a PN junction a component is created which has unidirectional current flow properties.

It should be made clear that in a PN junction the materials are not simply joined. The junction is a single chip of silicon crystal that has been doped alternately with arsenic and indium impurities while in its molten state. The cold crystal is then cut and wires are connected to the N and P areas of the crystal so it can be wired into a circuit.

The question we must now answer is, how does a PN junction prevent current flow in one direction but allow it in the other?

Consider a section of silicon, half of which is doped N and half doped P. The N section has many sites where electrons are not tightly bound to the material, while the P section has many sites where there are holes or subshells "looking" for an electron. Thus, because the crystal of the PN junction is continuous, some of these loosely-held electrons from the N section will move over to the P section to fill a hole. This action occurs at the interface of the two materials.

It is important to remember that the two sections of the crystal are initially neutral, as their electron-proton content is balanced. However, they now become charged as they either gain or lose electrons. The N section loses electrons to the P section, so a negative charge is built up on the P material and the N section becomes correspondingly positive. The charge of the P section prevents the wholesale diffusion of electrons from N to P. It is referred to as the *barrier potential*. If more electrons attempt to leave the N material and find their way to holes in the P section they encounter the wall of negative charge.

The magnitude of the barrier potential developed by this action is about 0.5 V.

When the electrons transfer into the P section, the section of the crystal at the interface becomes depleted of unbonded electrons and holes, or *charge carriers*. Together, the area that has given up electrons and the area that has gained electrons create a region where all

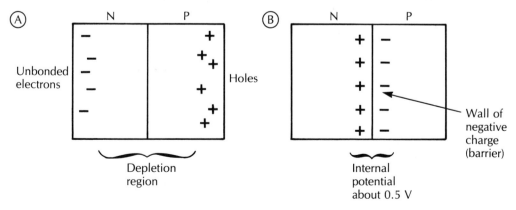

Figure 3.9 Barrier Formation

outer subshells are satisfied. This part of the crystal, called the *depletion region*, behaves just like pure silicon — it is an insulator.

We can now discuss the behaviour of the PN junction. See Figure 3.9. Consider what would happen if we applied an external potential (voltage) across the diode with negative to the N material and positive to the P material. This potential would tend to force unbonded electrons from the N section across the barrier and into holes in the P section. In other words, current will flow through the diode if the applied voltage is greater than the barrier voltage. The total circuit current through the diode, of course, would have to be limited by some form of circuit resistance.

Now consider what would happen if we reversed the polarity of the source. With a positive force at the N material and a negative force at the P, the unbonded electrons and holes are pulled to the ends of the crystal and the depletion region is strengthened. That is to say, the centre section of the crystal will have a greater area of insulation under these conditions. Conduction will not occur, because a large region of the crystal has satisfied outer subshells and a large external voltage would

be needed to drive current through it. For normal voltages, no current will flow when the source potential is applied in this direction.

The conducting direction of applied voltage is called the diode's *forward bias* while the non-conducting direction is called its *reverse bias*. See Figure 3.10.

Power Supplies

One of the most common uses of junction diodes is as rectifiers. Rectifiers convert AC (alternating current) to DC (direct current). This enables common AC energy to be used to power DC devices such as computers.

A rectifier, in its simplest form, consists of one diode connected between an AC source and a DC load. Figure 3.11 illustrates this.

Recall that current can only flow through a diode when its P material is positive. As a result the AC wave can only cause a current flow in the load during one of the half-cycles. This DC load current is a crude form of DC called pulsating DC.

Direct current in this form can be used for such things as battery charging and DC motor

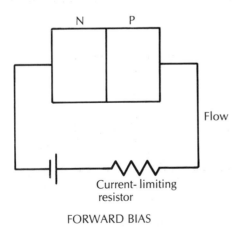

FORWARD BIAS

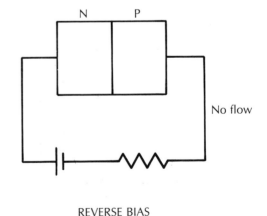

REVERSE BIAS

Figure 3.10 Diode Bias

currents. However, it is too unsteady for computer circuits. In order to make it suitable, the rectifier output must be filtered or smoothed out. This is generally done with a coil-capacitor arrangement. (Recall that capacitors are devices that store a charge when a DC voltage is applied to them.) One such arrangement is illustrated in Figure 3.12.

Capacitors C_1 and C_2 charge to the peak voltage of the AC wave. When the AC input voltage falls toward zero these capacitors discharge slowly through the DC load. They recharge to the peak value on the next half-cycle of the AC wave. If the capacitors are large enough the amount of ripple (voltage variation) is very small.

To reduce the ripple further, the induction coil L is used between the capacitors. When current through the coil changes, the electromagnetic field around the coil also changes.

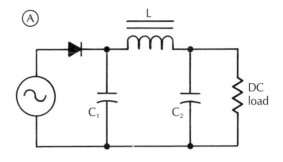

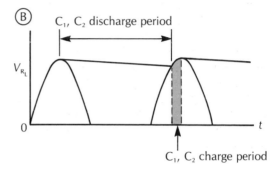

Figure 3.12 Coil-Capacitor Filter

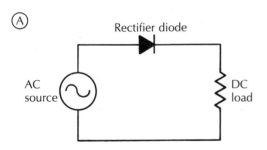

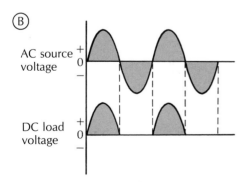

Figure 3.11 Basic Rectifier Circuit

This changing field causes a current to be generated in the coil by simple generator action. In generator action, electrons are caused to flow in a conductor when lines of magnetic force cut across it.

The direction of the generated current depends on the direction of the lines and their motion. A principle called Lenz's Law states that "generator action caused by a changing current in a coil always produces a generated current which opposes the change in source current."

Thus, there are two currents in the coil: the source current and the induced (generated) current. The induced current opposes the change in source current. If the source current is falling, the generated current in the coil flows in the same direction as the source current and helps keep the current up. If the source current is rising, the generated current flows in the opposite direction and helps hold the current down. The result is a steady, smooth load current — the ideal being a voltage without a trace of ripple.

We can see from Figure 3.12 that the DC output voltage is equal to the value of the peak AC wave. Normally this voltage is too high for electronic circuits. For most integrated circuit (IC) chips only 5 V is required. Therefore the peak AC voltage from a wall plug must be stepped down to about 5 V. This can be done with a step-down transformer. Generally, a step-down transformer with a centre-tapped secondary coil is used. This feature permits full-wave rectification. Figure 3.13 illustrates the advantages of a full-wave rectifier.

The secondary coil of the transformer is divided into two parts. The upper half connects to the filter and load via D_1. The lower half connects via D_2. On the half-cycle when point A is positive relative to C, D_1 will conduct and "send" DC to the filter and load. Point B will be negative relative to C and D_2 will not conduct.

On the opposite half-cycle, B will be positive relative to C. Now D_2 will "send" DC to the filter and load.

Notice that the load receives energy on both half-cycles. Therefore the filter discharge time is cut in half. This makes it easier to keep the DC output voltage steady.

Filtering the DC voltage is important, but keeping the DC voltage steady is also important. These two things are not the same. The voltage can be free of ripple, and yet rise and fall if the input AC voltage rises and falls. This would mean that the DC output would not stay steady at the prescribed voltage of, say, 5 V. This is a problem for TTL IC chips. Most of them are designed to work at a steady 5 V. If the DC voltage varies too far from this value, the chip will not operate properly.

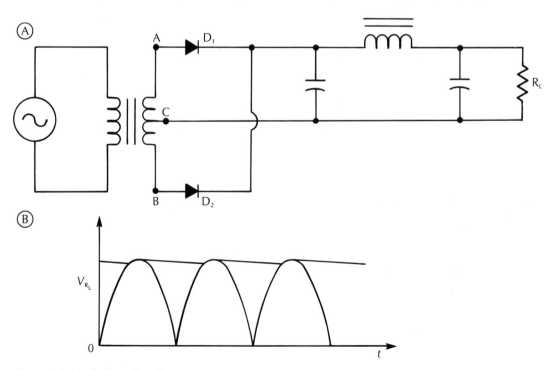

Figure 3.13 Full-Wave Rectifier

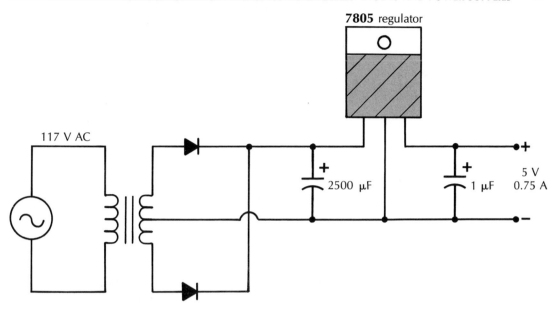

Figure 3.14 Five-Volt Line-operated Supply

To help keep the output voltage at its required value, regulators are used in conjunction with the rectifier. A regulator is itself an IC. It contains circuits that "watch" the output voltage and make corrections when the input voltage to the regulator changes. A regulator is often used between a battery supply and a circuit. It keeps the circuit voltage steady when the battery voltage changes. This application is described in Experiment 2.2.

Figure 3.14 illustrates the use of a common 7805 regulator. It is connected between a rectifier and a 5-V load.

Light-Emitting Diodes (LEDs)

Another interesting and useful property of certain junction diodes is their ability to radiate light energy when current flows through them. The principle is quite simple. When certain atoms have their outer-orbit electrons disturbed they radiate electromagnetic energy in the visible portion of the spectrum. In the case of junction diodes the outer-orbit electrons are constantly being disturbed when current is

flowing. As a result, electromagnetic energy is radiated. If the crystal is properly doped and if the surface is properly constructed, a significant quantity of visible electromagnetic energy

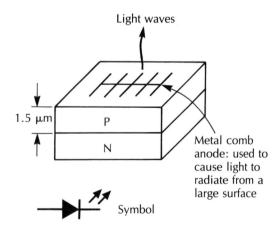

Figure 3.15 Light-Emitting Diode

(light) will be emitted from its surface. (See Figure 3.15). The colour of this light depends on the LED materials used. Reds and greens are the preferred spectral frequencies.

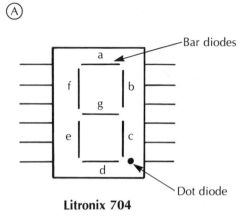

Ⓐ

Bar diodes

Dot diode

Litronix 704

Ⓑ

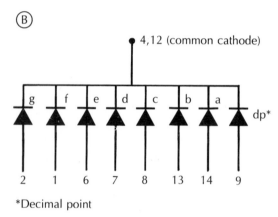

4,12 (common cathode)

g   f   e   d   c   b   a

dp*

2   1   6   7   8   13   14   9

*Decimal point

Figure 3.16 Seven-Segment Display

When LEDs are used in arrays such as the common seven-segment displays on calculators and digital watches, they can form alphanumeric readouts. Figure 3.16 shows the basic diode arrangement for a common seven-segment display. Actually, there are eight diodes in the unit because a diode is provided for the decimal point. The bar diodes are turned on individually. For example, when current flows from pin 4 to pin 14 in this unit, diode (a) will light up. The diode sections can be selected to display all the decimal digits and many letters.

3.3   Junction Transistors

This discussion will be limited to the basic characteristics of transistors, as the use of transistors in computer circuits is usually restricted to some form of switching function. We will appreciate this when we deal with some of the basic circuits.

The junction transistor is an extension of the junction diode, in that it consists of a pair of diodes that have a crystal section in common.

Notice that the transistor in Figure 3.17 is really just a pair of PN junctions with their P materials in common. Such an arrangement, with its extremely thin centre crystal, has a unique and remarkable property. If one section

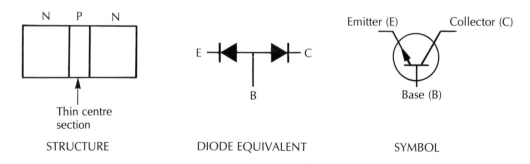

N   P   N

Thin centre section

STRUCTURE

E ◄—►— C

B

DIODE EQUIVALENT

Emitter (E)   Collector (C)

Base (B)

SYMBOL

Figure 3.17 Junction Transistor

is forward-biased and the other section re-verse-biased, current flows directly through the centre section and into the reverse-biased end of the crystal. Thus, the flow of current from end to end can be controlled by the centre section. This, and the fact that current flows out of a low-resistance, forward-biased section into a reverse-biased, high-resistance section, makes the junction transistor important for computers, as we will see.

Examine Figure 3.18 and notice that B_1 supplies the forward bias and B_2 the reverse bias for the NPN transistor.

If the forward-bias circuit were selected so that 10 mA of current flowed, then I_E would read 10 mA. Most of this current flows through the centre or base section and into the other end section or collector. Therefore, I_C would also read about 10 mA. A sensitive meter placed in the base path would read a tiny current flow, about 0.2 mA in this case. If we could watch the meters and open the base connection, both I_E and I_C would fall to zero. This means that the tiny base current — about 2% of I_E — can control the larger current flow through the device. We might compare this effect to a force of 2 N controlling a force of 100 N, or, in a hydraulic system, a trickle in a small pipe controlling a torrent in a large pipe.

Before we go further with this aspect of base current control, let us stop and discuss why the electrons flow through the base and into the reverse-biased collector section.

Consider an emitter electron in Figure 3.18. It is pushed out of the emitter crystal and past the barrier wall in the P-type base section. In a normal diode this electron would simply be attracted to the positive terminal of the battery B_1. In the transistor, however, the forces affecting this electron once it enters the base are quite different. Remember that the base is extremely thin — only a few atoms thick — and that next to it is the large positive depletion region in the collector crystal. The electron can

either work its way via the holes in the base to the battery B_1, or move directly out of the base section and over to the positive region in the collector crystal. This second force is immense compared to the force of B_1 and its source is only a few atoms away. As a result most electrons that appear in the base crystal are immediately captured by the depletion region

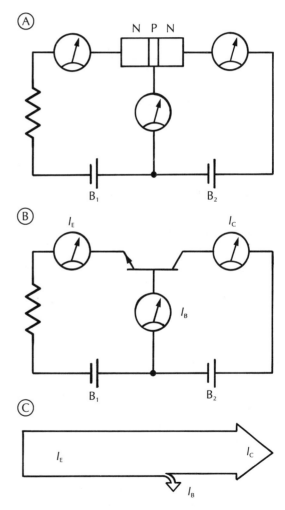

Figure 3.18 Transistor Current Division

in the collector crystal. Once an electron enters the collector section it is quickly whisked
to the outer end of the collector crystal and
onward to the positive terminal of battery B_2.
This means that the main current flow through
the transistor is from emitter to collector with
only a small trickle of flow to the base circuit.
Figure 3.19 illustrates the effect of the depletion region on charge movement through the
transistor.

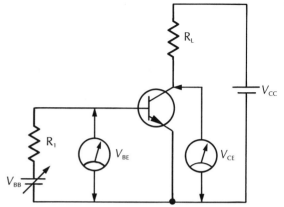

Figure 3.20 Voltage Amplification in a Common-
Emitter Transistor

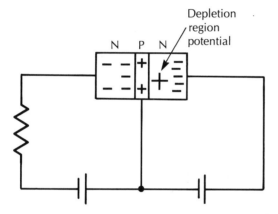

Figure 3.19 Collector Attraction

The fact that a small base current can control
a much larger flow is obviously important. Yet
a transistor can do even more. It can amplify
voltage variations and introduce a power gain
for varying currents.

The basics of voltage amplification can be
understood with the aid of Figure 3.20. The
battery marked V_{BB} supplies forward bias and
that marked V_{CC} reverse bias. Current flows
from emitter to collector as before, with a small
trickle of current flow to the base. Resistor R_1
is in the circuit to introduce a voltage drop
such that the correct forward bias is applied to
set up a safe level of current in the transistor.
Resistor R_L is used to introduce another voltage
drop. In this case we will assume that this second resistor has a voltage drop equal to one-
half of V_{CC}. If V_{CC} were supplied by a 9-V bat-

tery, the voltmeter marked V_{CE} would read 4.5
V. V_{BE}, which is the small forward bias that
pushes charge across the base barrier potential, would be about 0.5 V. If nothing in the
circuit changed we would have fixed readings
for V_{BE} and V_{CE}. The values of I_E, I_B, and I_C
would also be constant. If, however, we
changed the value of V_{BB}, all of our circuit
readings would change. Why? Assume that V_{BB}
rises. This would cause an increase in V_{BE} which
would produce a stronger forward bias. More
charge would flow out of the emitter and across
the barrier wall in the base. Most of this increase in current would flow directly through
the base section and into the collector crystal.
The increased collector circuit flow would cause
an increase in the voltage drop across R_L. There
would be a corresponding decrease in the voltage V_{CE} across the transistor. A set of actual
circuit measurements would show us that the
change in voltage across the transistor (V_{CE}) and
across R_L is much greater than the change in
base voltage (V_{BE}). We would find that a small
change in forward-bias voltage of about 0.1 V
would create a change in V_{CE} and V_{R_L} of about
1 or 2 V. This is voltage amplification. It is
almost like putting a dollar into a machine and
getting ten or twenty dollars out!

Amplification occurs in this circuit because of the extreme sensitivity of the base. The slightest change in base voltage causes a relatively large change in emitter and collector current and large changes in the voltages across R_L and the transistor.

Nevertheless, this is not a case of "getting something for nothing" in the circuit. Even though there is an amplified voltage, all of the circuit energy is supplied by the battery. We are really trading in relatively large amounts of DC energy for the tremendously great advantage of getting signal amplification.

We also get important energy gains in the signal — that is, in the changing voltages in the transistor. The energy gain can be seen by comparing the changing energy levels in the base circuit with the changing levels in the collector circuit.

Refer once again to Figure 3.20 to see how signal power gain occurs. The energy used to control the flow of current through the transistor is that of $V_{BE} \times I_B$. Voltage in volts times current in amperes expresses power in watts. So it is the forward-bias voltage V_{BE} and the resulting base current flow, I_B, that determine the energy required to control transistor current flow. Typical values for this circuit might be 0.5 V for V_{BE} and 0.1 mA for I_B. This equals a base circuit power of 50 μW. If we increase V_{BB} so that V_{BE} equals 0.6 V, I_B might rise to 0.15 mA. The base circuit power would now be 90 μW. Thus the change in voltage has produced a change in base circuit power of 40 μW.

The collector circuit power, on the other hand, is much greater. Remember the collector current is about fifty times that of the base current. If we select the values of $I_C = 5$ mA and $V_{R_L} = 4.5$ V, the power expended in R_L is:

$$P_{R_L} = V_{R_L} \times I_C$$
$$= 4.5 \times 5 \times 10^{-3}$$
$$= 22.5 \times 10^{-3} \text{ watts or } 22.5 \text{ mW}$$

If this set of values were to occur with a base current of 100 mA, the collector power expended in R_L would be 450 times as great as the power in the base circuit:

$$\frac{P_{R_L}}{P_{BASE}} = \frac{22.5}{0.05} = 450$$

If we further assume that the increase in base voltage increases the collector current from 5 mA to 7 mA, V_{R_L} would increase from 4.5 V to 6.3 V.

The 40% rise in I_C from 5 mA to 7 mA would cause a 40% rise in V_{R_L}, increasing it from 4.5 V to 6.3 V. The power expended in R_L would be 44.1 mW:

$$P_{R_L} = V_{R_L} \times I_C$$
$$= 6.3 \times 7 \times 10^{-3}$$
$$= 44.1 \times 10^{-3} \text{ watts or } 44.1 \text{ mW}$$

Thus the power expended in R_L increases by 21.6 mW when the power in the base circuit increases by 40 μW. This produces a power gain factor of 540 if we compare the change of power in the base circuit and the change of power in R_L:

$$\text{Power amplification} = \frac{P_{R_{L_1}} - P_{R_{L_2}}}{P_{B_1} - P_{B_2}}$$
$$= \frac{44.1 - 22.5}{0.090 - 0.050}$$
$$= \frac{21.6}{0.04}$$
$$= 540$$

Transistor power gains can be much larger than the value given in our example. The main point is that though the energy needed to cause a change in transistor current is small, it creates a corresponding change of energy in the collector circuit which is much greater.

This aspect of its operation makes the transistor useful as a switching device in computer circuits. A small voltage applied to the base of the transistor can cause the emitter-collector section to conduct heavily or to cut off current flow. The transistor behaves like a switch. When a forward-bias voltage is applied to the base, the transistor conducts. When a reverse-bias or no-bias voltage is applied, the transistor is cut off. Transistors have the advantages of speed and no moving parts. The simple circuit in Figure 3.21 shows how a transistor can be used as a switch to turn a light-emitting diode on and off.

When the control signal is producing a positive pulse, it turns the transistor on. Current will flow up from the emitter to the collector,

through the LED and R_2 to the $+V_{cc}$ point, energizing the diode. When there is no input pulse, the transistor will not conduct because it has no forward bias applied to its base. Transistors are used for a great many more switching functions in computer circuits. We will study some of them in the following chapters.

3.4 Field-Effect Transistors

Our previous discussion would seem to indicate that a junction transistor is an almost perfect device for switching and amplification. It has the disadvantage, however, of requiring energy in the base to regulate the collector current flow. Granted, this energy is small, but when great numbers of transistors are used in chips, the energy expenditure is important. There are other considerations as well that restrict the use of junction transistors. We will mention these in the following discussion of various types of *field-effect transistors* (FETs), which do not have such disadvantages.

The JFET (Junction Field-Effect Transistor)

The JFET is, in some ways, similar to a junction transistor. However, its main current flow is controlled by a reverse-biased gate rather than a forward-biased base. A perfect JFET would allow complete control of the main current by a zero-current control circuit.

The JFET consists of a section of N- or P-type silicon surrounded by a collar of oppositely doped silicon. Figure 3.22 shows the basic physical features of the JFET. Here a small cylinder of N-type silicon is surrounded by a section of P-type silicon. Basically we have a PN junction formation except that there are three connections instead of two.

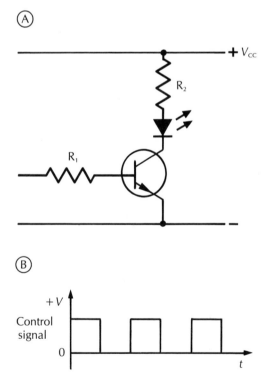

Figure 3.21 Transistor Acting as a Switch

STRUCTURE

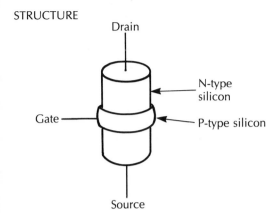

SYMBOL

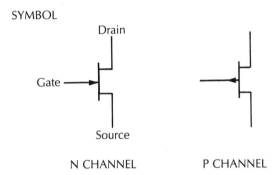

N CHANNEL   P CHANNEL

Figure 3.22 Junction Field-Effect Transistor (JFET)

When the JFET is operating, channel current flows from source to drain. With no gate connection the channel current would be limited by the applied voltage and the total resistance of the circuit, but when the gate is brought into the picture the current-flow condition is altered. The gate is normally connected to a reverse-bias potential applied between the gate and the source. This reverse bias creates a depletion region in the channel adjacent to the gate material. This inhibits the flow of current through the channel. The higher the reverse bias, the greater the depletion region and thus the higher the source-to-drain resistance. As might be expected, certain values of reverse

bias can cut off the channel current completely. With a fixed value of drain-to-source voltage (V_{DS}) there is a more or less direct relationship between the channel current and the reverse bias at the gate (V_{GS}). However, when the gate voltage is fixed and V_{DS} is varied, the channel current (I_D) rises linearly at first, then levels off as we increase the value of V_{DS}. This levelling is due to "pinch-off" in the silicon channel.

We can explain the pinch-off effect with the aid of Figure 3.23. Assume that the gate reverse bias is set at V_{GS}. Consider what happens as V_{DS} is increased from zero. The gate bias will have established a certain depletion in the crystal which presents a certain resistance in the channel. As V_{DS} is increased, more and more charge

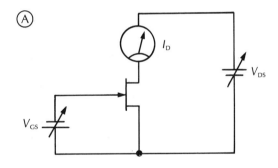

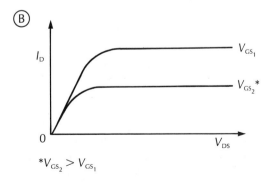

Figure 3.23 JFET V_{DS} versus I_D Characteristics

will flow through the channel. As V_{DS} rises, a new form of reverse bias presents itself. This reverse bias comes from the internal voltage distribution within the crystal supplied by V_{DS}. We can think of the channel as a long resistor. If we picked the midpoint of the resistor we would find 50% of the V_{DS} potential. As V_{DS} rises, the potential at this midpoint would rise proportionally. Thus, as V_{DS} rises the voltage at a point in the crystal adjacent to the gate rises. If we could measure the voltage at this point relative to the gate we could see the increase on the voltmeter. The meter would be measuring the increases in reverse bias due to increases in V_{DS}.

Now we have two actions taking place simultaneously. The rise in V_{DS} is trying to make I_D increase and the rise in the reverse bias is trying to make it decrease. One effect offsets the other and the overall action is such that I_D remains relatively constant over a wide range of values of V_{DS}. The point at which this levelling-off action begins to occur is called the pinch-off. Referring back to Figure 3.23 we can see that V_{GS} has a fairly direct control over I_D if V_{DS} is kept above the pinch-off level. Thus, the JFET can be used as a convenient switching or amplifying device similar to the junction transistor. Moreover, it has the advantage that it controls its main current flow with a gate circuit that requires no current.

Figure 3.24 shows a typical JFET amplifier circuit. When channel current flows, it creates voltage drops across resistors R_L and R_S. The voltage drops across R_S establish the reverse bias for the gate. The voltage drops across R_L make signal amplification possible in exactly the same way as described earlier for the junction transistor.

The bias that comes from R_S might need some clarification. Consider a voltmeter across R_S and assume that it reads a drop of 1 V. This means that the reverse bias from gate to source is 1 V. This is true because there is no gate

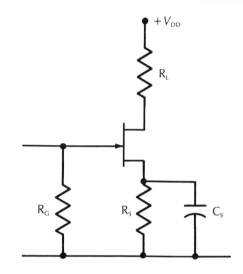

Figure 3.24 JFET Amplifier

current flow and thus no voltage drop across R_G. So the full voltage across R_S acts on the gate just as if R_G were not present. Indeed, R_G could be left out of the circuit and replaced by a short circuit as far as the bias is concerned. It is, however, needed to act as a load across which the input signal is developed. The input voltage that appears across R_G either adds to or subtracts from the bias and either increases or lowers the channel current. When the channel current is changed the voltage drop across R_L is changed. In this way a small input voltage causes a relatively large change in the voltage across R_L and consequently across the JFET.

If we think of the JFET as a switching device we can see that the application of a strong negative voltage at the gate would cause the channel current to drop to zero. With zero channel current there would be no voltage drop across R_L. Therefore the voltage across the JFET would be V_{DD}. Thus, a negative input signal causes a positive signal condition at the drain of the JFET. This feature of the JFET would make it usable as an inverter. Since the input condition is reversed at the output, it could be arranged so that a binary 0 input would appear at the output as a binary 1.

A disadvantage of the JFET is the leakage current that flows in the gate circuit. A perfect JFET would have no reverse-bias leakage current. This leakage current is a problem because it upsets the operating characteristics of a transistor. It can cause it to burn out, it lowers the input resistance to the JFET, and it represents an unwanted energy expenditure.

The MOSFET (Metal-Oxide-Semiconductor Field-Effect Transistor)

A MOSFET is a modified JFET. The name stands for metal-oxide-semiconductor field-effect transistor. It is sometimes called an *insulated gate FET*. As the name implies, the gate is not a PN junction but simply a thin metal layer separated from the conducting channel by an insulating layer of silicon dioxide. Figure 3.25 illustrates this arrangement.

The gate potential controls the current in the channel by either enriching the charge carriers in it or depleting them. If a positive gate potential is applied, electrons from the highly doped end sections of the channel are drawn into the thin channel section, lowering its resistance. If a negative gate potential is applied, electrons in the thin channel section are forced out, increasing its resistance. This response to gate potentials results in significant change in the channel current. This effect is similar to gate action in the JFET. Here, however, we have the advantage of response to both polarities of input, whereas the JFET could handle only one polarity of bias. Further, the insulating layer prevents gate leakage current, which reduces energy loss in the input circuit.

The Enhancement MOSFET

There is still another version of the field-effect transistor. It is called the *enhancement-mode MOSFET* or simply *enhancement MOSFET*. It has the advantage that it has no channel current flow unless there is a sufficiently strong gate voltage present. Recall that both the JFET and the conventional insulated gate MOSFET have channel current flow under normal circumstances. The application of a gate potential simply increases or decreases the existing channel current. In the enhancement MOSFET, there is no circuit current until a signal is present. This is a tremendous advantage in circuits where energy expenditure is critical. Figure 3.26 illustrates the basic structure of the enhancement MOSFET.

If we simply connect a battery between the source and drain terminals there will be no current flow as the channel is not continuous — the source and drain are like "islands" of N material. In fact, depletion regions will be

STRUCTURE

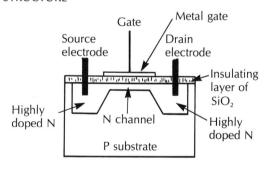

SYMBOL

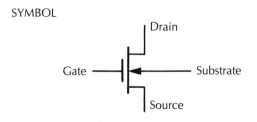

Figure 3.25 N-Channel MOSFET

STRUCTURE

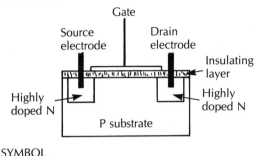

SYMBOL

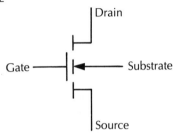

Figure 3.26 P-Substrate (N-Channel)
Enhancement MOSFET

present around these islands, which will further ensure that no current flows from source to drain. But when a positive potential is applied to the gate, charge (electrons in this case) is attracted to the region of the substrate under the gate. Thus electrons come from the source island and the drain island and from any free electrons present in the substrate. As a result a channel is created between the source and the drain which makes the section act as if it were continuous N material. Current can now flow from source to drain. But it will do so only when a positive potential is applied to the gate. If a negative potential is applied, the transistor will not conduct.

Figure 3.26 shows only one type of enhancement MOSFET. If the N and P materials in the transistor are reversed to create an N-substrate, P-channel type, a negative gate voltage is needed to cause conduction.

When a pair of opposite types of enhancement-mode MOSFETs are used in a switching circuit this is called a *complementary* system (abbreviated CMOS for "complementary metal-oxide semiconductor"). Circuits of this family have extremely low power dissipation. CMOSs are used extensively in all manner of digital circuits, such as those in wrist watches, calculators, and space apparatus.

Figure 3.27 shows how two opposite enhancement-mode transistors could be used as an inverter.

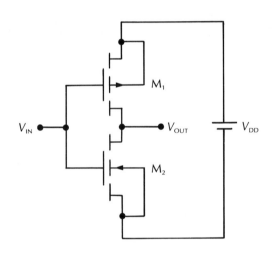

Figure 3.27 CMOS Circuit

If a positive input signal is present it will turn on transistor M_2 and turn off transistor M_1. In this state we can think of M_2 as a closed switch and M_1 as a high resistance. As a result V_{OUT} will be low or zero relative to the battery negative point in the circuit. The opposite set of conditions applies to a low or negative input signal.

Questions

1. Name the three essential parts of a basic circuit.
2. Define *source, conducting path*, and *load*.
3. Define *voltage, charge, current, resistance*, and *insulator*.
4. Explain why current flow is the same in all parts of a simple circuit.
5. State the Ohm's Law relationship for current and voltage and for current and resistance.
6. Find R if $V = 12$ V and $I = 10$ mA.
7. Find V if $R = 1$ kΩ and $I = 10$ mA.
8. Find I if $R = 1.7$ kΩ and $V = 6$ V.
9. Why are resistor colour codes used?
10. How is total circuit resistance affected when resistors are connected in parallel?
11. How is total circuit resistance affected when resistors are connected in series?
12. Explain the basic function of a diode in a circuit.
13. Why is a diode often referred to as a polarity-sensitive switch?
14. In a circuit, can current flow between two points having positive charges? Explain.
15. In a circuit, can current flow between two points having negative charges? Explain.
16. Explain why pure silicon is an insulator.
17. Define *covalent bond, doping, N-type silicon*, and *P-type silicon*.
18. Describe the subshell distribution of electrons in silicon.
19. Does a section of N-type silicon bear a negative charge? Explain.
20. Does P-type silicon become positively charged due to doping? Explain.
21. Explain how a barrier potential is formed in a PN junction.
22. Define *reverse bias* and *forward bias*.
23. Explain why current does not flow in a reverse-biased diode.
24. Explain how forward bias causes diode current flow.
25. Explain how current flow in N material differs from current flow in P material.
26. Explain how current flow in a light-emitting diode causes light energy to be radiated.
27. Explain the purpose of the base section in a junction transistor.
28. Explain why current flows into the reverse-biased collector section of a junction transistor.
29. Explain the reason for calling a junction transistor a current amplifier.
30. Explain how transistors can introduce a power gain.
31. Explain how a transistor can be used as an electronic switch.
32. How does a JFET differ from a junction transistor?
33. Explain the meaning of pinch-off in a JFET.
34. What is the main advantage of a JFET over a junction transistor?
35. How does a MOSFET differ from a JFET?
36. Explain how the gate in a MOSFET controls the channel current.
37. What is the main advantage of a MOSFET over a JFET?
38. Explain the basic difference between an enhancement MOSFET and a depletion MOSFET.
39. What are complementary MOSFETs?
40. Can a JFET accept two polarities of gate bias? Explain.
41. What is the advantage of a full-wave power supply over the half-wave type?
42. Explain the action of a coil-capacitor power supply filter.
43. Explain the need for a regulator at the output of a DC power supply.

Experiments

Experiment 3.1

Object

To show the effect of parallel and series resistance on current flow.

Circuit

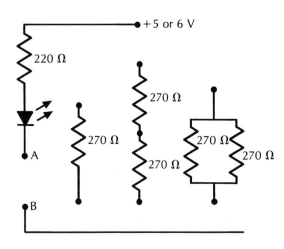

Figure E3.1

Steps

1. Connect the 270-Ω resistor to points A and B. Observe the brightness of the LED.
2. Connect the two 270-Ω resistors joined in series, to points A and B. Observe the brightness of the LED.
3. Connect the two 270-Ω resistors joined in parallel, to points A and B. Observe the brightness of the LED.
4. How is LED brightness related to current flow?
5. If you measured with an ohmmeter the resistance between points A and B in each of the three cases, what would the readings be?

Experiment 3.2

Object

To show the conditions under which current will flow between two points.

Circuit

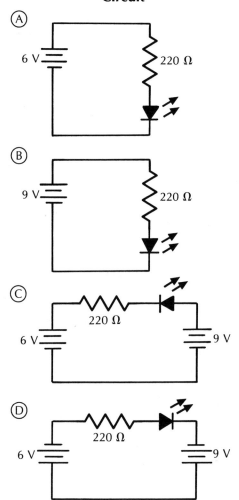

Figure E3.2

Steps

1. Connect circuit A. Observe the brightness of the LED.
2. Connect circuit B. Observe the brightness of the LED.

3. Connect circuit C. Observe the brightness of the LED.
4. Connect circuit D. Observe the brightness of the LED.
5. Will current flow between two negative points?
6. Will current flow between two positive points?
7. What is the effective voltage in circuit C? Circuit D?

4. Calculate the internal resistance of the LED in circuits A and B.
5. Why is the series resistance needed in the circuits?
6. If you connected the LED directly to a 1-V source, would it glow?
7. If you reversed the LED in circuit A, what readings would you get for V and I?

Experiment 3.3

Object

To show the operating characteristics of an LED.

Circuit

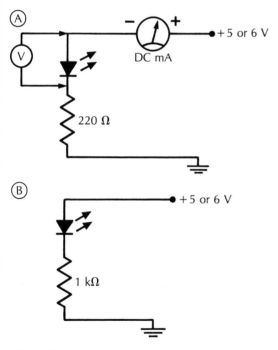

Figure E3.3

Steps

1. Connect circuit A. Record the current flow.
2. Use a high-impedance DCVM to measure the voltage across the LED.
3. Connect circuit B. Again measure I and V.

Experiment 3.4

Object

To become familiar with the operation of a MAN 72A seven-segment display.

Circuit

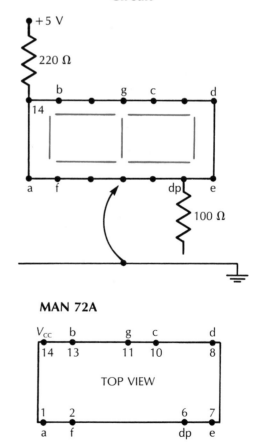

Figure E3.4

Steps

1. Connect pin 14 to the positive 5- or 6-V source via the 220-Ω resistor.
2. Use a small probe wire to touch, in turn, each remaining pin on the display, except pin 6, to the negative side of the source. Record the display response for each pin.
3. Connect pin 6 to ground via a 100-Ω resistor.
4. Why is the 200-Ω resistor required at the common anode?

Experiment 3.5

Object

To show how current flows in a junction transistor.

Circuit

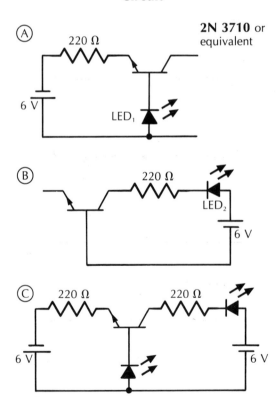

Figure E3.5

Steps

1. Connect circuit A. Observe the brightness of the LED.
2. Replace the LED in circuit A with a milliammeter and record *I*.
3. Connect circuit B and observe the LED.
4. Connect circuit C. Observe the brightness of both LEDs.
5. Replace the LEDs in circuit C with milliammeters and record the currents.
6. What percentage of the emitter current transfers to the collector in circuit C?

Experiment 3.6

Object

To show the voltage distribution in an active junction transistor circuit.

Circuit

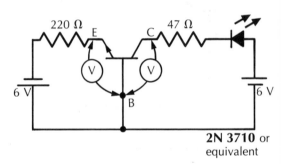

Figure E3.6

Steps

1. Connect the circuit. Observe the LED.
2. Use a high-impedance DCVM to measure the emitter-base and base-collector voltages.
3. Measure the voltage drops across the 220-Ω and 47-Ω resistors.
4. Measure the voltage drop across the LED.
5. Why is the 220-Ω resistor needed?
6. With the circuit operating, place a short across the 47-Ω resistor. Does the LED brightness change? Explain.

Experiment 3.7

Object

To show the operation of an active, common-emitter, junction transistor.

Circuit

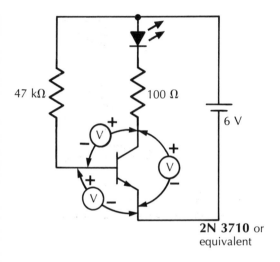

Figure E3.7

Steps

1. Connect the circuit. Observe the brightness of the LED.
2. Using a high-impedance DCVM, measure the following voltages: base to emitter; base to collector; collector to emitter.
3. Replace the 47-kΩ base resistor with a 10-kΩ. Observe the brightness of the LED.
4. Calculate the base current flow through the 47-kΩ resistor.
5. Why is the 100-Ω resistor used in the collector circuit?

Experiment 3.8

Object

To show how a common-emitter junction transistor can introduce a voltage gain.

Circuit

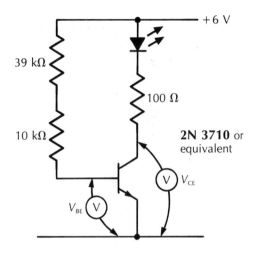

Figure E3.8

Steps

1. Connect the circuit. Observe the brightness of the LED.
2. Measure the following voltages: base to emitter; collector to emitter.
3. Short out the 39-kΩ base resistor and repeat the measurements of step 2.
4. Determine the changes in the base and collector voltages from steps 2 and 3.
5. Calculate the voltage gain by:

$$\text{Gain} = \frac{\Delta V_{CE}}{\Delta V_{BE}}$$

6. Why is the LED brighter in step 3?

Experiment 3.9

Object

To show the operating characteristics of a JFET.

Circuit

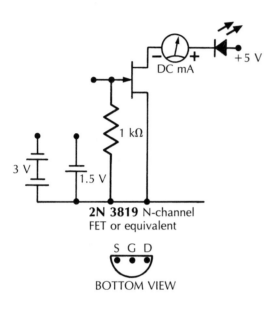

Figure E3.9

Steps

1. Connect the circuit. Record the drain current.
2. Place a short across the 1-kΩ gate resistor. Does the drain current change?
3. If a variable power supply is available, step the voltage from 0 to 9 V in 1-V steps. Record the drain current for each step.
4. With V_{DS} set at 5 V, connect the gate to the 1.5-V battery. Record I_D.
5. With V_{DS} set at 5 V, connect the gate to the 3-V battery. Record I_D.
6. Make a graph of the data obtained in step 3.

Experiment 3.10

Object

To show the conduction characteristics of a depletion MOSFET.

Circuit

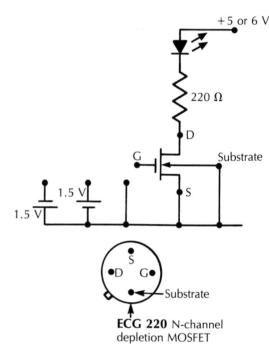

Figure E3.10

Steps

1. Connect the circuit. Connect G to ground. Observe the brightness of the LED.
2. Remove the ground from the gate and connect the gate to the positive terminal of the 1.5-V battery. Observe the brightness of the LED.
3. Connect the gate to the negative terminal of the 1.5-V battery. Observe the brightness of the LED.
4. How can two polarities be used at the gate without damaging the transistor?

Experiment 3.11

Object

To show the operation of an enhancement-mode MOSFET.

Circuit

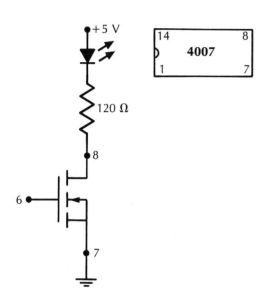

Figure E3.11

Steps

1. Connect the circuit. Connect the gate to ground. Observe the LED.
2. Connect the gate to + 5 V. Observe the LED.
3. Why should MOSFET gates be shorted to ground (substrate) when being handled?

Experiment 3.12

Object

To show the operation of a CMOS inverter.

Circuit

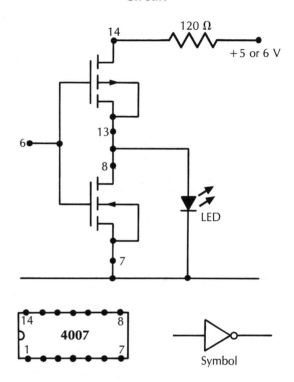

Figure E3.12

Steps

1. Connect the circuit.
2. Connect the gate to ground. Observe the LED.
3. Connect the gate high (pin 14). Observe the LED.
4. How do the two series transistors differ?

CHAPTER 4

Gates and Logic

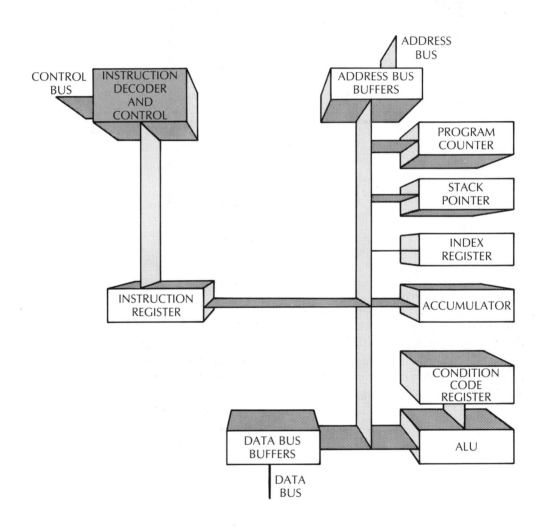

CONTROL BUS

INSTRUCTION DECODER AND CONTROL

ADDRESS BUS

ADDRESS BUS BUFFERS

PROGRAM COUNTER

STACK POINTER

INDEX REGISTER

INSTRUCTION REGISTER

ACCUMULATOR

CONDITION CODE REGISTER

DATA BUS BUFFERS

ALU

DATA BUS

MICROPROCESSOR UNITS

■ INTRODUCTION ■

In this chapter, we will examine basic logic gates. Gates are the electronic circuits that control all of the binary processes that occur in a computer. They are circuits that produce a definite two-state output in response to various binary input conditions. This characteristic of gates makes it possible for them to do the many kinds of mathematical calculations with great accuracy.

This chapter will show that a computer does not consist of masses of tremendously complex circuits. Rather, it has relatively few and rather simple circuits, which, however, are used in large numbers to process binary data.

Integrated Circuit
Courtesy of Kurt Schick

4.1 Gates

In nontechnical use, the word *gate* describes a device that is used to allow — or not allow — passage through a barrier such as a fence. Computer gates are logic circuits with one output and one or more inputs, which allow the passage of binary signals through the gate for certain input combinations.

A simple PN junction diode can act as a gate. It will conduct if the correct polarity of voltage is applied and not conduct if the polarity is reversed. Figure 4.1 illustrates this gate function. When a forward bias is present, the diode acts as a closed switch and the battery voltage (input) appears across the resistor (output). When a reverse bias is present, the diode does not conduct and the input voltage does not appear at the output. In this second situation the diode is working like a polarity-sensitive switch or gate. It lets the positive voltage pass but stops or blocks a negative potential.

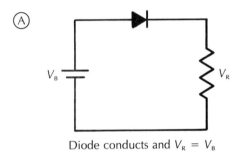

Diode conducts and $V_R = V_B$

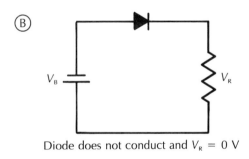

Diode does not conduct and $V_R = 0$ V

Figure 4.1 Diode Gate

The transistors discussed in Chapter 3 can act in exactly the same way as diodes. When the correct form of bias signal is applied to the base, or gate, of the device, current is either caused to flow or cut off, depending on the input signal polarity. We will now examine specific types of circuits that provide a variety of gate actions. When used in combination they can do arithmetic and the whole range of logical functions unique to computers. From studying these circuits it will be seen that logic gates can be constructed in a variety of ways.

As we have seen, there is diode logic. Also, transistors, with associated circuit resistors, can be used as gates. These circuits are called *resistor-transistor logic* (RTL) types. Similarly, transistors can be used in combination to form gates. This arrangement is known as *transistor-transistor logic* (TTL). Other circuit arrangements are named similarly — that is, according to their specific features. All of these logic "families" are employed in integrated circuits (ICs), where large numbers of gates have been formed on incredibly small silicon chips.

The AND Gate

The AND gate is a common computer gate. It has an output only when all inputs are present. By "output" we mean a *non-zero* output — in other words, a binary 1 condition. In computers, binary 1 is normally represented by the presence of a voltage, and binary 0 by the absence of a voltage or a low-voltage condition.

Figure 4.2 shows a typical diode AND gate. Notice how simple the circuit is. The input points are A and B. When either switch is connected to the battery B_1, a positive potential is applied to its diode, preventing it from conducting. In this condition the diode acts like an open switch, as discussed in Chapter 3. This positive potential can be considered as a binary 1. When either switch is connected to the common bottom point of the circuit, its diode is placed in a conducting condition and acts like a closed switch. When one or both of the diodes conducts, current flows up through the diode or diodes and up through the resistor to

battery B_2. All, or nearly all, of the B_2 voltage will appear as a voltage drop across the resistor. The output voltage, measured from Y to the common (bottom) point in the circuit, will be zero. The only way a voltage can be present at Y is for both diodes to be cut off, and this only occurs when both A and B are at a positive level (binary 1). We can see, then, that both inputs must be at a binary 1 level in order for a binary 1 to appear at the output.

In an AND circuit with four inputs, all of them would have to be at a binary 1 level in order for the output to be at binary 1.

The characteristics of an AND circuit can be summarized in a "table of combinations" which is normally called a *truth table*. The truth table of a logic circuit shows all the input-output

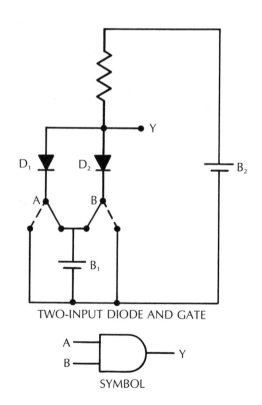

TWO-INPUT DIODE AND GATE

SYMBOL

Figure 4.2 AND Gate

relationships that apply to the circuit. (The letters A, B, and Y correspond to points in Figure 4.2.)

AND Gate Truth Table

Input		Output
A	B	Y
0	0	0
0	1	0
1	0	0
1	1	1

As shown, the AND circuit operates on an "all-or-nothing" principle. All inputs must be high (at binary 1) in order for the output to be high.

Two transistors could be used in place of the diodes to form an AND circuit. A basic circuit of this type is shown in Figure 4.3.

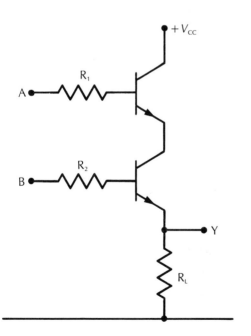

Figure 4.3 Two-Transistor AND Circuit

In order to get a voltage across resistor R_L which would represent a binary 1, it would be necessary to have a positive potential at the base of both transistors. The transistors are in series and both must be in a conducting state in order to produce such a voltage drop. As can be seen, the truth-table conditions that applied to the previous AND circuit are present here.

Compare the basic AND circuits in Figures 4.2 and 4.3. In Figure 4.2 the diode circuit operates such that the input circuits (A and B) are in the path of the main current flow. In Figure 4.3, on the other hand, the input circuits A and B are in the transistor base current paths and not in the main current path through the transistors. Thus the input or control circuit currents can be much smaller than in the diode circuit. There are two advantages in this. The first has to do with control-signal energy. Logic gates are normally turned on and off by small sequential pulses of voltage and not by switches connected to batteries. These pulse signals have limited energy levels and cannot control high-energy circuits. The second advantage is that the lower loading effect of the transistor circuit makes multiple input control possible.

Many other circuits have been devised to add flexibility to logic systems. One such device is the *multiple-emitter transistor*. IC design techniques have made it possible to form transistors that have several emitter segments. A dual-emitter transistor could replace the two individual transistors used in Figure 4.3.

Figure 4.4 shows an AND circuit in which a multiple-emitter transistor is used to simplify the circuit. Remember that this circuit is just one of many circuits contained in a single IC chip.

Notice that the input control leads A and B act on the same transistor, whereas two transistors were used to effect input control in Figure 4.3. It is true that we are using a second transistor here to deliver an output condition

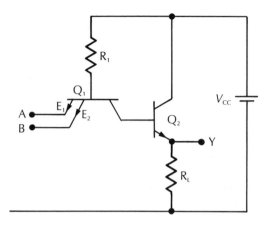

Figure 4.4 Dual-Emitter Input TTL AND Circuit

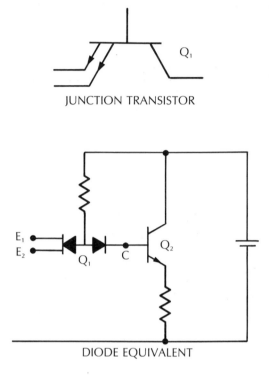

Figure 4.5 Diode Equivalent of Junction Transistor Q_1 in Figure 4.4

across R_L, but as we will see shortly, actual chip circuits are greatly simplified by the multiple-emitter arrangement. There are other advantages which will be discussed later.

It is important here to discuss in detail the function of the junction transistor Q_1 in Figure 4.4. In order clearly to understand the circuit we must look upon Q_1 as a pair of diodes. Remember that a junction transistor is really just two diodes that share a centre section. Thus Q_1 can be considered in terms of its diode-pair equivalent shown in Figure 4.5.

If the base has a positive potential and either the emitter or the collector is connected to ground, current will flow to the base through the diode section that completes the circuit. Similarly, if both E and C are connected to ground and the base is positive, current will flow to the base through both diode sections.

Transistor Operating Modes

At this point in the discussion we must consider the three basic modes of operation for a transistor. These are:

1. The *cut-off* mode, wherein the transistor acts as an open circuit.

2. The *saturation* mode, wherein the transistor is conducting at or near its maximum current level in the circuit and can be considered as a closed switch.
3. The *active* or *linear* mode, wherein the transistor is between these extremes and acts as a nearly linear amplifier.

The active and the cut-off modes are familiar to us (see Chapter 3). The saturation mode, on the other hand, is much different from transistor behaviour in normal amplifier circuits. It is different both in terms of the voltage distribution in the transistor and in terms of its current-flow pattern. Figure 4.6 illustrates the differences in the voltage distribution in the transistor for these three modes.

In the cut-off mode in Figure 4.6A there is no conduction except for leakage current, and thus no voltage drop across resistor R_L. Con-

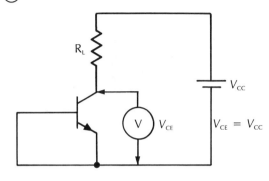

(A) CUT-OFF MODE

$V_{CE} = V_{CC}$

(B) ACTIVE MODE

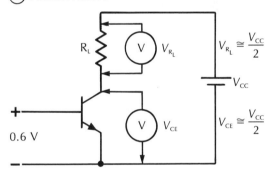

0.6 V

$V_{R_L} \cong \dfrac{V_{CC}}{2}$

$V_{CE} \cong \dfrac{V_{CC}}{2}$

(C) SATURATION MODE

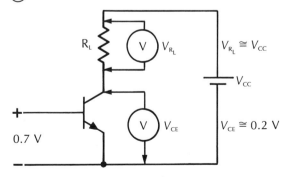

0.7 V

$V_{R_L} \cong V_{CC}$

$V_{CE} \cong 0.2\ V$

Figure 4.6 Transistor Voltage Distribution and Operating Mode

sequently all of the battery voltage appears across the transistor.

The active or linear mode of operation in 4.6B has the transistor conducting at an intermediate level. The voltage drops across R_L and the transistor are approximately equal and about half of V_{CC}. As mentioned earlier, this mode is the normal mode of operation for transistor amplifiers. In logic circuits, however, the transistor is generally used as a switch or a gate and not as an amplifier. Hence, the transistors are generally operated at one extreme or the other.

The saturation mode illustrated in 4.6C applies to a transistor that is conducting heavily and acting like a closed switch. The voltage across this transistor (V_{CE}) is typically 0.2 V. When we examine all voltages present at the transistor we find that both sections of the transistor are actually forward-biased.

The base-emitter voltage is about 0.7 V and acts as a forward bias on this section. The base-collector voltage must be about 0.5 V as the collector is at $+0.2$ V while the base is at $+0.7$ V. This set of potentials creates a difference voltage of 0.5 V. The base is positive relative to the collector. This is, of course, a forward bias on this section.

This operating mode causes an interesting set of conditions in the transistor. Current flows from emitter to base due to the forward bias V_{BE}. From there it flows on into the collector as a normal collector current. As well, there is the usual contribution of base current from this flow.

Along with this flow there is another current present. This flows from collector to base due to the forward bias present at saturation. This second current flow diminishes I_C and increases I_B. This is not to say that we have current flowing simultaneously in two directions in the collector circuit. Rather, there is a two-current tendency, but the "normal" collector current flow predominates. When we experiment with this conduction mode we find that as we go deeper into saturation, I_B rises steeply and I_C rises gradually. This is due to the current-flow conditions we have just described. The important overall effect is that the transistor acts like an extremely low resistance when it is saturated.

We have analyzed transistor saturation with reference to Figure 4.6C. The whole discussion started, however, in reference to transistor Q_1 in Figure 4.4. This transistor, as we saw, behaves like a pair of diodes and conducts differently than the transistor in Figure 4.6C. Figure 4.7 illustrates some of the similarities and differences between these two transistors.

In Figure 4.7A the transistor is acting like a pair of diodes where one diode circuit has more resistance than the other. They are both forward-biased. If we assume V_{BE} to be 0.7 V and V_{BC} to be 0.5 V (as in Figure 4.6C), V_{CE} will read 0.2 V. Thus in terms of the voltage across the emitter-collector leads, we would not be able to distinguish between the two transistor conditions. Strictly speaking, the transistor in A is not saturated in the sense that the one in B is. However, in terms of the voltage V_{CE}, it acts as if it were. For example, if R_L in circuit A represented the internal resistance of a voltmeter, it would measure V_{CE}, which would be about 0.2 V. Similarly, if R_L represented the base circuit of Q_2 in Figure 4.4, it would see this same potential (essentially zero volts) and would not turn on. Finally, the saturation current in Figure 4.7B is different from the transistor current pattern in A; however, the voltage drop presented across the emitter-base sections is similar.

Now we can return to our AND circuit in Figure 4.4. When both A and B inputs are open or at a positive potential, so that there is a reverse bias between emitter and base, this section of the transistor will be inactive. The base-collector section, on the other hand, will be conducting, as it is forward-biased from V_{CC}. This section of Q_1 allows base current flow from Q_2, which is limited to an appropriate

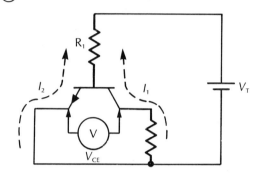

(A) PARALLEL DIODE EFFECT

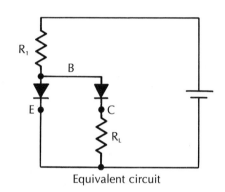

Equivalent circuit

(B) SATURATION

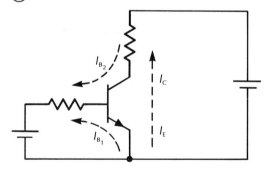

Figure 4.7 Transistor Saturation and Parallel Diode Action

value by R_1. This current-flow path turns Q_2 on and produces a "high" output across R_L. Thus, with both inputs high, there is a high

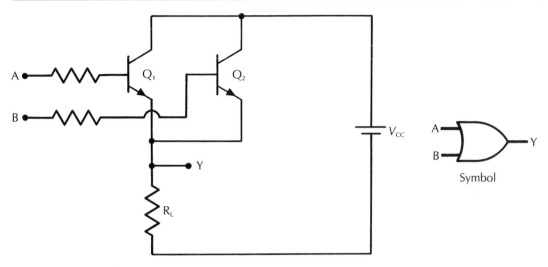

Figure 4.8 RTL OR Circuit

output — which satisfies one condition of an AND circuit. If either emitter of Q_1 is grounded, or if both are, the base voltage at Q_2 will drop to practically 0 V and Q_2 will quickly cut off. The collector circuit of Q_1 will now stop conducting. With Q_2 cut off, V_{R_L} is 0 V. A zero input (or ground) at either A or B will cause a 0 output at Y. All conditions are satisfied, then, for an AND circuit.

The OR Gate

The OR gate is another common gate. As its truth table shows, it is really the exact opposite of the AND gate.

OR Gate Truth Table

Input		Output
A	B	Y
0	0	0
1	0	1
0	1	1
1	1	1

Figure 4.8 shows a circuit using a resistor-transistor combination for this logic circuit. If a forward bias is applied to either transistor, it

will conduct and produce a binary 1 condition across R_L. The only input combination that will drop V_R to zero volts is binary 0 at both A and B.

The OR circuit could just as easily be constructed using diode resistor logic as in Figure 4.9.

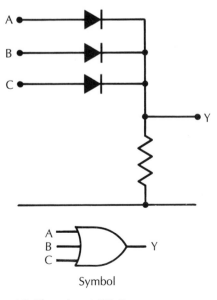

Figure 4.9 Three-Input OR Gate

Let us now take a slightly different approach to gate control. Consider the two-input OR gate in Figure 4.10. The inputs are supplied from a signal source rather than a pair of switch inputs. The signal source we are dealing with is delivering a chain of on-off pulses to input A. Simultaneously it is delivering a chain of such pulses to input B. The frequency of the pulses at A is higher than at B. Observe the chain of output pulses from Y as a result of the two signals.

Recall that an OR circuit delivers a binary 1 output when either A or B is at binary 1. The circuit output will remain at binary 1 all the time that one or the other input is at binary 1. The result is an output pulse chain that is lower in frequency than A or B.

At this point, where we have examined only the AND and the OR logic circuits, the reader might wonder how they are used in a computer or calculator to do arithmetic and many other

functions of such devices. As we will see shortly, however, these logic circuits are used in combination with several others to do all kinds of logical operations such as binary addition.

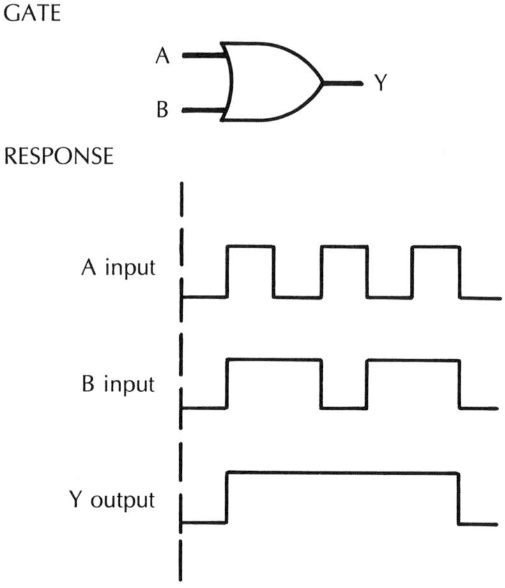

The NOT Gate

The NOT gate is sometimes called an inverter. Its function is to change an input condition to its binary opposite. Thus the circuit has only one input and one output.

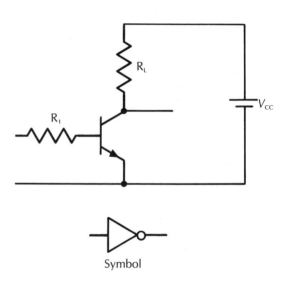

Figure 4.11 shows a basic NOT circuit and its symbol. When a binary 1 is applied to the input (high level), the transistor saturates and the collector voltage drops to nearly 0. Conversely, when a binary 0 is applied (low level), the transistor is cut off and its collector voltage will be at the V_{CC} value.

This circuit is used whenever a binary digit has to be changed to its opposite.

Figure 4.12 shows a NOT circuit which uses a pair of enhancement MOSFETs, as described

GATE

RESPONSE

Figure 4.10 Signal Response in a Two-Input OR Gate

Symbol

Figure 4.11 NOT Circuit

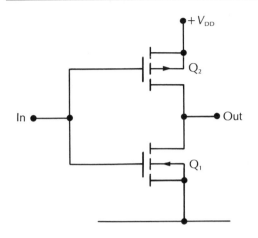

Figure 4.12 CMOS Inverter

Speaking in terms of binary signals, the NAND circuit produces an output that is the complement or negation of that of an AND circuit. It does this by means of an inverter connected to an AND gate. NAND gates can be produced using a variety of logic types. Figure 4.13 shows a basic NAND circuit using TTL.

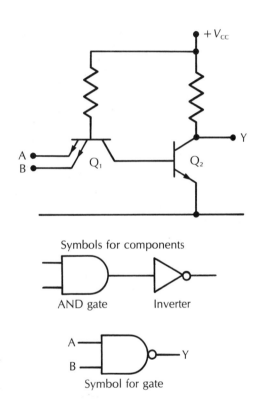

Figure 4.13 TTL NAND Gate

in Chapter 3. When the common gate terminals are connected to zero volts, the upper, P-channel transistor Q_2 is switched on and the lower, N-channel transistor Q_1 is switched off. This condition causes the output voltage to be high and approximately equal to V_{DD}. When a binary 1 is applied at the input, Q_2 is switched off and Q_1 on with the result that the output voltage drops to 0.

This type of inverter circuit consumes far less energy than the circuit used in Figure 4.11. Moreover, the "packing density" in chips can be very high with CMOS elements.

The NAND Gate

A NAND gate produces a low output when both of its inputs are high, as indicated by the following truth table for a two-input gate.

NAND Gate Truth Table

Input		Output
A	B	Y
0	0	1
0	1	1
1	0	1
1	1	0

This circuit is familiar and we can easily relate its binary action to the NAND truth table. If either A or B is low (binary 0), Q_1 will be saturated and the base potential on Q_2 will be zero. Q_2 will be cut off and its collector voltage will be high (binary 1). In order to get a low output at the collector of Q_2 we must deliver a forward bias to its base. This will only be possible when Q_1 has both of its emitters reverse-biased. We can see that all of the conditions of the NAND truth table are met with this circuit.

Figure 4.14 shows a typical example of a NAND circuit found in many TTL integrated circuits. It uses the popular *totem-pole circuit* formation and a multiple-emitter transistor as an input control element.

As before, Q_1 is controlled by the binary conditions at A and B. Assume that A and B are both at binary 1, which causes the emitter-base sections to be reverse-biased. Base current in Q_2, however, will flow through the collector-base section of Q_1, as it will be forward-biased. The collector-base section of Q_1 acts like a simple diode in series with R_1 and the base of Q_2. This condition in Q_1, of course, turns on Q_2. When Q_2 is on, its saturation current in conjunction with R_2 and R_3 creates a pair of potentials that are used to control Q_3 and Q_4. The potential, or voltage drop, across R_2 is used as the forward bias that turns on Q_4.

The potential at the collector of Q_2 is the potential that controls Q_3. When Q_2 is on, its collector potential will be the sum of the voltage drop across R_2 and the saturation voltage from emitter to collector on Q_2. If we assume that V_{R_2} is about 0.7 V when Q_2 conducts, then the collector potential relative to ground will be about 0.9 V. This voltage by itself would be sufficient to turn on Q_3, but the emitter of Q_3 is not connected directly to ground. Therefore it is not at zero potential relative to its base. The only way current could flow through Q_3 in Figure 4.14 is up through Q_4, then through diode D_1 and finally through Q_3. In order for this current to flow, electrons would have to overcome the internal barrier potential of D_1. This would be about 0.7 V. Thus the effective forward bias on Q_3 is only about 0.2 V when its base is at 0.9 V. This is much too small to cause Q_3 to conduct.

However, conduction will occur in the collector circuit of Q_4 if there is an output load

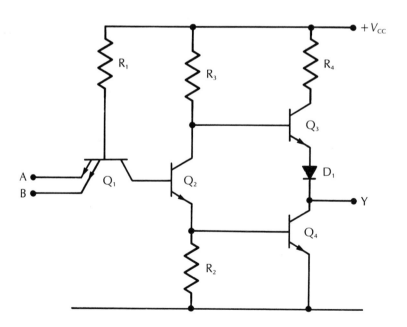

Figure 4.14 Two-Input TTL NAND Gate

present in its collector circuit which connects to the point labelled V_{CC}. If, on the other hand, the collector of Q_4 is connected to ground through a load resistance, the conduction from collector to base in Q_4, due to its saturated condition, would be essentially zero. This is because the voltage at the collector of Q_4 is essentially zero.

Consider now a low input condition at A or B or both A and B. Conduction will occur in Q_1 from emitter to base and saturate the transistor. This saturation will cause the collector potential of Q_1 to drop to about 0.2 V. This small potential is too low to forward-bias Q_2. Therefore Q_2 cuts off. With Q_2 cut off, Q_4 is also cut off, as there is no forward bias developed across R_2. At the same time, the voltage at the base of Q_3 rises because of the reduced voltage drop across R_3 now that Q_2 is not delivering current. This increased voltage at the base of Q_3 causes Q_3 to conduct if a conducting path is provided at the circuit output. If a load resistance of some kind is present from the output terminal to ground, current will flow up through this resistor, up through D_1, and on through Q_3. This flow will deliver a high voltage condition or a binary 1 across the output load resistor.

These load conditions are illustrated in Figure 4.15. If Q_4 is on and Q_3 is off, current will flow up through the saturated Q_4, then up through R_5 and LED_1. This current, if sufficient, will light LED_1. LED_2 will be off because the voltage across Q_4 is only about 0.2. When Q_4 is turned off and Q_3 on, current will flow up through LED_2 and R_6, then up through D_1, and finally through Q_3. LED_2 will now be lit and LED_1 will be off. LED_1 will be off because the voltage at the junction of R_5 and R_6 will be high (only slightly less than V_{CC}). The difference between this junction voltage and V_{CC} will be only that of the forward bias on D_1, plus the saturation voltage of Q_3, plus the small voltage drop across R_4. Typically there will be about

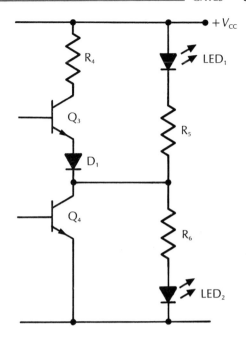

Figure 4.15 Totem-Pole Load Current

a 1-V difference between V_{CC} and the junction voltage R_5-R_6. It is this difference potential that acts across LED_1 and its series resistor R_5. This voltage is too low to operate LED_1, so LED_1 remains off when Q_3 is conducting.

Suppose the output load in Figure 4.15 were simply a single resistor across Q_4. It would then have a high voltage across it when Q_3 was on and a low or zero voltage across it when Q_4 was on.

It can be seen that the output load for the gate is usually another gate or a "fan-out" of many gates connected to the circuit output terminal.

The NOR Gate

A NOR gate is formed by combining an OR gate with an inverter. The presence of the inverter makes the combined output NOT OR or simply NOR. Its truth table is the complement or negation of that of an OR gate.

NOR Gate Truth Table

Input		Output
A	B	Y
0	0	1
0	1	0
1	0	0
1	1	0

We have spent some time now discussing in detail how transistors switch on and off. Also, we have analyzed the totem-pole circuit. With this background it is possible to understand a wide variety of gates in various logic families.

Figure 4.16 shows how two basic integrated circuits are connected to perform the NOR-gate function. A quick look at the circuit reveals that it has a totem-pole output and emitter control at the input. If this circuit is to deliver

the NOR-gate conditions it must produce a high output when the two inputs are at zero. Conversely when either or both inputs are at binary 1 the output must be at zero.

Consider A and B to be at zero (ground). Grounded emitters on Q_1 and Q_4 cause them to saturate. Therefore, the base potentials on Q_2 and Q_3 drop to nearly zero. This cuts off Q_2 and Q_3. Also, the voltage across R_4 drops to zero and the potential at the bottom of R_2 rises (goes high). This condition causes Q_5 to cut off and Q_6 to turn on. If there is a load connected between Y and ground (a voltmeter will provide a load), it will have a "high" voltage across it.

If either or both A and B inputs are high, the Y output will go to 0.

Now consider A high and B low. Q_1 will have no emitter current, but Q_4 will. Q_2 will be turned on and Q_3 off. With Q_2 on, there will be a voltage drop across R_4. This will turn on Q_5. The potential at the bottom of R_2 will

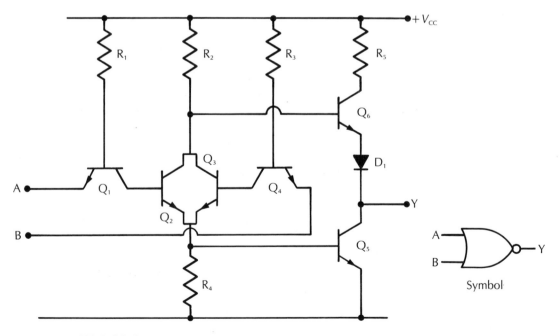

Figure 4.16 TTL NOR Gate

be too low to turn on Q_6. Thus the Y output goes low when either or both A and B inputs are high.

Our circuit section in Figure 4.16 is basically like the NOR circuits found in a 7402 TTL IC. We will now look at a basic NOR circuit in a CMOS IC similar to the circuit used in a 4001 chip. In Figure 4.17, the Q_1 and Q_2 enhancement-mode MOSFETs are P-channel types while Q_3 and Q_4 are N-channel. Notice also that the P substrates of Q_3 and Q_4 connect to the negative side of the circuit, while the N-substrates of Q_1 and Q_2 go to the point labelled V_{DD}.

Consider a binary 1 to be at A. This positive potential will cause the P channel in Q_1 to deplete further and keep Q_1 turned off. Q_4, however, will have its N channel enriched with charge and it will turn on. So with a binary 1 at A, Q_4 acts like a low resistance or a closed switch, and Q_1 the opposite. This condition at A produces a low or zero voltage at Y. The same set of conditions occurs for a binary 1 at B, this time involving Q_2 and Q_3. If both A and B are at binary 1, the output will still be zero, because both Q_3 and Q_4 are acting like closed switches keeping Y low.

The output will go high if and only if both A and B are at binary 0, for with A and B at binary 0 there is a ground potential on all gates. This potential further depletes the channels in Q_3 and Q_4, cutting them off. The upper transistors Q_1 and Q_2 have holes pulled into their P channels. They turn on and act like closed switches. This low-resistance condition in Q_1 and Q_2 brings the potential at Y close to V_{DD}.

It may be noted that the two NOR circuits discussed in Figures 4.16 and 4.17 do the same thing. Why, then, are both types used? We already know that the CMOS circuit expends less energy than the junction-transistor type. This fact alone might seem like a good enough reason to scrap the circuit in Figure 4.16. However, the matter is not quite that simple. CMOS circuits do have the advantage of low power dissipation, but they are slower-acting and more noise-sensitive than the TTL types. We will examine these two characteristics in detail a little later.

The EXCLUSIVE OR (XOR) Gate

The EXCLUSIVE OR (XOR) gate is important and commonly used. It really consists of three gates and two inverters, as shown in Figure 4.18. As will be seen in Chapter 5, one of its many uses is in arithmetic circuits.

The XOR gate really compares its two input signals. As shown in the truth table, if the two inputs are the same it produces a 0 output, and if they are different it produces a binary 1 output.

EXCLUSIVE OR Gate Truth Table

Input		Output
A	B	Y
0	0	0
0	1	1
1	0	1
1	1	0

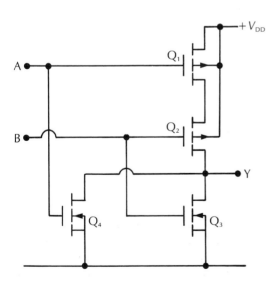

Figure 4.17 NOR CMOS Integrated Circuit

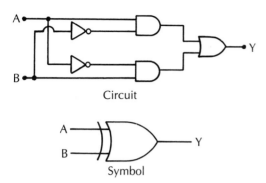

Circuit

A ———
B ——— Y

Symbol

Figure 4.18 EXCLUSIVE OR Gate

to have either an even or an odd number of binary 1s. If, due to noise in the system, extra binary 1 pulses enter, they will be detected by the receiving terminal.

Figure 4.19 shows the gate arrangement for a basic parity-bit generator. This generator examines each four-bit binary word. It then generates a binary 1 output if the word has an odd number of binary 1s. If, on the other hand, the

Our knowledge of the three basic circuits allows us to follow the condition sequence from input to output and check to see if the truth-table conditions are met.

Assume binary 0 inputs at A and B. The inverters change the zeros to ones, so both the upper and the lower AND circuits have a zero-one input. The output of both AND circuits will be 0 and the inputs to the OR circuit will be a pair of zeros. The OR circuit will deliver a 0 output.

If A and B are both at binary 1, the output will also be 0. Follow the condition through. Once again the AND circuits will have zero-one pairs as inputs and their outputs will be zeros. Again the OR circuit will have a zero-zero input and a zero output.

A zero-one input combination results in a binary 1 output. If A is at 1 and B at 0, the upper AND circuit will have a one-one input while the lower AND circuit will have a zero-zero input. The upper AND circuit will produce a binary 1 output, and the lower a binary 0 output. The OR circuit now has a zero-one input and will produce a binary 1 output.

Another common use for the XOR gate is as a *parity-bit generator*. At the end of Chapter 2 we discussed the need for parity bits in data transmission systems. All binary words are made

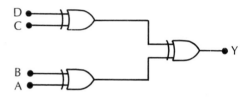

D ●
C ●   ● Y

B ●
A ●

Truth Table

A	B	C	D	Y
0	0	0	0	0
0	0	0	1	1
0	0	1	0	1
0	0	1	1	0
0	1	0	0	1
0	1	0	1	0
0	1	1	0	0
0	1	1	1	1
1	0	0	0	1
1	0	0	1	0
1	0	1	0	0
1	0	1	1	1
1	1	0	0	0
1	1	0	1	1
1	1	1	0	1
1	1	1	1	0

Figure 4.19 Even Parity-Bit Generator

word has an even number of binary 1s, the generator produces a binary 0. Thus, this circuit is designed for *even*-parity transmission.

The computer receiving these binary words would have a circuit for checking parity. If any word came in without an even number of binary 1s, the computer would immediately recognize an error and order a rerun of the data.

4.2 Boolean Algebra

Mathematical expressions are used to simplify and condense the various processes involved in computations and theory. Boolean algebra, similarly, is used to simplify logic circuits.

For hundreds of years, humans have tried to reduce language and thought processes to a simplified, logical form so that truth can be extracted from assumptions. One man who made an enormous contribution in this area was George Boole (1815–1864). In 1854 he published a work entitled *An Investigation of the Laws of Thought on Which Are Founded the Mathemetical Theories of Logic and Probabilities*. Boole used mathematical formulas and symbols to represent human reasoning. His system of logic was found to be perfectly suited to the characteristics of digital computer circuits.

In 1938 a Bell Telephone Company research assistant, Claude Shannon, used Boole's system of logic and applied it to the design and simplification of telephone dialing networks. He applied logic to switch combinations and produced a system of mathematical expressions and the calculus to manipulate them which became known as Boolean algebra.

Whole books have been written on Boolean algebra and colleges and universities offer a wide variety of courses on it. Thus, a comprehensive treatment is beyond the scope of this book, but the basics of Boolean algebra will be presented to show how it is used both to analyze and to simplify logic circuits.

To see the necessity of simplifying logic circuits, examine Figure 4.20. Circuit A employs 3 gates and 5 inverters. Yet circuit B, which uses only 2 gates, delivers the same output

conditions as the more costly and complex circuit.

We will see as we proceed that Boolean algebra can be used to reduce a logic circuit to its most elementary form. Conversely, circuit function can be determined by examining its Boolean output expression.

The first thing we should learn about Boolean algebra is the meaning of its various signs. There are three basic operations to be indicated: AND, OR, and NOT.

1. The AND operation, also known as *conjunction*, gives the logical product of two terms. The conjunction of A and B is written AB (or, by some authors, A · B).
2. The OR operation, also known as *disjunction*, gives the logical sum of two terms. The disjunction of A and B is written A + B.
3. The NOT operation, also known as *negation*, gives the logical negation of a single term. The negation of A is written $\overline{A}$; of AB, $\overline{AB}$; of A + B, $\overline{A + B}$.

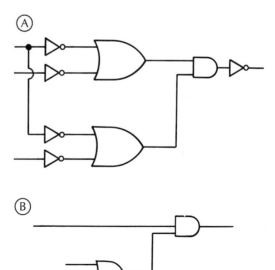

Figure 4.20 Equivalent Logic Circuits

Example 1

AB (or A · B) is read "A and B."

A + B is read "A or B."

$\overline{A}$ is read "not A" or "A not."

We must review for a moment the truth tables for AND, OR, and NOT logic. We will see that the OR function relates to logical addition while the AND function relates to logical multiplication. The NOT circuit or inverter results in complementation.

AND Truth Table	OR Truth Table	NOT Truth Table
AB = Y	A + B = Y	$\overline{A}$ = Y
0 × 0 = 0	0 + 0 = 0	0 negated = 1
0 × 1 = 0	0 + 1 = 1	1 negated = 0
1 × 0 = 0	1 + 0 = 1	
1 × 1 = 1	1 + 1 = 1	

Now we can apply Boolean ideas to the circuits in Figure 4.21.

Gate A produces AND logic. The output will be at binary 1 if and only if A and B are both at binary 1. The expression Y = AB is read "Y is at binary 1 if both A and B are at binary 1." Similarly, the OR gate B is read "Y is at binary 1 if either A or B is at binary 1."

Gate C, called an *inverter*, produces NOT logic. Its Y output will always be the binary opposite of its input.

Gate D produces NAND logic. Y will be at binary 1 if A and B are not both at binary 1. This can be confusing if we are not careful! Gate D consists of an AND circuit and an inverter. Therefore, its output will be the complement of that of the AND gate.

NAND Truth Table

Input		Output
A	B	Y
0	0	1
1	0	1
0	1	1
1	1	0

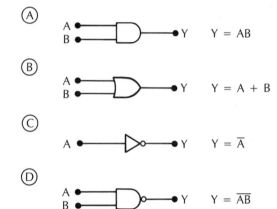
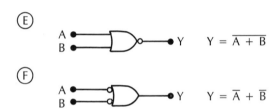
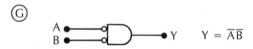

(A) A, B → Y   Y = AB

(B) A, B → Y   Y = A + B

(C) A → Y   Y = $\overline{A}$

(D) A, B → Y   Y = $\overline{AB}$

(E) A, B → Y   Y = $\overline{A + B}$

(F) A, B → Y   Y = $\overline{A} + \overline{B}$

(G) A, B → Y   Y = $\overline{A}\overline{B}$

Figure 4.21 Logic Gates and Their Boolean Expressions

If we return to our original statement for D, we see from the truth table that Y is at binary 1 when A and B are not both at binary 1. When A and B are both at binary 1 the Y output is at binary 0.

Gate E produces NOR logic. Y is at binary 1 when neither A nor B is at binary 1. If either A or B or both are at binary 1, Y will be at binary 0.

Gate G also produces NOR logic. However, the inversion or complementation occurs in the input rather than the output of the circuit. The Boolean expression is changed to reflect this by placing the NOT symbol over the A and the B individually. Y is at binary 1 when input A or input B are not at binary 1. As before, if either A or B or both are at binary 1, Y is at binary 0.

Gate F produces NAND logic just like D. Y will be at binary 1 if A and B are not both at binary 1. Again the NOT symbol is placed above A and B individually to show that complementation occurs at the input.

We see from the above examples that all Boolean expressions are made equal to binary 1. It is conventional to do this, so that all of the logic circuits are analyzed in terms of the input conditions required to deliver a binary 1 output. Figure 4.22 will illustrate this further.

Consider the meaning of the Boolean expression for circuit A in the figure, $Y = \overline{A} + B$. The equation translates: "Y is at binary 1 when $\overline{A}$, or binary 0, is present at A or binary 1 is present at B." We can readily see that either of these inputs will activate the OR circuit to produce a binary 1 output.

In case this is still confusing, consider the expression in another way. $Y = \overline{A} + B$ can be read "Y is at binary 1 when not A is equal to 1 or B is equal to 1."

We can go a step further and check all the input combinations to see if they agree with the Boolean expression for the circuit.

1. A = 0, B = 0
   $Y = \overline{A} + B$
   $= \overline{0} + 0$
   $= 1 + 0$
   $= 1$

2. A = 0, B = 1
   $Y = \overline{A} + B$
   $= \overline{0} + 1$
   $= 1 + 1$
   $= 1$

3. A = 1, B = 0
   $Y = \overline{A} + B$
   $= \overline{1} + 0$
   $= 0 + 0$
   $= 0$

4. A = 1, B = 1
   $Y = \overline{A} + B$
   $= \overline{1} + 1$
   $= 0 + 1$
   $= 1$

At first glance, solution 3 may seem to show an error in the system because Y does not work out to binary 1. However, return to the translation of the formula, $Y = \overline{A} + B$. It states that Y is at binary 1 when not A or B is at binary 1. With an input of A = 1 and B = 0, not A is 0 and B is 0; thus, the circuit output at Y is binary 0.

We should now be able to understand the translation of the Boolean expressions for parts B and C in Figure 4.22.

In B we find Y at binary 1 when not A is binary 1 or not B is binary 1. Again, this is just another way of saying Y is binary 1 when either A or B is at binary 0.

In C we have two stages of complementation. In order to have Y at binary 1, the AND gate output must be 0. The gate output will be 0 if its direct inputs are any binary combination other than 1, 1. Therefore Y will be at 1 for any combination of the inputs except for A = 0, B = 1.

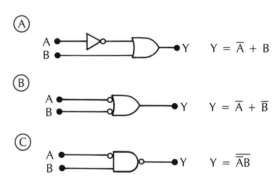

(A)
A
B
Y $Y = \overline{A} + B$

(B)
A
B
Y $Y = \overline{A} + \overline{B}$

(C)
A
B
Y $Y = \overline{AB}$

Figure 4.22 Fitting Boolean Equations to Circuits

Thus, the Boolean expression of gate C is translated "Y will be at 1 when it is not true that A is 0 and B is 1." The truth table for this gate illustrates the translation.

Input		Output
A	B	Y
0	0	1
0	1	0
1	0	1
1	1	1

$Y = \overline{AB}$

This method of analysis can be applied to any basic gate combination. With practice the Boolean equation for a circuit can be written quickly.

Deriving Logic Circuits from Boolean Expressions

Sometimes it is necessary to derive a working logic circuit from a given Boolean expression. This is really just the opposite of what we have been doing.

Let us derive a working circuit to satisfy the expression:

$$Y = \overline{A + \overline{B}} \; \overline{AB}$$

The first step in problems of this kind is to recognize the various parts of the equation in terms of their circuit equivalents. For example, AB corresponds to an AND gate, $\overline{AB}$ to a NAND gate, $A + B$ to an OR gate, $\overline{A + B}$ to a NOR gate, and $A\overline{B}$ to an AND gate with inverted inputs. Once we recognize these basic logic forms we can proceed to build the overall circuit. It should be mentioned at once that there is more than one way to "build" a logic circuit. However, the designer will always look for the simplest circuit possible.

Returning to the expression $Y = \overline{A + \overline{B}} \; \overline{AB}$, the first factor $A + \overline{B}$ relates to a NOR gate (with a minor variation) and the second $\overline{AB}$ relates to a NAND gate. The minor variation in the first factor is the $\overline{B}$. The conventional NOR-gate logic is $\overline{A + B}$. However, the $\overline{B}$ can be made into a B with an inverter, as will be seen later.

Next, it is understood that the two factors are tied with an AND symbol. The output gate, then, will be an AND gate.

Figure 4.23 illustrates how the above reasoning is applied. The elements of the Boolean expression are the beginning step. Work back from the output to determine the sequence of basic logic gates required to do the job. Work out the fine points as needed. For example, an inverter circuit is used to provide the $\overline{B}$ at the input of the NOR gate. The final result is a combination of basic gates that satisfies the conditions of the Boolean expression.

Simplifying Boolean Expressions

Boolean expressions help us to recognize the function of a circuit. This recognition allows us to select the correct logic. Figure 4.23 was an example of the conversion.

Boolean expressions can be manipulated and simplified. They should always be reduced to their simplest form before they are translated into their logic equivalents.

One way to simplify Boolean expressions is to apply Boolean theorems and postulates. These

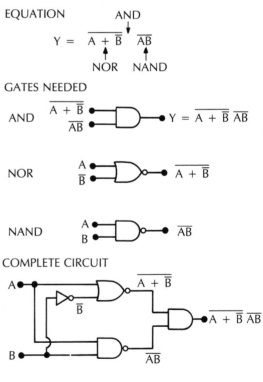

Figure 4.23 Designing Circuits from Boolean Equations

theorems exist in pairs: a theorem derived for an AND function has a corresponding theorem for an OR function. This aspect of the theorems is called *duality* and is illustrated in the list below. (Note the double complementation in 1.)

Boolean Theorems

OR:

1. $\overline{\overline{A}} = A$
2. $0 + A = A$
3. $1 + A = 1$
4. $A + A = A$
5. $A + \overline{A} = 1$
6. $A + B$
   $= B + A$
7. $A + (B + C)$
   $= (A + B) + C$
8. $A + AB = A$
9. $A + \overline{A}B$
   $= A + B$
10. $A (B + C)$
    $= AB + AC$
11. $\overline{A + B} = \overline{A}\overline{B}$

AND:

1. $\overline{\overline{A}} = A$
2. $1A = A$
3. $0A = 0$
4. $AA = A$
5. $A\overline{A} = 0$
6. AB
   $= BA$
7. $A (BC)$
   $= (AB) C$
8. $A (A + B) = A$
9. $A (\overline{A} + B)$
   $= AB$
10. $A + BC$
    $= (A + B) (A + C)$
11. $\overline{AB} = \overline{A} + \overline{B}$

Pairing is illustrated when we compare an OR gate to an AND gate with inverted inputs and output. They have the same logic. Similarly, comparing an AND gate to an OR gate with inverted inputs and output shows that they have the same logic. This duality is helpful in circuit simplification. It means that, given any Boolean identity, we can produce a logically identical expression by changing OR signs to AND signs and vice versa, and complementing all binary numbers.

Each of the theorems can be proved by applying the conditions of the statement to the correct logic gate or gates. Their usefulness is illustrated in Figure 4.24.

CIRCUIT

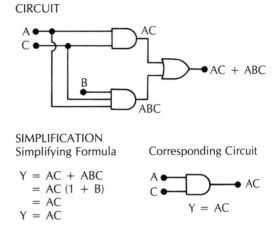

SIMPLIFICATION
Simplifying Formula   Corresponding Circuit

$Y = AC + ABC$
$\ = AC (1 + B)$
$\ = AC$
$Y = AC$

$Y = AC$

Figure 4.24 Simplifying Logic Using Boolean Theorems

Theorem 4(OR) states that $A + A = A$. Applied to the expression $Y = AC + ABC$ it is evident that A is ORed with A, and C with C. This means that the lower AND gate is redundant.

Input B can only present a binary 1 to the OR gate when A and C are also at binary 1. This means that input B makes no contribution to the output condition.

DeMorganizing

The pair of theorems numbered 11 in the list are sometimes called DeMorgan's Theorems. DeMorgan was a friend of Boole and he contributed these important theorems to the mathematics of logic. The first states:

"The complement of a sum equals the product of the complements."

The second states:

"The complement of a product equals the sum of the complements."

The two are often collectively referred to as *DeMorgan's Theorem.*

These theorems show that any logic function can be performed either by the use of AND and INVERT (complementation) or by the use of OR and INVERT. They can be used to simplify logic and to convert from one form of gating to another. For example, logic functions must sometimes be performed by only one type of gate, because the design must make use of the gates available.

The rules for applying DeMorgan's Theorem — DeMorganizing — are:

1. Complement each term, variable, and factor in the expression.
2. Change all ORs to ANDs and all ANDs to ORs.
3. Complement the whole expression.

Figure 4.25 illustrates the steps.

EQUIVALENT CIRCUITS

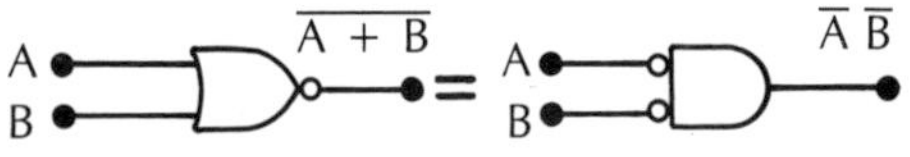

EXPRESSION TO BE DEMORGANIZED

$\overline{A + B}$

DEMORGANIZING PROCESS

1. $\overline{\overline{A} + \overline{B}}$ Complementing each term

2. $\overline{\overline{A}\overline{B}}$ Changing OR to AND

3. $\overline{A}\overline{B}$ Complementing whole expression

Figure 4.25 DeMorganizing the Expression $\overline{A + B}$

With practice some shortcuts can be found. The following example will show this.

Example 2

Use DeMorgan's Theorem to simplify:

$Y = \overline{\overline{AB} + A\overline{B}C}$

$Y = (A + \overline{B})(\overline{A} + B + C)$

If any variables are doubly complemented, the complementation is removed. The AND and OR signs are then changed. Parentheses are used to avoid confusion. If we wish, just one part of a Boolean expression can be DeMorganized. This does not change the function of the expression; it simply expresses it differently. One or a few of the terms, factors, variables, or combinations of variables can be selected for DeMorganizing.

Example 3

$Y = \overline{(\overline{A} + \overline{B})\ \overline{(\overline{C} + D)}}$

DeMorganizing two terms:

$\overline{(\overline{A} + \overline{B})\ \overline{(\overline{C} + D)}}$

$\overline{(\overline{A} + \overline{B}) + \overline{(\overline{C} + D)}}$

$\overline{A} + \overline{B} + \overline{\overline{C}} + D$

DeMorganizing all variables:

$\overline{(\overline{A} + \overline{B})(C + \overline{D})}$

$\overline{(\overline{AB}) + (C\,\overline{D})}$

$\overline{A}\,\overline{B} + C\overline{D}$

We can DeMorganize logic circuits as well as Boolean expressions. Figure 4.26 shows the procedure.

CIRCUIT TO BE
DEMORGANIZED

BOOLEAN
EXPRESSION
FOR CIRCUIT

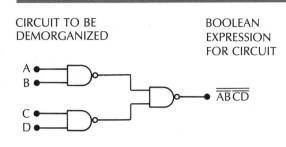

$\overline{\overline{AB}\,\overline{CD}}$

DEMORGANIZING PROCESS

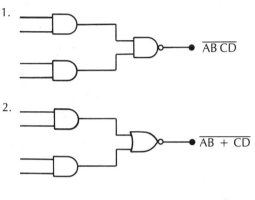

1.

$\overline{\overline{AB}\,\overline{CD}}$

2.

$\overline{AB + CD}$

3.

AB + CD

Figure 4.26 DeMorganizing Logic Circuits

Sometimes more than one theorem must be used to simplify a Boolean expression properly.

Example 4

Simplify:

$\overline{\overline{AB}\,\overline{A}}$

Applying DeMorgan theorem 11(AND):

AB + A

Applying theorem 8(OR):

A

The above shows that the original expression can be reduced to one condition. That is, the logical "output" of the original expression is identical with the condition of input A. Figure 4.27 shows this.

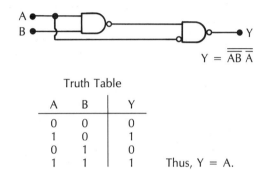

$Y = \overline{\overline{AB}\,\overline{A}}$

Truth Table

A	B	Y
0	0	0
1	0	1
0	1	0
1	1	1

Thus, Y = A.

Figure 4.27 Boolean Simplifications

The topic of finding circuit combinations to satisfy given Boolean formulas is immense. When there are so many possibilities and variations for each circuit, the task can be very complex. For the purposes of this text, the student should merely grasp the necessity for and basic method of simplifying logic circuits.

The *Karnaugh map* is an extension of the study of logic-circuit simplification. Karnaugh mapping is an alternative method of solving and simplifying logic circuits — more a diagrammatic representation of a logic statement than an algebraic one. Those who are familiar with Venn diagrams will find Karnaugh maps similar.

Questions

1. Define *logic gate*.
2. Define *TTL logic*.
3. Define *high* and *low* as applied to logic circuits.
4. Explain the purpose of an AND gate.
5. Explain the purpose of a truth table as it relates to a logic gate.
6. Explain how multiple-emitter transistors simplify logic gates.
7. Explain how a transistor can be used as a control device to turn another transistor on or off.
8. Define the following transistor operating modes: *cut-off, active, saturated*.
9. Which transistor operating mode is used for gates? Why?
10. Explain why the voltage across a saturated transistor drops to 0.2 V.
11. Explain the operating characteristics of a transistor OR gate.
12. Show how a transistor can be connected to act as a NOT circuit.
13. Write the truth table for a NAND and an AND gate. How does the logic differ?
14. Explain the purpose of a totem-pole circuit at the output of a TTL gate.
15. Refer to Figure 4.15. Explain how the totem-pole circuit controls the LEDs.
16. Refer to Figure 4.16. Explain why a binary 1 (high) at A or B will cause a binary 0 (low) at Y.
17. What is the advantage of the CMOS circuit of Figure 4.17 over the TTL circuit in Figure 4.16?
18. The XOR gate is called a comparator. Why?
19. Explain the meaning of parity and explain the purpose of parity bits.
20. Explain why the AND function is equivalent to multiplication.
21. Explain why the OR function is equivalent to addition.

22. Write the Boolean expressions for the following gates: AND, OR, NAND, NOR.
23. Is the logic for an OR gate with an inverted output the same as for one with inverted inputs? Explain.
24. Explain how Boolean theorems can be used to simplify logic circuit design.
25. Simplify the following Boolean expressions using DeMorgan's Theorem:

$$\overline{(A + B)\ (\overline{C} + \overline{D})} \quad , \quad \overline{(A + B) + (C\overline{D})}$$

26. Simplify the following:

$$\overline{AB} + \overline{A}B + AC \quad , \quad \overline{(AB\overline{D})\ \overline{(AB)}\ \overline{(AB\overline{D})}}$$

27. When one is performing the DeMorganizing process on a Boolean expression, must every part be DeMorganized? Explain.
28. Can a logic circuit consisting of OR gates and inverters be duplicated with AND gates and inverters only? Give an example.

Experiments

Experiment 4.1

Object

To show the operation of a diode-logic AND gate.

Circuit

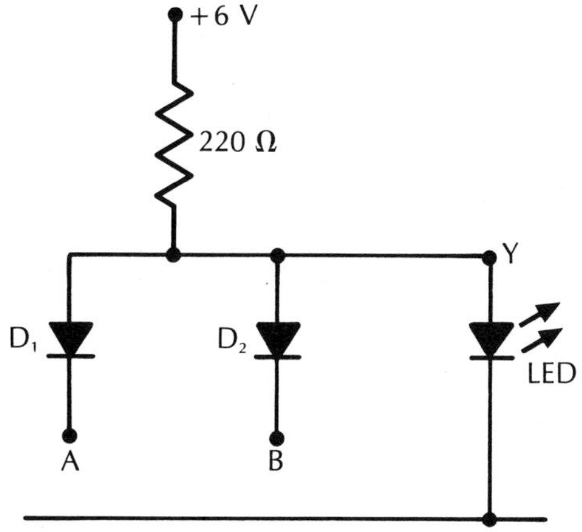

+6 V

220 Ω

Y

D₁ D₂

LED

A B

Truth Table

A—⊐D— Y
B—

Symbol

A	B	Y
0	0	0
0	1	0
1	0	0
1	1	1

Figure E4.1

Steps
1. Connect the circuit.
2. Ground A and B. Observe the LED.
3. Ground A and connect B to +6 V. Observe the LED.
4. Ground B and connect A to +6 V.
5. Connect both A and B to +6 V. Observe the LED.
6. Why does the LED stay dark when either A or B is grounded?

Experiment 4.2

Object

To show the operation of a transistor-logic AND gate.

Circuit

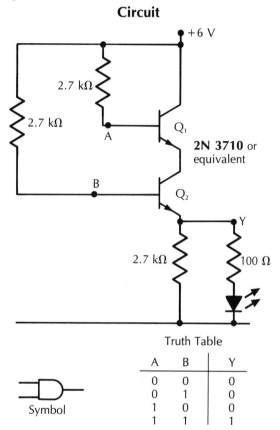

+6 V

2.7 kΩ

2.7 kΩ

A

Q₁

2N 3710 or equivalent

B

Q₂

Y

2.7 kΩ 100 Ω

Truth Table

—⊐D—

Symbol

A	B	Y
0	0	0
0	1	0
1	0	0
1	1	1

Figure E4.2

Steps
1. Connect the circuit. Ground both A and B. Observe the LED.
2. Remove the ground from A. Observe the LED.
3. Ground A and remove the ground from B. Observe the LED.
4. Remove both grounds. Observe the LED.
5. Would this circuit work without the 2.7-kΩ resistor? Explain.

Experiment 4.3

Object

To show the operation of a diode-logic OR gate.

Circuit

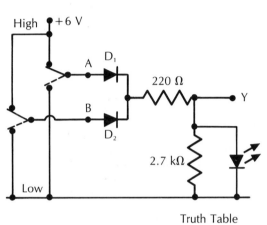

Figure E4.3

A ⎯⎤⎬⎯ Y
B ⎯⎦

Symbol

Truth Table

A	B	Y
0	0	0
1	0	1
0	1	1
1	1	1

Steps

1. Connect the circuit. Switch A and B to ground. Observe the LED.
2. Switch A high and B low. Observe the LED.
3. Switch B high and A low. Observe the LED.
4. Switch both A and B high. Observe the LED.
5. When A is high and B is low, why isn't there a short circuit through D_1 and D_2?

Experiment 4.4

Object

To show the operation of an OR gate with RTL (resistor-transistor logic).

Circuit

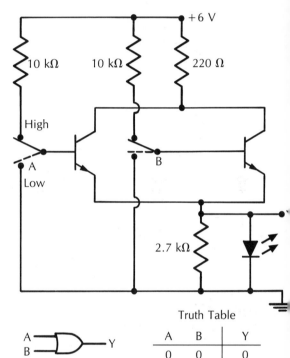

A ⎯⎤⎬⎯ Y
B ⎯⎦

Symbol

Figure E4.4

Truth Table

A	B	Y
0	0	0
1	0	1
0	1	1
1	1	1

Steps

1. Connect the circuit.
2. Switch both A and B to ground. Observe the LED.
3. Switch A high and B low. Observe the LED.
4. Switch B high and A low. Observe the LED.
5. Switch both A and B high. Observe the LED.
6. Are the transistors connected in series or parallel?

Experiment 4.5

Object

To show the operation of a single-transistor inverter circuit.

Circuit

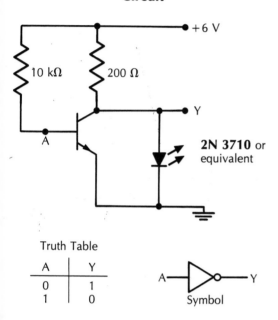

Truth Table

A	Y
0	1
1	0

Symbol

Figure E4.5

Steps

1. Connect the circuit. Observe the LED.
2. Short A to ground. Observe the LED.
3. Why is the LED off when A is high?

Experiment 4.6

Object

To show the three modes of transistor operation.

Circuit

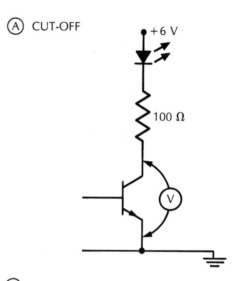

(A) CUT-OFF

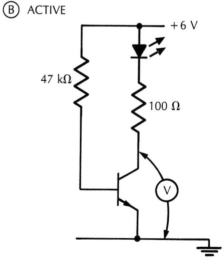

(B) ACTIVE

Figure E4.6

(C) SATURATION

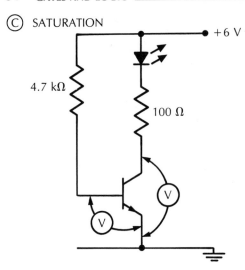

Figure E4.6 (cont.)

Steps

1. Connect circuit A. Observe the LED. Measure V_{CE}.
2. Connect B. Observe the LED. Measure V_{CE}.
3. Connect C. Observe the LED. Measure V_{CE}.
4. Which mode is suited for signal amplification? Why?
5. Which is the switching mode? Why?

Experiment 4.7

Object

To show the action of a junction transistor when it is used as a diode pair.

Circuit

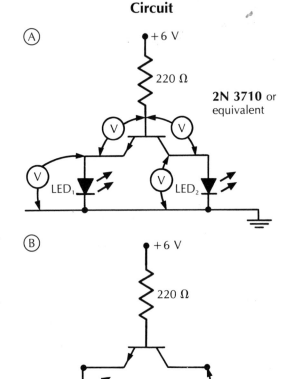

Figure E4.7

Steps

1. Connect circuit A. Record the meter readings for the four voltages shown.
2. Remove LED₁. Does LED₂ still glow?
3. Connect circuit B. Measure the voltage indicated. Short the emitter to ground and observe the voltmeter reading.
4. Does the collector-base circuit act independently of the emitter-base circuit? Explain.

Experiment 4.8

Object

To show how a transistor can be used as an on-off device to control another transistor.

Circuit

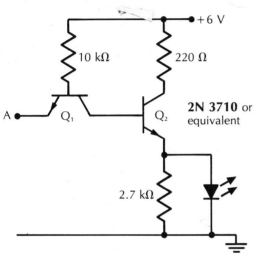

Figure E4.8

Steps

1. Connect the circuit. Observe the LED. Measure the voltage from the base of Q_2 to ground.
2. Short point A to ground. Observe the LED. Measure the voltage from the base of Q_2 to ground.
3. When A is open, does Q_1 act like a transistor? Explain.

Experiment 4.9

Object

To show the operation of a totem-pole circuit.

Circuit

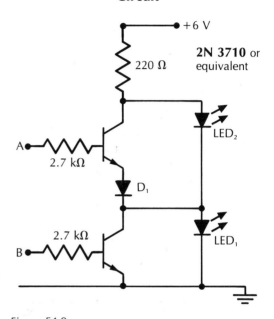

Figure E4.9

Steps

1. Connect the circuit. Connect A to +6 V (high) and B to ground (low). Observe both LEDs.
2. Connect B high and A low. Observe both LEDs.
3. Trace the conducting path for LED_1.
4. Trace the conducting path for LED_2.
5. Why do both LEDs glow if both A and B are low?

Experiment 4.10

Object

To show the control of a totem-pole circuit.

Circuit

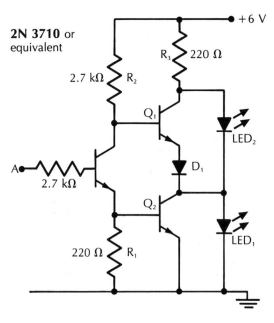

Figure E4.10

Steps

1. Connect the circuit. Connect A to ground. Observe both LEDS.
2. Connect A to +6 V. Observe both LEDs.
3. What voltage would be present across R₁ when LED₂ is on?
4. What keeps LED₂ off when Q₁ is on?
5. Why is D₁ used in the circuit?

Experiment 4.11

Object

To show the logic of an IC AND gate.

Circuit

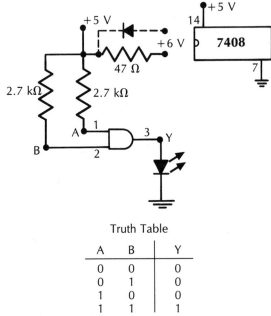

Truth Table

A	B	Y
0	0	0
0	1	0
1	0	0
1	1	1

Figure E4.11

Steps

Note: If a 6-V source is used, connect via the 47-Ω resistor or a diode to drop the battery voltage to approximately 5 V.

1. Connect the circuit and observe the LED.
2. Short A to ground. Observe the LED. Remove short.
3. Short B to ground. Observe the LED.
4. Short both A and B to ground. Observe the LED.
5. Write the Boolean expression for this gate.

Experiment 4.12

Object

To show the operation of an IC OR gate.

Circuit

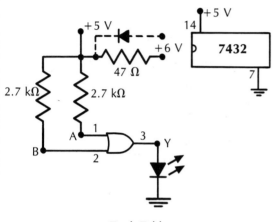

Figure E4.12

Truth Table

A	B	Y
0	0	0
1	0	1
0	1	1
1	1	1

Steps

Note: If a 6-V source is used, connect via a 47-Ω resistor or a diode to drop the battery voltage to approximately 5 V.

1. Connect the circuit. Observe the LED.
2. Ground A. Observe the LED.
3. Remove ground from A. Ground B. Observe the LED.
4. Ground both A and B. Observe the LED.
5. Write the Boolean expression for this gate.

Experiment 4.13

Object

To show the operation of an IC inverter.

Circuit

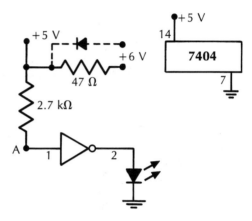

Figure E4.13

Steps

Note: If a 6-V source is used, connect via a 47-Ω resistor or a diode to drop the battery voltage to approximately 5 V.

1. Connect the circuit. Observe the LED.
2. Ground A. Observe the LED.
3. If a binary 0 is applied to the input, what binary value will be present at the output?

Experiment 4.14

Object

To show the operation of an IC NAND gate.

Circuit

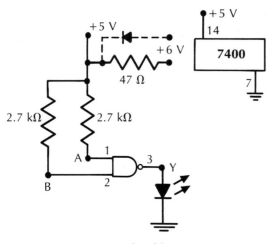

Figure E4.14

Truth Table

A	B	Y
0	0	1
0	1	1
1	0	1
1	1	0

Steps

Note: If a 6-V source is used, connect via a 47-Ω resistor or a diode to drop the battery voltage to approximately 5 V.

1. Connect the circuit. Observe the LED.
2. Ground A. Observe the LED.
3. Ground only B. Observe the LED.
4. Ground both A and B. Observe the LED.
5. Write the Boolean expression for this gate.

Experiment 4.15

Object

To show the operation of an IC NOR gate.

Circuit

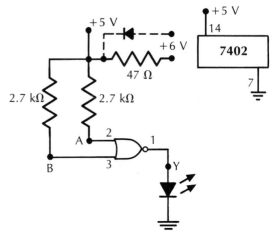

Figure E4.15

Truth Table

A	B	Y
1	1	0
1	0	0
0	1	0
0	0	1

Steps

Note: If a 6-V source is used, connect via a 47-Ω resistor or a diode to drop the battery voltage to approximately 5 V.

1. Connect the circuit. Observe the LED.
2. Ground A. Observe the LED.
3. Ground B only. Observe the LED.
4. Ground both A and B. Observe the LED.
5. Write the Boolean expression for this gate.

Experiment 4.16

Object
To show the operation of an XOR gate.

Circuit

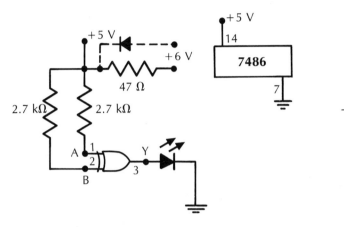

Truth Table

A	B	Y
0	0	0
0	1	1
1	0	1
1	1	0

Figure E4.16

Steps

Note: If a 6-V source is used, connect via a 47-Ω resistor or a diode to drop the battery voltage to approximately 5 V.

1. Connect the circuit. Ground A and B. Observe the LED.
2. Connect A low and B high. Observe the LED.
3. Connect A high and B low. Observe the LED.
4. Connect both A and B high. Observe the LED.
5. Why can we call this gate a comparator?

Experiment 4.17

Object

To show the logic of an XOR gate using two chips.

Circuit

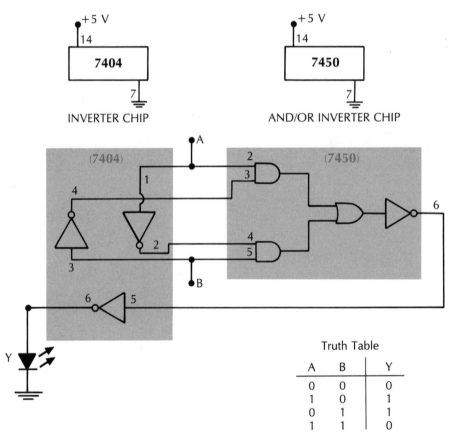

Figure E4.17

Truth Table

A	B	Y
0	0	0
1	0	1
0	1	1
1	1	0

Steps

Note: If a 6-V source is used, connect via a 47-Ω resistor or a diode to drop the battery voltage to approximately 5 V.

1. Connect the circuit. Ground A and B. Observe the LED.
2. Ground B and connect A high. Observe the LED.
3. Ground A and connect B high. Observe the LED.
4. Connect both A and B high. Observe the LED.
5. Show the binary conditions at all points when A is 0 and B is 1.

Experiment 4.18

Object

To show how different gate combinations can produce the same logic.

Circuit

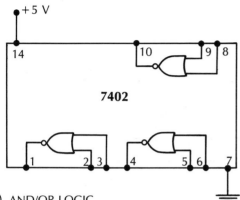

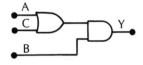

(A) AND/OR LOGIC

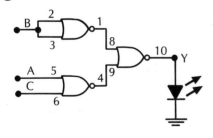

(B) NOR LOGIC

Truth Table

A	B	C	Y
0	0	0	0
0	0	1	0
0	1	0	0
0	1	1	1
1	0	0	0
1	0	1	0
1	1	0	1
1	1	1	1

Figure E4.18

Steps

Note: If a 6-V source is used, connect via a 47-Ω resistor or a diode to drop the battery voltage to approximately 5 V.

1. Examine circuit A. Determine if the logic of circuit A fits the truth table.

2. Connect circuit B. Apply the input combinations shown in the truth table. Observe the LED in each case.

3. When would we use circuit B in preference to circuit A?

Experiment 4.19

Object

To compare the logic of an AND gate with an inverted output to that of an AND gate with inverted inputs.

Circuit

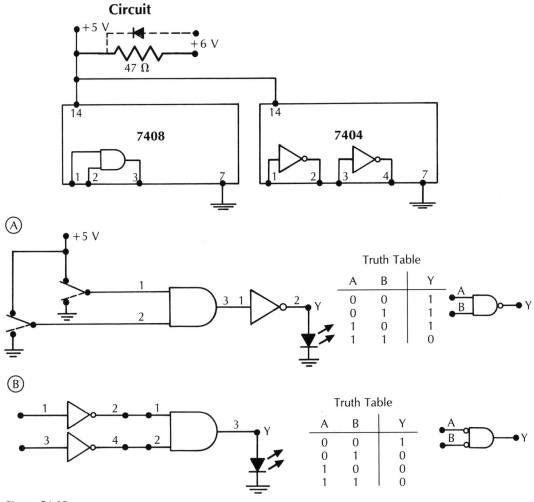

Figure E4.19

Steps

Note: If a 6-V source is used, connect via a 47-Ω resistor or a diode to drop the battery voltage to approximately 5 V.

1. Connect circuit A. Apply the input combinations shown and observe the LED.

2. Connect circuit B. Apply the input combinations shown and observe the LED.
3. What gate is equivalent to A?
4. What gate is equivalent to B?

Experiment 4.20

Object

To compare the logic of an OR gate with an inverted output to that of an OR gate with inverted inputs.

Circuit

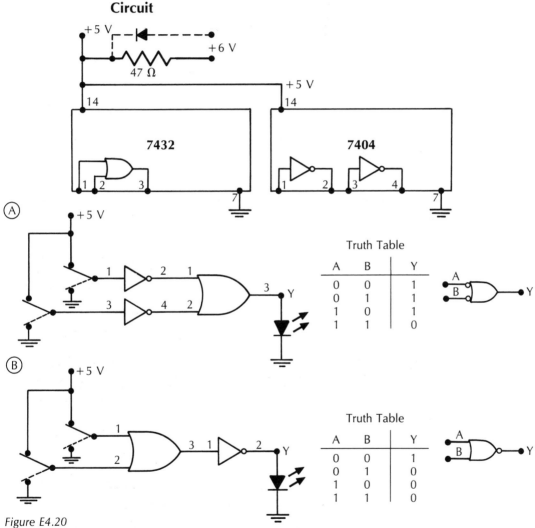

Figure E4.20

Steps

Note: If a 6-V source is used, connect via a 47-Ω resistor or a diode to drop the battery voltage to approximately 5 V.

1. Connect circuit A. Apply the input combinations shown and observe the LED.

2. Connect circuit B. Apply the input combinations shown and observe the LED.
3. What gate is equivalent to A?
4. What gate is equivalent to B?

CHAPTER 5

Digital Circuits at Work

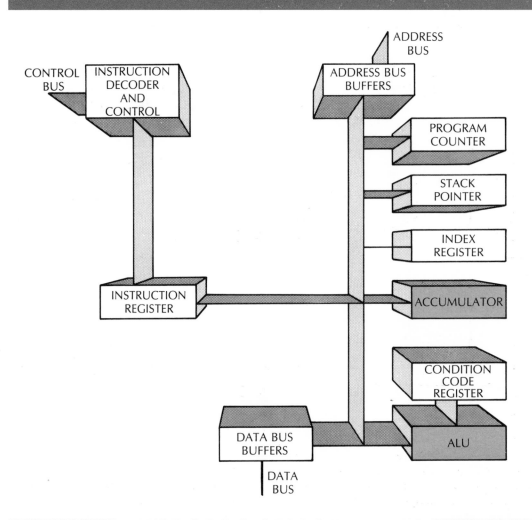

■ INTRODUCTION ■

In this chapter we will examine some of the basic arithmetic operations as they are performed in computers. In all computers, from the largest kinds to the simplest pocket calculator, the basic method is the same — addition, subtraction, multiplication, and division can all be done with a basic adder circuit.

As we saw in Chapter 1, subtraction can be done by addition of the complement; multiplication is just repeated addition; and division is just repeated subtraction. So an adder circuit can be used to do all of the basic arithmetic operations. Other arithmetic and algebraic processes require special circuits and memory, but the heart of the arithmetic units is the binary adder. Not only do these circuits allow the computer to duplicate human mental processes, but they do it with amazing speed and accuracy.

The basic arithmetic logic circuits that we study here will show us how the computer does calculations and will help us to appreciate the function of other basic circuits required in computers.

5.1   Computer Addition

Binary Addition: A Review

In Chapter 1 we learned how to add binary numbers. The rules are:

$0 + 0 = 0$
$1 + 0 = 1$
$0 + 1 = 1$
$1 + 1 = 1$ carry 1

For example, if we are doing $15 + 7$, we convert to binary and add following the above rules.

Example 1

Decimal

```
  15
 +7
  22
```

Binary

```
   1111
 +  111
 10110
```

When we do $1 + 1$ in the first column we get 0 with a 1 carry to the next column. In the next column we have the same addition ($1 + 1$), which equals binary 0 with a 1 carry to the third column; however, the previous 1 carry remains in the second column, so the sum for this column is 1. This process is continued for all columns.

The addition process presented here is a review. We are now interested in the way logic circuits respond to these binary signals and produce a sum in agreement with the binary rules of addition.

The Binary Half-Adder

It may be surprising to see how easy it is for basic logic circuits to do binary addition. In the section on the XOR circuit in Chapter 4, it was mentioned that the circuit is commonly used for arithmetic operations. We will now see how easy it is to use the XOR circuit along with an AND circuit to do basic binary addition. Figure 5.1 shows how the two basic gates involved can be arranged to add two binary digits. Figure 5.1A shows the logic of the XOR gate found in 5.1B.[1]

---

1. Notice that as circuits get more complex they are drawn as labelled boxes with the appropriate inputs and outputs.

XOR GATE

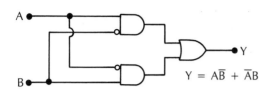

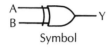

Symbol

Input		Output	
A	B	Sum	Carry
0	0	0	0
0	1	1	0
1	0	1	0
1	1	0	1

It can be seen that the truth table is identical to the rules of binary addition.

It is also apparent how simply this basic circuit adds binary digits. Consider the binary half-adder in Figure 5.2, which performs the same operation but uses two AND gates, an OR gate, and an inverter.

HALF-ADDER

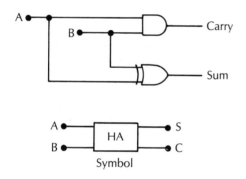

Symbol

Figure 5.1 Binary Half-Adder

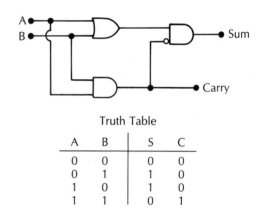

Truth Table

A	B	S	C
0	0	0	0
0	1	1	0
1	0	1	0
1	1	0	1

Figure 5.2 More Complex Binary Half-Adder

An XOR circuit only produces a binary 1 output when its two inputs are different. If the two inputs are the same the output is binary 0. The translation of its Boolean expression states the same thing. Y is at binary 1 when A is 1 and not B ($\overline{B}$) is 1, or when not A ($\overline{A}$) is 1 and B is 1.

When we couple the XOR circuit to an AND circuit it becomes a perfect 1-bit binary adder. Consider the four possible input combinations:

Obviously, binary addition will generally involve more than just a pair of 1-bit digits. The example in Section 5.1 shows that addition involves a carry. Therefore a circuit is needed that can handle *three* binary digits at a time. To do this, two half-adders are connected and combined with an OR gate to form what is called a *full-adder*.

The Binary Full-Adder

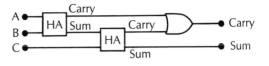

A binary full-adder can add three digits at a time. The full-adder circuit arrangement is illustrated in Figure 5.3.

We can verify the output for each of the input combinations by following the binary conditions through each circuit. If A, B, and C are all at binary 1, the top HA will have a 0 sum and a 1 carry. Thus, the bottom HA will have a 0, 1 input. This means it will have an output of binary 1 at S and 0 at C. The OR circuit will have a binary 1 input from the top HA and a 0 from the bottom HA. Thus the OR output will be at binary 1. This set of inputs causes a binary 1, 1 output.

We have examined circuits that can add up to three binary digits. Now there is a need to expand the circuits further so multi-digit binary numbers can be added. This can be achieved by either of two methods. The first, known as *parallel binary addition*, consists of increasing the number of full-adders, and is illustrated by Figure 5.4.

In the parallel adder all of the adders work at the same time, hence the name. If a larger

Truth Table

A	B	C	Carry	Sum
0	0	0	0	0
0	0	1	0	1
0	1	0	0	1
0	1	1	1	0
1	0	0	0	1
1	0	1	1	0
1	1	0	1	0
1	1	1	1	1

Figure 5.3 Binary Full-Adder

binary number is to be added, more circuit sections are used.

The second method, known as *serial binary addition*, is more complex. A serial adder will do the binary addition shown in Figure 5.4, but it is slower than the parallel adder. Yet it has the advantages that it uses less logic circuitry and that it can simplify the arithmetic

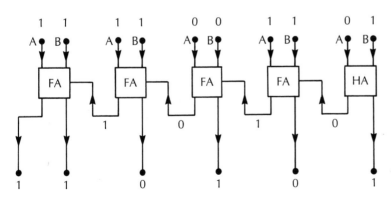

Binary number input at A: 11010
Binary number input at B: 11011
Adder output: 110101

Figure 5.4 Parallel Binary Adder

process when complex functions are to be performed. On the other hand, the serial adder requires associated circuitry that the parallel adder does not. This circuitry, which includes the registers, will be studied in Chapter 6. For now, we will simply look at the serial adder in terms of how it compares with the parallel adder. See Figure 5.5.

Unlike the parallel adder, the serial adder adds the binary digits step by step (serially), starting with the least significant bits. For example, if we are adding the binary numbers 101 and 100, 1 and 0 would be added first. Then the circuit would shift to the next column and add it, and so on. In a very general way, the serial adder responds to binary inputs as follows: the two binary numbers are stored in two *input registers* A and B. The least significant digits in these registers are applied to the serial adder as inputs. The adder produces an output in the usual way and stores this output in an *output register*. If there is a carry present, it is cycled through a *delay circuit* which causes it to be added in the next step. A *shift pulse* now causes the process to be repeated by shifting the registers to the next set of binary digits to be added.

In Chapters 6 and 7 we will study the operation of the above-mentioned new circuit elements — the register, the pulse generator or clock, and the delay flip-flop.

BCD Addition

Many computers use binary for the arithmetic operations, but some use binary-coded decimal (BCD) numbers, which we studied in Chapter 2. There, it was explained how the decimal digits 0 through 9 can be coded with 4-bit binary numbers. Computers that add using this BCD system must use a modified logic circuit.

Let us review the BCD system and then relate it to BCD adder circuitry.

In BCD, or the 8421 code as it is sometimes called, decimal digits are transformed into their 4-bit binary equivalents.

Example 2

3	2	0	Decimal digit
0011	0010	0000	Binary code

As was pointed out in Chapter 2, six 4-bit combinations cannot be used: 1010, 1011,

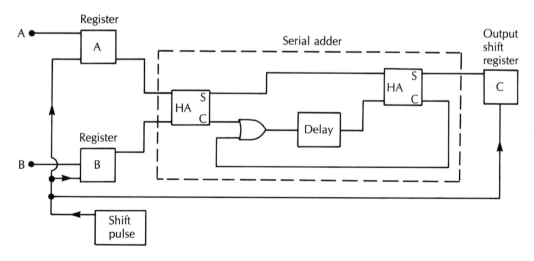

Figure 5.5 Serial Adder Circuit Arrangement

1100, 1101, 1110, and 1111. Since they do not correspond to any decimal digit, these combinations are meaningless. To add BCD numbers, logic circuits must be arranged so that these six combinations are ignored.

Example 3

8		1000
+4		+0100
12		1100

The binary sum 1100 is fine as far as binary numbers are concerned, but it is meaningless in BCD.

The BCD code for 12 is 0001 0010. Thus, when the sum of two binary digits exceeds 9, the next six combinations must be skipped and a new 4-bit code sequence started. We can do this by simply adding 6 (0110) to the binary sum. This will then put us back into BCD. Zeros are often added on the left (where they are not significant) to form the needed four digits in BCDs.

Example 4

8		1000	
+4		+0100	
12		1100	Bin. equiv. of 12
		+0110	Adding 6
		00010010	BCD for 12

Zeros added

Example 5

7		0111	
+6		+0110	
13		1101	Binary 13
		+0110	Adding 6
		00010011	BCD 13

Zeros added

Figure 5.6 illustrates the operation of a 4-bit BCD adder. Keep in mind here that we are adding just two decimal digits, in this case 8 and 5. These two numbers are put into the

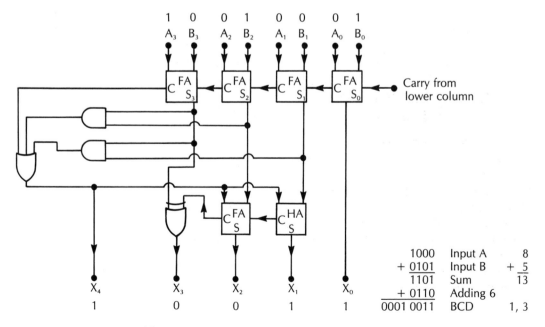

		1000	Input A	8
		+ 0101	Input B	+ 5
		1101	Sum	13
		+ 0110	Adding 6	
		0001 0011	BCD	1, 3

Figure 5.6 Four-Bit BCD Adder

adder in BCD form. The inputs are 1000 at A and 0101 at B. The adder does two basic things:

1. It adds the two binary numbers and produces the binary sum at the output of the full-adders. In this example the output is 01101. This is the correct equivalent for binary 13.
2. The additional logic circuitry now comes into play.

The pair of AND gates and the OR gate are used to recognize a sum greater than 9. Therefore, the binary equivalent of 6 must be added. The OR circuit output delivers binary 6 (0110) to the bottom adders to make the output read in BCD. The required output is 10011. In BCD this is one-three, understood to stand for 13.

Note that this circuit deals with only one column of digits. If we were adding three columns, the circuit in Figure 5.6 would have to be tripled — that is, the IC logic must be increased in density. By expanding the circuit, numbers of any size can be added.

5.2 Computer Subtraction

Binary Subtraction: A Review

It has been shown in Chapter 1 that subtraction can be done by addition if complementation is used. Computer circuits can be kept simple by applying the complementation method to binary subtraction.

Binary subtraction can be accomplished by computer circuits in a variety of ways, but there are only two basic methods, involving the one's complement and the two's complement. Let us briefly review them.

One's Complement Method

The complement of the subtrahend is added to the minuend. If there is a final carry, it is added to the difference as an end-around carry. When such a carry exists, the answer is positive and in its true (uncomplemented) form. When there is no final carry, the answer is negative and in its one's complement form.

Example 6

10	Minuend	1010
-6	Subtrahend	-0110
4	Difference	0100

```
 1010    Minuend
+1001    Complement of subtrahend
10011
↑
Carry

 0011
+   1    End-around carry
 0100    Answer, uncomplemented
```

When subtracting a larger number from a smaller as in the next example, we actually reverse the process to get the absolute value of the difference, remembering that it will be negative.

Example 7

5		0101
-9		-1001
-4		-0100

Instead of subtracting 1001 from 0101 we do the converse.

```
 1001
-0101
 0100    Answer, absolute value

-0100    Answer
```

Of course, the computer will do the subtraction by complementation and addition:

```
  0101
+ 0110    One's complement of 9
 01011
```

There is no final carry. Hence:

−0100   Answer

Two's Complement Method

Recall from Chapter 1 that the two's complement method of subtraction eliminates the end-around carry.

Example 8

```
 10              1010
 −6            − 0110
 ───           ──────
  4              0100
```

The subtrahend is converted to its two's complement form by complementing and adding one. Then it is added to the minuend.

```
  1010
+ 1010    Two's complement
 10100
 ↑
 Carry (ignored)
```

Here there is a 1 carry. This tells us that the answer is positive and is the true binary difference. Nothing further is done with the carry, and of course it is not part of the answer.

0100   Answer

Example 9

```
  5              0101
 −9            − 1001
 ───           ──────
 −4            − 0100
```

```
  0101
+ 0111    Two's complement
  1100
```

There is no carry. Therefore the above answer is negative and in its two's complement form.

−0100   Answer

The Binary Subtractor

Though there are many rules to be remembered when doing subtraction manually, computers do it automatically and with great speed.

Figure 5.7 shows how a 4-bit binary number can be subtracted using the one's complement system. The binary number (or word) inserted at the B inputs is subtracted from the binary number inserted at the A inputs. The inverters in the B leads change all Bs to $\bar{B}$s. The two binary numbers are now added by the full-adders and the end-around carry is also added in. If there is an end-around carry present, the

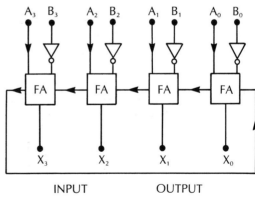

```
INPUT          OUTPUT
A: 0100         X: 1100
B: 0111
```

True binary difference: 0011 (negative)

Figure 5.7 Parallel Binary Subtractor

result is positive and in binary form. If there is not, the output is recognized as negative and in the one's complement form for the subtraction involved. For example, assume that binary 0100 is entered at A and 0111 is entered at B. This means that 7 is to be subtracted from 4. The inverters convert 0111 to 1000 at the B inputs to the full-adders. The adders add 0100 to 1000 and produce 1100 at the X outputs. Since there is no end-around carry the circuit recognizes that this is a negative value and is in the one's complement form. The binary output is simply inverted to get the correct negative value — in this case 0011 (4 − 7 = −3). Obviously, extra circuitry is required to do this. Nevertheless, it is a relatively simple addition to the basic subtractor circuit.

The subtractor shown in Figure 5.8 is a dual-purpose circuit. As well as subtracting in the two's complement system, it also adds. Which it does depends on the condition of the subtractor (SUB) line.

If the SUB line is at binary 0, the circuit adds the binary numbers at inputs A and B. If the SUB line is at binary 1, the input at B is inverted and added in two's complement form.

Assume that binary 0111 is applied to A and binary 0011 to B, and that they are to be added. (This is not the example shown below the figure.) In this case the SUB line is at 0. As a result there is no carry input to the first full-adder. A binary 0 input is connected to each XOR circuit. The XOR circuit will now produce a 0 output when its B input is zero and a 1 output when the B input is 1. In other words, the B inputs go straight through the XOR circuits as if they were transparent. The full-adders now do their job of adding the A and B inputs. A sum of up to four binary digits can be handled by this circuit.

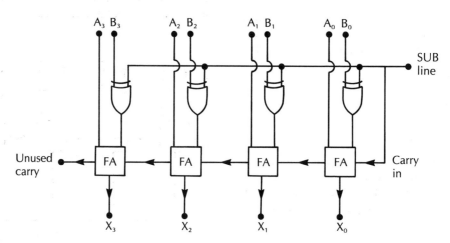

A: 1001
B: 0011
Carry in: 1
X output: 0110

Figure 5.8 Two's Complement Subtractor or Adder

When subtraction is called for, the SUB line is placed at binary 1. Now binary 1s at the B inputs come out of the XOR circuits as zeros, and binary 0s as 1s. Also, there is a binary 1 supplied to the carry input of the first full-adder. The XOR circuits change the B input into its complement form. The addition of the binary 1 at the first full-adder converts the result to its two's complement form.

The full-adder output at X is the difference of the A and B inputs.

For example, assume that binary 1001 is entered at A and binary 0011 at B. Since subtraction is called for, the SUB line is at binary 1. The XOR outputs will be 1100. The full-adders will see inputs of (B) 1100 and (A) 1001 along with a carry input of 1. The X outputs, then, will be 0110 with a final carry of 1 which is ignored.

Example 10

9		1001	A
−3		−0011	B
6		0110	

Full-Adder Inputs

```
  1001
+ 1101
 10110    X output
↑
Carry (ignored)
```

We have seen how basic circuits are used to add binary numbers. We have also seen that the addition process is basic to all of the arithmetic operations — it is simply a matter of modifying the adder circuit to make it subtract or multiply or divide. Obviously, a great deal of circuitry is needed to handle these functions. Some of this circuitry has yet to be discussed. For example, binary numbers have to be delivered to the adder circuits and extracted from them; there must be circuitry to "see" if there are end-around carries present; and there have to be circuits to hold or store binary numbers before and after they are added. The circuits required for these functions will be examined in the following chapters.

Questions

1. Explain how a binary half-adder combines XOR and AND logic to add two binary digits.
2. Can a half-adder add two digits plus a carry input? Explain.
3. Refer to Figure 5.3 and explain the logical operation of the full-adder.
4. Review the parallel adder illustrated in Figure 5.4. Why is the end adder a half-adder?
5. Refer to Figure 5.6 and explain how binary-coded decimal addition differs from the system illustrated in Figure 5.4.
6. What is the advantage of binary-coded decimal number representations?
7. Explain how addition in a serial adder differs from addition in a parallel adder.
8. Refer to Figure 5.7 and explain how the full adders work together to subtract.
9. Refer to Figure 5.8. Explain how this circuit can be used to either add or subtract binary numbers.
10. How is the value of a binary number affected if the binary point is shifted one place to the right? How is it affected if the binary point is shifted one place to the left?

Experiments

Experiment 5.1

Object

To show the operation and logic of a binary half-adder.

Circuit

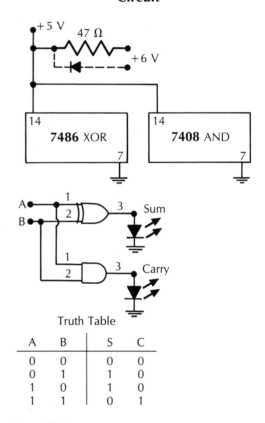

Figure E5.1

Steps

Note: If a 6-V source is used, connect via a 47-Ω resistor or a diode to drop the battery voltage to approximately 5 V.

1. Connect the circuit. Apply the input combinations shown in the truth table and observe the sum and carry LEDs.
2. What are the limitations of this adder?

Experiment 5.2

Object

To show the operation of a full-adder.

Circuit

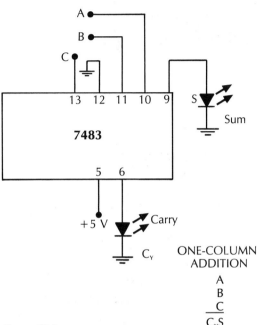

Figure E5.2

ONE-COLUMN
ADDITION

$$A$$
$$B$$
$$\underline{C}$$
$$C_Y S$$

Steps

Note: If a 6-V source is used, connect via a 47-Ω resistor or a diode to drop the battery voltage to approximately 5 V.

1. Connect the circuit.
2. Insert all combinations of A, B, and C and record the output response of the LEDs.
3. How many binary digits can this circuit add?

Experiment 5.3

Object

To show the operation of a two-stage full-adder.

Circuit

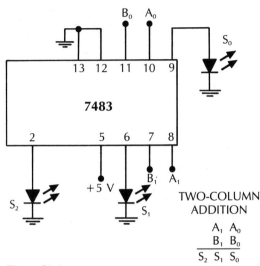

Figure E5.3

TWO-COLUMN
ADDITION

$$A_1 \ A_0$$
$$\underline{B_1 \ B_0}$$
$$S_2 \ S_1 \ S_0$$

Steps

Note: If a 6-V source is used, connect via a 47-Ω resistor or a diode to drop the battery voltage to approximately 5V.

1. Connect the circuit. Connect pins 7, 8, 10, and 11 to ground. Observe the LEDs.
2. Insert all combinations of binary digits into A_0, B_0, A_1, and B_1 and observe the LEDs in each case.
3. How many columns of binary digits can this circuit add?

CHAPTER 6

Flip-Flop Circuits and Binary Storage

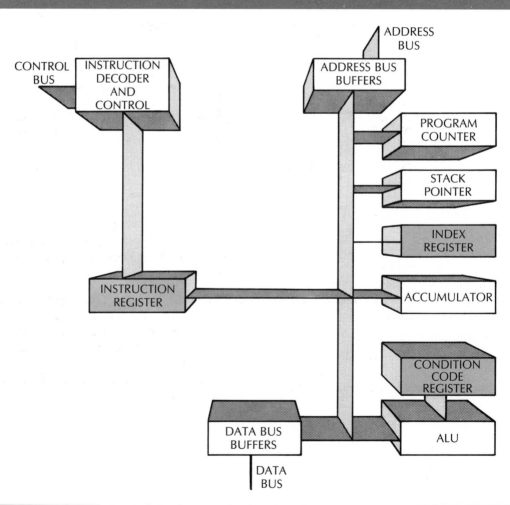

ADDRESS
BUS

CONTROL
BUS

INSTRUCTION
DECODER
AND
CONTROL

ADDRESS BUS
BUFFERS

PROGRAM
COUNTER

STACK
POINTER

INDEX
REGISTER

INSTRUCTION
REGISTER

ACCUMULATOR

CONDITION
CODE
REGISTER

DATA BUS
BUFFERS

ALU

DATA
BUS

MICROPROCESSOR UNITS

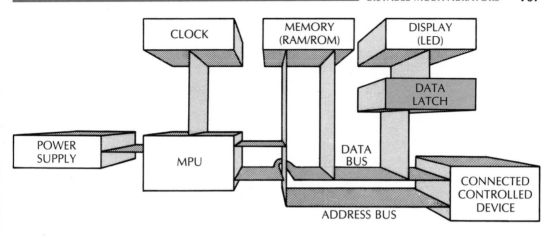

COMPUTER SYSTEM

■■ INTRODUCTION ■■

The logic circuits used in computers are designed only to make decisions and do arithmetic. They have no memory. In order to produce a given output condition, these circuits require certain input conditions. Once those conditions are removed the circuit has no way of "remembering" the result. However, there is a need for computers to remember or store data for both short and long periods of time while the data is being processed. This is much like human data processing: if we wish to add two numbers, we must remember momentarily what they are, add them, and then remember the sum.

A computer gets its ability to store data temporarily from its *flip-flop circuits*. These circuits can store binary data, count pulses, and synchronize the operation of the many circuits necessary in a computer. Because flip-flop circuits are so important, we must understand clearly their basic operation and circuit applications.

6.1 Bistable Multivibrators

A multivibrator (MV) is a circuit consisting of a pair of transistors which alternately turn each other off. Multivibrators come in two basic classes: free-running and controlled. Their use as computer memory devices calls for the controlled type — i.e., flip-flops that have their output condition controlled by input trigger pulses — while their use as computer clocks calls for the free-running type. We will examine clock circuits in Chapter 8; here we will confine our interest to memory devices.

The *basic flip-flop* or *bistable MV* is an easy circuit to understand. We have already dealt with circuits in which saturated transistors are used. The same operating conditions are present here.

Figure 6.1 shows a basic circuit for a bistable MV. This circuit is called bistable because it will remain in one of two possible conditions until some external control is applied to change it. Consider this circuit when the battery is first

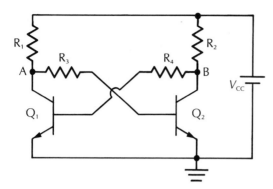

Figure 6.1 Basic Bistable Multivibrator Circuit

connected. Assume that Q_1 conducts slightly ahead of Q_2, since no transistor pair would ever be perfectly identical. As the Q_1 collector current rises, the voltage at A will drop lower and lower until it reaches about 0.2 V, when Q_1 is saturated. The falling voltage at A causes the current in Q_2 to fall, as A is connected to the base of Q_2 via R_3. This action is cumulative. The voltage at A is falling as Q_1 goes into saturation and the voltage at B is rising as Q_2 goes into cut-off. Once these extremes are reached, the two transistors remain in this state until some external condition is applied to change it. Here Q_1 is conducting at saturation and Q_2 is cut off. Current flow in the circuit will be present in Q_1, R_1, R_4, and R_2. Collector current will flow up through Q_1 and R_1. Base current in Q_1 will flow up through R_4 and R_2. There will be no current in Q_2.

If we measure the voltages in the circuit we find about 0.2 V across Q_1 emitter-collector (V_{CE}). The emitter-base voltage is about 0.7 V. These voltages, you recall, are typical for a saturated silicon transistor. The voltages for Q_2 would be consistent with its cut-off condition. Its base-emitter voltage would be 0.2 V, since it is connected across Q_1. The voltage at the collector of Q_2 would be equal to V_{CC} minus

the V_{R_2} potential caused by the base current flow from Q_1.

This operating condition (Q_1 on, Q_2 off) can be changed by simply dropping V_{BE} on Q_1 to zero. We can do this by momentarily shorting the base-emitter section of Q_1.

When we short V_{BE} on Q_1 to zero this removes its forward bias and cuts Q_1 off. As it quickly goes to cut-off, its collector voltage rises at point A. This causes the base voltage of Q_2 to rise, allowing Q_2 to conduct. As Q_2 begins to conduct, the voltage drop across its collector load resistor R_2 increases. Also, the voltage at B drops and continues to drop to about 0.2 V at B, when Q_2 is saturated. This low voltage at B is now used to hold Q_1 in a cut-off condition. Once again, the circuit will rest in this condition until it is caused to change by some external action.

Let us relate the voltages at A and B to binary conditions. Let a high voltage represent 1 and a low voltage represent 0. Now we have a 0, 1 condition at outputs A and B which can be reversed. If Q_1 is on and Q_2 is off, point A will be at 0 and B at 1. This condition will be held indefinitely as long as the circuit is energized. If the condition of Q_1, Q_2 is reversed, the conditions at A and B will reverse.

Clearly there is a need for a control mechanism in a flip-flop circuit. We must be able to tell the circuit what the binary output is to be and we must also be able to instruct the circuit to change the output condition. There are many ways in which such a control can be introduced in a circuit. We will now examine several common control circuits.

Consider the circuit in Figure 6.2, which provides for complete control of the circuit output. When the power supply is connected to this circuit, Q_2 and Q_3 behave in exactly the same way as the transistors did in Figure 6.1. This time, however, we have two additional

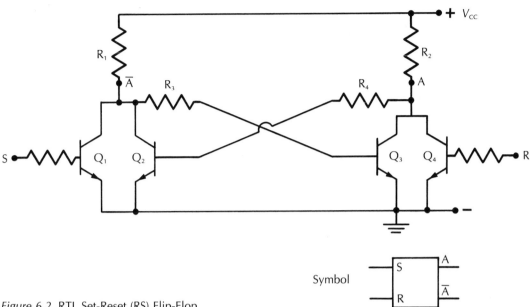

Figure 6.2 RTL Set-Reset (RS) Flip-Flop

transistors (Q_1 and Q_4), which act in parallel with Q_2 and Q_3.

Assume that the circuit is energized and Q_2 is on and Q_3 is off. If we turned Q_1 on by applying a forward bias at S it would not change anything in the circuit. This is because the voltage across Q_2 is already held at 0.2 V by the saturation of Q_2. However, if we turn Q_4 on by applying a forward bias at R, the circuit will transfer to its opposite state. When Q_4 is turned on, it will conduct and saturate, as there is a high-voltage condition present at A. This action by Q_4 will drop the voltage at A to 0.2 V. It will also cause Q_2 to cut off, because Q_2 gets its bias from point A. This sequence causes the voltage conditions at A and $\overline{A}$ to reverse.

Notice that the voltage applied at R does not have to be maintained. A simple pulse of forward bias will cause Q_4 to saturate. This, in turn, will cause the flip-flop circuit to cycle and change state. While the circuit is in this

state the further application of a pulse of forward bias at R will have no effect.

The operating response possibilities for the set-reset (RS) flip-flop are summarized in the following table.

R (Reset)	S (Set)	A
0	0	Last value (0 or 1)
0	1	1
1	0	0
1	1	Not allowed

We will look at the RS features of the circuit later in this chapter.

When S is at binary 1, A must either be at or go to binary 1. When R is at binary 1, A must be at or go to binary 0. We see now that the circuit causes the output at A to be stuck or "latched" in its last state. It will only change its state when an appropriate pulse is applied at either S or R.

In terms of logic circuits, the RS flip-flop is a pair of interconnected NOR circuits, as shown in Figure 6.3. Consider the action of the circuit. With no signals applied to R and S, the outputs will hold at one condition. Assume that A is at 1 and $\overline{A}$ at 0. In this state the input to the top gate is 0, 1, which produces a NOR output of 0. The bottom NOR gate has a 0, 0 input which causes an output of 1 at A.

If S receives a binary 1 pulse, its input will now be 1, 1. This still calls for a NOR output of 0, so nothing will change in the circuit. However, if R now receives a binary 1 pulse, the bottom NOR gate will have a 0, 1 input. Its output will change from 1 to 0. Once this happens the top gate sees a 0, 0 input. Its output will now switch from 0 to 1. We can see that the circuit satisfies all the conditions for RS flip-flop action.

This RS flip-flop circuit requires two input signals for full control. However, it is possible to achieve this same control with one input signal on one input line. This method of control is known as *symmetrical triggering*. With it the circuit state is changed each time an input pulse is applied. Again, there are many ways in which flip-flop circuits can be arranged for symmetrical triggering. We will examine one common type known as a *T flip-flop* or *toggle flip-flop*. The basic circuit is illustrated in Figure 6.4.

The circuit looks rather complicated at first glance but it is really quite similar to our previous RS flip-flop. It should also be mentioned that our circuit in Figure 6.4 normally would have a bias divider circuit included. However, it is left out for the moment to simplify the circuit description. The circuit shown is a working arrangement, but without the extra bias source it would be rather noise-sensitive. We will come back to this point later.

If our circuit were energized and there were no input at T, then either Q_1 or Q_2, randomly, would saturate while its counterpart would cut off. This would be similar to the RS flip-flop. Under these conditions the trigger circuit components C_1, C_2, R_1, R_2, D_1, D_2 do nothing.

The circuit is designed so that the appearance of a binary 1 pulse at T will change the output condition of Q_1 and Q_2. If the pulse is removed and then reapplied, it will once again change the output condition of Q_1 and Q_2.

In order to understand how this happens we must carefully follow the action of the trigger circuit. We will assume that Q_1 is on and Q_2 off. Since Q_1 is saturated, its collector and base voltages are very low — less than 1 V. Since Q_2 is cut off, its collector voltage will be high — about the value of V_{CC}. At the same time its

NOR LOGIC

Truth Table

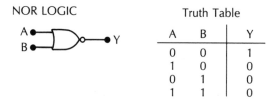

A	B	Y
0	0	1
1	0	0
0	1	0
1	1	0

FLIP-FLOP LOGIC

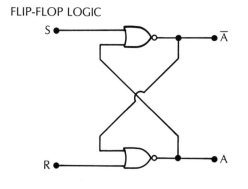

SYMBOL

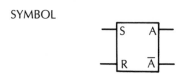

Figure 6.3 RS Flip-Flop Logic

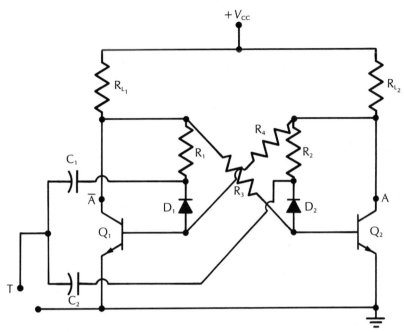

Figure 6.4 Toggle Flip-Flop

base voltage is low — about 0 V. Under these general conditions we can consider the action of the trigger circuit with the aid of Figure 6.5.

We will look at the circuit in each of its three operating states: (1) When Q_1 is on and Q_2 is off and there is no trigger pulse, i.e., the T

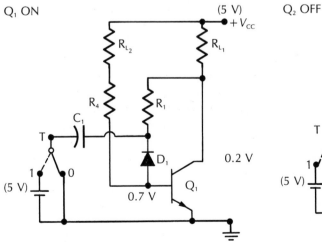

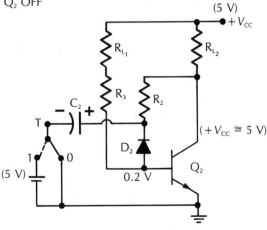

Figure 6.5 Trigger Circuit Analysis

input is resting at 0 V. (2) When the T input receives a positive pulse voltage. (3) When the positive pulse voltage at T drops back to 0 V.

1. When Q_1 is on and T is resting at 0 V, there is no charge action on C_1 and D_1 will not conduct. The voltage across C_1 is essentially 0 V as the collector potential is about 0.2 V and T is at 0 V. The potential across D_1 is only about 0.5 V.

   At the same time, Q_2 is off and its collector potential is at nearly V_{CC} — we will assume 5 V. If T is resting at 0 V, there will be a difference potential of about 5 V across C_2. C_2 will charge to this potential with the polarities shown. D_2 will not conduct as it has a reverse bias.

2. When a binary 1 (5-V) condition appears on the trigger line, C_1 quickly charges to this 5 V through R_1. The capacitor sees a difference of potential of approximately 5 V between the $+5$ V at T and the $+0.2$ V at the collector of Q_1. This charge action has no effect on D_1 as the potential at the junction of D_1 and R_1 is a reverse bias for D_1.

   C_2, on the other hand, sees $+5$ V at T and about $+5$ V at the collector of Q_2. Remember also that C_2 is charged to 5 V from the discussion of state 1. This places the junction of D_2 and R_2 at $+10$ V. However, C_2 will quickly discharge through R_2 and drop the potential here to $+5$ V. This returns the charge on C_2 to 0 V, as it now sits between the two $+5$-V points. D_2 will not conduct because the positive potential at the D_2-R_2 junction is a reverse bias.

3. We have now come to the point where the circuit is made to change its output condition. When the short-duration $+5$-V pulse at T drops to 0 V, the on transistor is turned off and the off transistor is turned on. When T drops suddenly to 0 V from $+5$ V, it does so with C_1 charged to 5 V and C_2 at 0 V. C_1 discharges quickly through R_1 and places

its -5-V potential at the junction of R_1 and D_1. This gives a forward bias to D_1 and transfers this pulse of -5 V to the base of Q_1. This spike of voltage causes Q_1 to cut off.

At this moment the T input at C_2 goes from $+5$ to 0 V. C_2 is discharged at this time. It will now quickly start to charge to the 5-V potential it sees between T and the collector of Q_2. This charge action drops the voltage at the junction of R_2-D_2 to nearly 0 V as C_2 charges through R_2. D_2 is cut off during this period.

All this takes place in a very short period of time, during which the circuit is in transition: Q_1 is being turned off and Q_2 on.

The toggle flip-flop circuit of Figure 6.4 usually has base bias supplied from a negative voltage source as shown in Figure 6.6. The transistor which is cut off is held at about -1.5 V. Therefore a stronger pulse or voltage change is needed to trigger it on. For example, if we consider Q_1 on and Q_2 off, the bias voltage on the base of Q_2 will be determined mainly by the voltage drops across R_6 and R_3.

6.2 Astable Multivibrators

The *astable* or *free-running MV* is a common computer circuit. It has no stable state, but constantly switches back and forth on its own at a rate determined by its component values. If it is designed so that each transistor conducts for an equal time, the output signal is a square wave.

This circuit is used for many computer operations. One of its common functions is as a computer clock. It acts as a control device to turn various circuit sections on or off in unison.

A basic free-running MV circuit is shown in Figure 6.7. Assume that Q_1 is on (saturated)

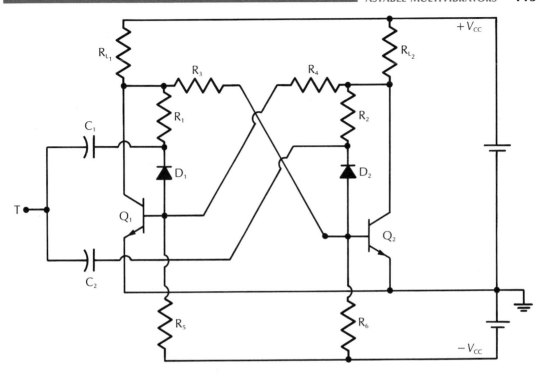

Figure 6.6 T Flip-Flop with $-V_{cc}$ Bias

and Q_2 is off. With Q_1 saturated its base and collector voltages are essentially zero, while the collector voltage of Q_2 will be about V_{cc}.

With Q_1 conducting heavily, C_2 quickly charges to V_{cc} through the low resistance of R_2 and, of course, through the base circuit of Q_1. If it were not for C_1, Q_1 would just stay on and Q_2 would stay off. However, while Q_1 is on, C_1 is slowly discharging through Q_1 and R_3. Remember that C_1 on the previous cycle would charge to V_{cc} just as C_2 did on this cycle. At this point, C_1 is charged to V_{cc} with its collector side positive. Now C_1 sees ground potential at the collector of Q_1, since Q_1 is saturated. C_1 starts to discharge through Q_1 and the high resistance of R_3, and would lose its charge and continue to charge up to V_{cc} in the opposite direction if nothing else stopped it. When C_1 is discharged and then starts to charge to V_{cc},

the base voltage of Q_2 starts to become positive. Q_2 quickly conducts. This causes the circuit to cycle.

The saturated Q_2 connects the collector end

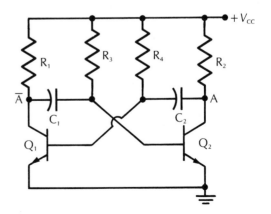

Figure 6.7 Free-Running Multivibrator Circuit

Q₁ ON

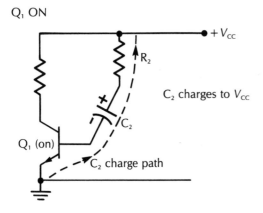

Q₂ ON

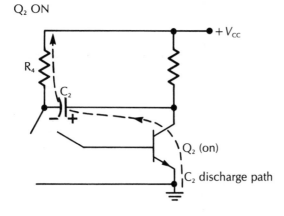

WAVEFORMS

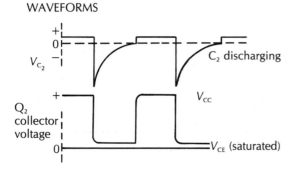

Figure 6.8 Astable MV Waveforms and Capacitor Charge-Discharge Action

of C_2 to ground. This, in turn, causes the base voltage of Q_1 to "see," or sense, the negative charge potential of C_2. This situation causes Q_1 suddenly to cut off. Q_1 remains cut off until C_2 has time to lose its charge and start charging to the opposite polarity. Thus, the circuit cycles back and forth, at a rate determined by the values of C_1, C_2, R_3, and R_4. If C_1-R_3 and C_2-R_4 are similar, the on-off time for Q_1 and Q_2 will be the same. This results in square-wave output pulses.

Figure 6.8 shows the waveforms and charge-discharge action for the circuit. We see that C_2 charges to V_{cc} when Q_1 is on. When Q_2 is on, C_2 wants to charge to V_{cc} through R_4. To do this it must first discharge, then begin to charge with opposite polarities.

6.3 Monostable (One-Shot) Multivibrators

Another common computer circuit is the *monostable* or *one-shot MV*. It has one stable state but can be triggered into the opposite state for a short period of time, after which it returns to its original state. As we will see when we examine the circuit in Figure 6.9, this MV can only be triggered when it is in its stable state. It can not be falsely triggered once the initial trigger pulse has been applied. This reduces the problem of accidental triggering, especially in a system where there is a lot of noise present. Later we will discuss other special features of the one-shot MV, such as pulse-shaping and pulse-delay.

The normal or stable state for the circuit in Figure 6.9 is Q_2 on and Q_1 off. In this state, Q_2 is saturated and its collector potential is nearly 0 V. Since the base of Q_1 is connected

CIRCUIT

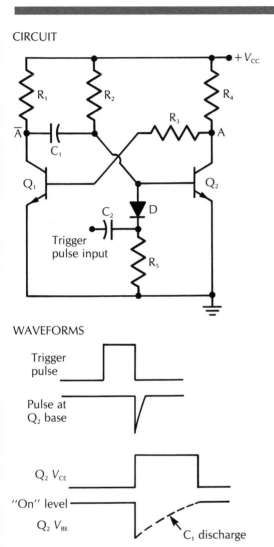

WAVEFORMS

Trigger
pulse

Pulse at
Q_2 base

$Q_2 V_{CE}$

"On" level

$Q_2 V_{BE}$

C_1 discharge

Figure 6.9 Basic One-Shot Multivibrator Circuit

to the collector of Q_2 via R_3, Q_1 is cut off and so its collector potential will be V_{CC}. Thus C_1 will charge to V_{CC} through the conducting base of Q_2. The circuit will remain in this state until a trigger pulse is applied. This state causes a high (binary 1) condition at A and a low (binary 0) at $\overline{A}$.

When a trigger pulse is applied, a "spiked" voltage (i.e., one of short duration) is produced across R_5 due to the fast charge action of C_2. When the input pulse drops to zero, another spike of voltage appears across R_5 due to the fast discharge of C_2. The negative spike causes diode D to conduct. This delivers the spike of voltage to the base of Q_2, which in turn drives Q_2 to cut-off.

The cut-off of Q_2 suddenly drives the base of Q_1 into conduction. This happens because the collector voltage of Q_2 now rises to V_{CC} and delivers a forward bias to the base of Q_1 via R_3.

With Q_1 saturated and Q_2 cut off, C_1 has its collector end connected essentially to ground, via Q_1. The full charge voltage on C_1 (V_{CC}) is now applied to the base of Q_2. This charge potential is negative at the junction of C_1 and R_2. Thus the base of Q_2 is highly reverse-biased. C_1 starts to discharge to 0 V and then charge to V_{CC} through R_2 and the conducting Q_1. As soon as C_1 charges slightly positive, Q_2 senses a forward bias and once again becomes saturated, cutting off Q_1. The circuit rests in this state until another trigger pulse is applied.

We see that Q_2 is kept off for a period determined by the time constant of C_1-R_2. We can also see that another trigger pulse will not affect the circuit if it is applied while Q_2 is off. Notice also that the circuit has the effect of delaying the output pulse relative to the input pulse. From the waveforms we see that the output pulse $Q_2 V_{CE}$ (the collector-to-emitter voltage of transistor Q_2) falls to zero at a later time than does the trigger pulse. We will discuss an application for this circuit feature in another chapter.

We have looked at three basic MV types:

set-reset, free-running, and monostable (one-shot). These can be either used directly to do a variety of jobs in a computer or modified and expanded to perform complex computer functions. For example, flip-flops in computers are generally *clocked*, i.e., synchronized and controlled by a chain of pulses from a clock circuit. In the case of the RS flip-flop, its output condition would change only when the clock pulse was present. Figure 6.10 gives the logic diagram for a clocked RS flip-flop.

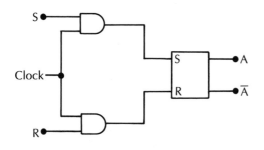

Figure 6.10 Clocked RS Flip-Flop

We see that a *set* pulse or a *reset* pulse can only be transferred to the flip-flop if the AND gates are *enabled* (turned on) by the clock pulse. In systems where hundreds, or even thousands, of flip-flops are present, the clock is used to synchronize their operation.

It can be seen that a set or a reset pulse in Figure 6.10 will not cause the flip-flop to switch. It is actually the clock pulse that causes this. Of course, a binary 1 condition must be present at S or R, but it can do nothing until the clock pulse arrives.

We have learned that the bistable MV (RS type) responds to a binary 1 condition at either of its two inputs. If the S input "sees" a binary

1 then the A output will be at binary 1, as described in Figure 6.2. The flip-flop will hold this condition until the R input gets a binary 1.

Once the circuit has been set it remains set and will not switch, even if a binary 1 is reapplied to the S input. This makes the RS MV useful as a *switch debouncer*. When switches (such as input keys) are operated, the spring contacts can open and close several times before they settle down, causing error data and noise in logic circuits. When an RS flip-flop is used, this problem is eliminated.

Figure 6.11 shows how an RS flip-flop can be connected to debounce a switch.

CIRCUIT

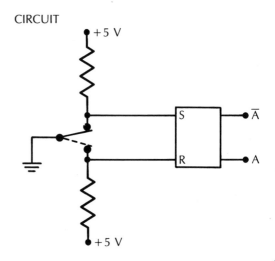

WAVEFORMS

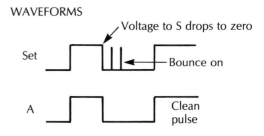

Figure 6.11 SR Flip-Flop Used to Debounce a Switch

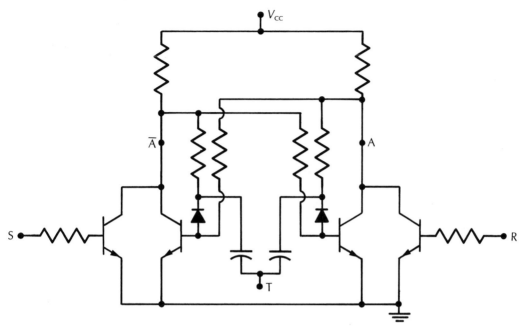

Figure 6.12 Basic RST Flip-Flop

6.4 RST Flip-Flops

The *RST flip-flop* is just a combined RS and toggle flip-flop. We have already examined this circuit in detail, so we will simply consider its general characteristics here. We can think of this circuit as Figures 6.2 and 6.6 combined into one. This circuit can *toggle* — switch the outputs — only when both the set and reset inputs are at 0. If the set input is at binary 1, the output at A holds at binary 1. The circuit stays set and the toggle input has no effect. Similarly, if the reset input is at binary 1, the circuit remains reset with $\overline{A}$ at binary 1. Again, the toggle input has no effect.

Figure 6.12 shows a basic RST flip-flop circuit. We see that it is just a union of Figures 6.2 and 6.6.

6.5 JK Flip-Flops

As we consider computer circuits in more and more detail we see that timed or *clocked* operation is vital. For example, when logic circuits are activated to make decisions or to do arithmetic they must do it quickly and without ambiguity. The clocking of the circuit enables operation only on "instructions" from the clock pulse. This positive control by the clock exactly times all of the logic circuit operations.

The *JK flip-flop*[1] was designed to refine RS circuit operation. It responds only to rapidly changing pulses at its *clock* input. This aspect

---

1. The designation JK has no important meaning except as a means of differentiation from the RS flip-flop.

LOGIC

TIMING

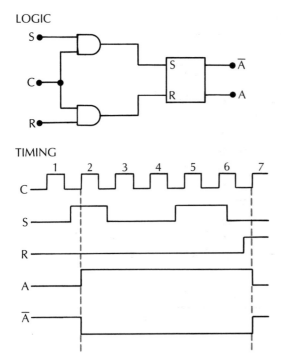

Figure 6.13 Timing for Clocked RS Flip-Flop

pinpoints the exact moment when the flip-flop can change states. As a result more precise timing and control are achieved.

Before studying the JK flip-flop in detail we will discuss two main weaknesses of the RS flip-flop. Figure 6.13 shows the timing for a clocked RS circuit. Compare the S (set) pulse with A. When the S pulse appears, the output does not change from binary 0 to binary 1 at A until the clock pulse goes to binary 1. Conversely, if the S pulse arrives sometime during the clock pulse the output will switch. Thus, one weakness is that the time of circuit transfer varies — it can occur anywhere within the period of the clock pulse.

The other weakness of the RS flip-flop is the forbidden input of two binary 1s. The JK flip-flop overcomes these problems. A basic logic circuit for JK flip-flop operation is shown in Figure 6.14.

Notice that a 0 input to both J and K prevents a change in output when the clock pulse arrives. However, a binary 1 at J causes A to jump to binary 1 at the leading edge of the clock pulse. Similarly, when J is 0 and K is 1

TIMING

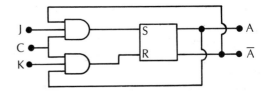

LOGIC

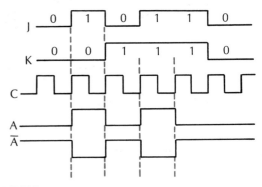

Truth Table

J	K	Circuit Action
0	0	Last state
1	0	Sets
0	1	Resets
1	1	Toggles

Figure 6.14 Basic JK Flip-Flop Logic

the output state switches at the leading edge of the clock pulse. Also, when both J and K are at 1 the output state switches at the leading edge of each clock pulse.

This type of triggering is called *positive edge triggering*, but the circuit can also be triggered at the falling edge of the clock pulse. In that case it would exhibit *negative edge triggering*.

The JK flip-flop seems to have done away with the weaknesses present in the RS type. There is, however, one possible problem. Notice that the JK outputs are connected to the AND gate inputs. A delay in getting the signals

transferred from input to output can cause a problem known as *race-around*: an output may try to change several times for a single input. This problem is overcome by expanding the JK flip-flop to form a *master-slave JK flip-flop*.

Before examining this circuit, we will consider a basic JK flip-flop schematic. Of course, such basic circuits represent only one of a number of forms that logic circuits can take. Also, today these logic circuits are fabricated in quantity on IC chips, and the circuit in Figure 6.15 would be only one small section of an IC.

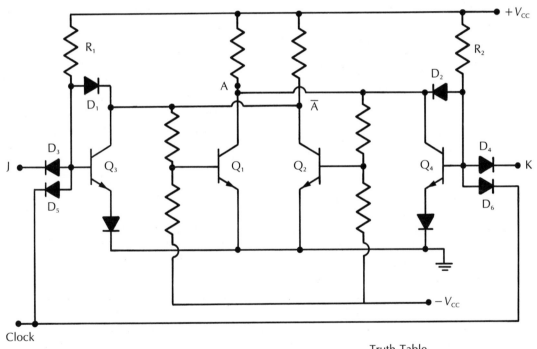

Truth Table

J	K	C	A	$\overline{A}$
0	0	1	No change	No change
0	1	1	0	1 (resets)
1	0	1	1	0 (sets)
1	1	1	Toggles	

Figure 6.15 Basic JK Flip-Flop

Follow the action of the circuit for the four input possibilities discussed next.

1. J is at 0 and K is at 0. D_3 and D_4 are forward-biased and Q_3 and Q_4 are kept off as their base potentials are held to 0 V. A clock input of 1 (positive) puts a reverse bias on D_5 and D_6, so it has no effect. The output at A and $\overline{A}$ will remain in its former state.

2. J is 1 and K is 0. Assume Q_1 is on and Q_2 is off. D_1 is reverse-biased. A clock input of 1 reverse-biases D_5 and D_6. Also, the 0 input at K holds the base of Q_4 at zero, ensuring that Q_4 stays off.

   D_1, D_3, and D_5 are all reverse-biased when the clock pulse arrives. At the arrival of a positive clock pulse, Q_3 turns on. A saturated Q_3 drops the collector voltage of Q_2 and the base voltage of Q_1 to 0 V. This causes Q_1 to switch off and Q_2 on. This leaves the circuit output in the set condition.

   Notice that when Q_2 is on it places a 0-V potential on the base of Q_3 via D_1. This holds Q_3 off. The clock input is now *disabled* and has no effect as long as the J and K inputs are present.

3. J is at 0 and K is at 1. The sequence described in possibility 2 is repeated on the opposite "side" of the circuit. Once again, only the first clock pulse will be effective in changing the circuit state.

4. J is at 1 and K is at 1. With this input combination the clock pulse causes the circuit output to toggle — switch back and forth.

   D_3 and D_4 are reverse-biased.

   Assume that Q_2 is on and Q_1 off. Thus D_1 is forward-biased and D_2 is reverse-biased. The forward bias on D_1 causes Q_3 to be turned off. Q_4 is also off until the clock pulse becomes positive.

   The presence of a positive clock pulse turns Q_4 on as D_6 now has a reverse bias.

When Q_4 turns on, it switches Q_2 off and Q_1 on. The next clock pulse reverses the procedure.

The Master-Slave JK

Basically, a master-slave JK flip-flop is just two JK flip-flops in series. It has the advantage that it overcomes the race-around or "feedback" problem of the basic JK flip-flop. This improvement is realized by having the first or master circuit react to its inputs, after which the second or slave circuit "copies" the output of the master.

A basic logic diagram will show how the circuit does this. See Figure 6.16.

1. Follow the logic when J is 1 and K is 0. When the positive clock pulse (C) arrives, the master flip-flop produces a set output (A_M is 1, $\overline{A}$ is 0). When the clock pulse (C) drops to zero, the inverted clock pulse ($\overline{C}$) clocks the slave flip-flop on. Its J input comes from A_M, so the slave output is binary 1 at A. Very simply, the slave copies the master.

2. The opposite set of input pulses cause the circuits to reset in turn.

3. If both J and K are high (binary 1), the master toggles on the leading edge of the clock pulse and the slave toggles on the trailing edge of the clock pulse (C).

Notice the difference between the master and the slave circuit symbols in the figure. The arrowhead at the clock input of the master indicates edge triggering. On the slave symbol there is a bubble at the clock input terminal. This indicates the clock signal has been inverted.

The master-slave JK flip-flop is a remarkably versatile device. It can complement (change the state of) its binary outputs; it has no invalid input combinations; it does not race-around.

LOGIC

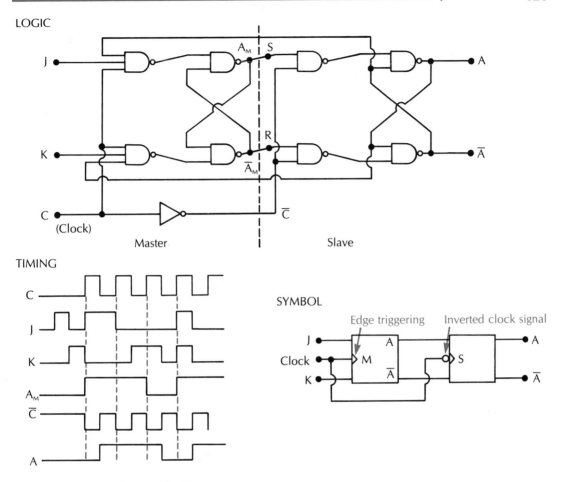

TIMING

Figure 6.16 Master-Slave JK Flip-Flop

This versatility makes it excellent for counting pulses. We will examine counting circuits in the next chapter.

Before leaving the topic of flip-flops it should be stated that flip-flop circuits can be constructed in many different ways. A variety of basic gates can be used to achieve the same end. We have examined only a few of the basic arrangements. It should also be mentioned that clock pulses which control flip-flops and gates are often differentiated. That is, the relatively long duration of the pulse is converted into a pair of spiked pulses. One spike is produced by the leading edge of the clock pulse and another by the trailing edge. These spikes create a shorter period of time in which the flip-flop can react to input data. JK flip-flops are often edge-triggered by spikes as opposed to level pulses. The flip-flops can only change state when the clock pulse is changing state (low to high or high to low) on the edge of its pulse.

LOGIC

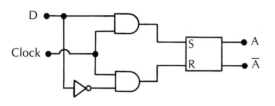

SYMBOL

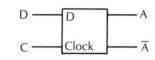

Truth Table

Clock	D	A	$\overline{A}$
0	Don't care	Last state	
1	0	0	1
1	1	1	0

Figure 6.17 D Flip-Flop

6.6 Registers

Computers require both temporary and permanent (or semi-permanent) storage. Permanent storage is usually handled by *memory devices*. Temporary storage is handled by *registers*.

Registers are logic circuits, usually flip-flops. They are arranged to allow for the storage and processing of data in binary form. There are two basic kinds: *storage registers* and *shift registers*. As their names imply, the storage register holds binary data and the shift register processes it.

A register is really a group of flip-flops used to store a binary word. Each digit requires a flip-flop. If the word consists of four binary digits, four flip-flops are called for. Before we go on, it should be mentioned that registers can do more than just store binary data. They

can also complement binary bits and perform multiplication and division.

One simple form of register (or *latch*) is a *D flip-flop*. A D flip-flop is basically an RS flip-flop (bistable) preceded by two AND gates and a NOT gate. The logic circuit and symbol are shown in Figure 6.17.

If the clock pulse is low (binary 0) we see that the data input has no effect on the output. In the industry this is referred to as the *don't care* condition. The outputs at A and $\overline{A}$ will simply stay in the last state. When the clock pulse goes high (binary 1), the output copies the value of D. Similarly, as D goes to 1, A also goes to 1. In summary, the data input is copied at A and is held until new data is present with the clock pulse.

Figure 6.18 shows a 4-bit register that will temporarily store a 4-bit binary word. If the

D LATCHES

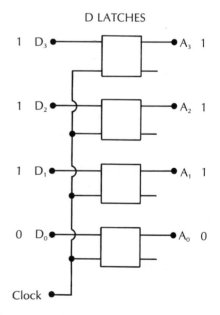

Input: 0111
Output (stored): 0111

Figure 6.18 Temporary Storage in a 4-Bit Register

word 0111 is presented as input data, it will be transferred through to the A outputs where the clock pulse appears. If the clock pulse remains at 0 and the binary input data changes it will have no effect on the output. The output word is latched or stored in the register until new data is clocked in.

Preset and Clear

The temporary storage of binary data necessitates a means of *clearing* a register as well as *setting* it. When the system is first turned on the register must be *preset* so that its condition is "known" before data is entered. Similarly, when new data is to be stored the old data must be removed from the register.

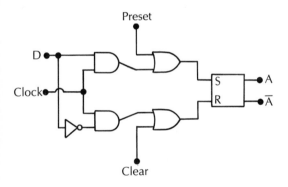

Figure 6.19 Preset and Clear in a D Flip-Flop

The logic circuit which provides for presetting and clearing is shown in Figure 6.19. A binary 1 at Preset causes output A to set at 1. A binary 1 at Clear causes output A to reset to

0. Pulses on these lines can ready the register for new data.

6.7 Shift Registers

We have seen how registers can store binary data. The latches in Figure 6.18 were able to store a 4-bit binary word. Now we will look at a register that has some flexibility. The *shift register* can do a variety of jobs: store numbers and computer instruction data; hold or delay data in the system for a certain time; convert a sequence of pulses into a "parallel" presentation of the same pulses; and act as a pulse-train generator.

First we will look at a basic shift register using D flip-flops. A D flip-flop simply copies the input data and presents it at output A. This copy or transfer is done under control of the clock pulse. The binary data transferred to the A output is held there until the next clock pulse. At the next clock pulse the data present at the input will again be copied.

Look at the four D flip-flops in Figure 6.20. Assume that only one bit of binary data appears at the input and all registers are reset. The data line voltage delivers one pulse and falls to zero, where it stays. The following then occurs:

1. The clock pulse that appears along with the data pulse will transfer this binary 1 to the A output of the first register. There it is stored. The clock pulse drops to zero and nothing further happens.

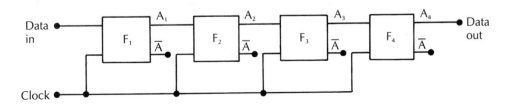

Figure 6.20 Four-Bit Shift Register

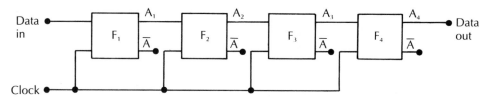

2. On the next clock pulse, there is a binary 0 input to the shift register. Therefore, the first flip-flop goes to 0 at A. The second register sees its 1 input. This 1 is transferred to its A output.
3. On the next clock pulse, the data input is still 0, so there is no change in the output of the first flip-flop. The output of the second flip-flop is 1 and its input is 0. The second flip-flop is switched to a 0 at A. The third has its output set at 1.
4. Finally, on the next clock pulse, the 1 at the output of the third flip-flop sets the output of the last flip-flop to 1. The output of the third flip-flop is now set to 0.

We can see from this analysis that the shift register simply steps an input pulse along the register. The pulse moves down one each time a clock pulse is applied to the circuit. If a string of pulses is applied, the pulses simply march down the register in order.

If the data is to be held in the register once it is filled, the clock pulses must be kept off. If we continue to clock the register, it will simply shift the stored data out the end of the register.

It is often helpful to analyze the shift register in terms of its timing diagram. Consider an input of 1010 to be entered and briefly stored in the 4-bit shift register just discussed.

Figure 6.21 shows that the flip-flops have positive edge triggering. That is, the output changes state at the start (rise) of the clock pulse.

At time t_1 the clock pulse, along with an LSB (least significant bit) data input of 0, sets A_1 to 0. A_2, A_3, and A_4 lines are at 0.

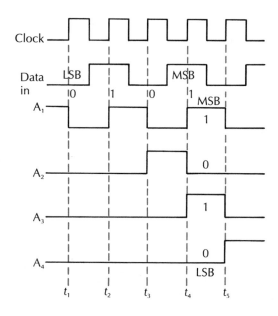

Figure 6.21 Shift Register Timing Diagram

At t_2, F_1 sees the binary 1 on the data input line and A_1 goes to 1. A_2 stays at 0 as F_2 input is at 0.

At t_3, F_1 input is 0. A_1 goes to 0 while A_2 goes to 1. A_2 goes to 1 because the F_2 input senses A_1 going to 0. A_3 and A_4 are still at 0.

At t_4, F_1 sees the MSB (most significant bit) on the data input. A_1 goes to 1. A_2 now goes to 0. A_3 goes to 1 and A_4 stays at 0.

Now the four binary digits have been shifted into the register, the LSB having been entered first.

Data stored in a register can be either shifted out and read or sampled at the individual gate outputs. The register discussed here is "loaded" bit by bit on each clock cycle. As a result this type of register is rather slow to load and slow to read. We will now discuss a much faster type of register.

The Parallel Entry Shift Register

The entry of binary data into a *parallel entry shift register* requires only two clock cycles, as illustrated in Figure 6.22. When the circuit is reset, the A outputs go to 0 on the trailing edge of the clock pulse (negative edge triggering).

Once the binary input data is on the input lines, the shift pulse is applied to shift the data into the register. A binary 1 on any of the input lines gets through the AND gate and causes the flip-flop to set. If the input is a 0, the AND output is 0. Therefore, the flip-flop stays reset. This causes the flip-flop output to be 0 at A.

Thus, the binary word is shifted into the register all at once, not bit by bit.

As we mentioned earlier, shift registers can do more than just store data. They can also multiply and divide binary numbers. This is done by means of what is referred to as a shift-left, shift-right operation.

The Shift Right-Left Operation

If binary numbers are shifted one place *left* as shown below, they are *multiplied* by two.

Example 1

$101_2 = 5_{10}$
$1010_2 = 10_{10}$

Similarly, if they are shifted two places left, they are multiplied by four.

Example 2

$101_2 = 5_{10}$
$10100_2 = 20_{10}$

If binary numbers are shifted one place *right*, they are *divided* by two.

Example 3

$101_2 = 5_{10}$
$10.1_2 = 2.5_{10}$

Similarly, if they are shifted two places right, they are divided by four.

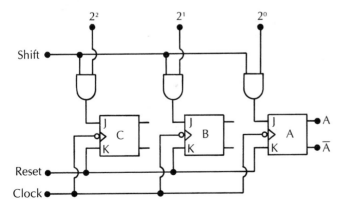

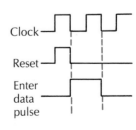

Figure 6.22 Parallel Entry Shift Register

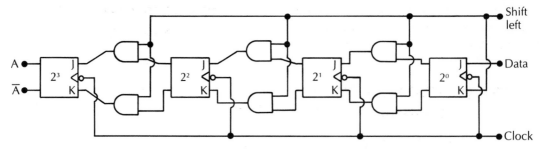

Data input line held at 0 for shift-left pulse

Figure 6.23 Shift-Left Logic Circuit

Example 4

$$101_2 = 5_{10}$$
$$1.01_2 = 1.25_{10}$$

The logic circuit shown in Figure 6.23 permits a shift left for multiplication of the input data. Assume that the register holds 101_2 in the first three "sub-registers." The contents of the register will be shifted one place left each time the clock completes a cycle (pulse) when the shift-left line is high.

The input data line must be held at 0 when the shift line goes high. This ensures that a 0 is placed to the left of the binary point. The binary condition on the A lines will shift left one step when the clock pulse appears. The left-hand flip-flop is required to hold the MSB that has been shifted left.

If the shift-left line is held high for two clock cycles, the stored data will shift two places left. This is equivalent to multiplying the register contents by four.

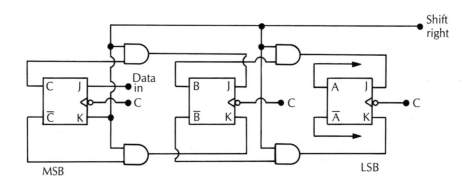

Figure 6.24 Shift-Right Logic Circuit

A shift-right sequence can be provided by the logic circuit in Figure 6.24. This circuit behaves in basically the same way as the shift-left type. Notice that the Data In line must be held at 0 when the shift occurs. This is so the MSB will have a zero-fill. We divide by two by stepping one place right and by four by stepping two places.

We have seen the value of the basic shift register as a storage device and as an arithmetic function circuit. Now we will briefly look at one more application of the shift register.

The Sequence Generator

A *sequence generator* produces a word, a code, or a character. The flip-flops in the register are preset to give the right output. When the clock is activated, the stored pulses are delivered to the circuit from the register. At the same time, the pulses are fed back into the register. We now have a register that will repeat its output continuously. This function is often referred to as *dynamic memory* or a *shift register read-only memory*.

Questions

1. Refer to Figure 6.1 and describe the characteristics of a bistable MV.
2. Refer to Figure 6.1 and explain how Q_2 is held off if Q_1 is on. How could the condition be transferred and Q_2 turned on?
3. Explain the purpose of R_3 and R_4 in Figure 6.1.
4. If Q_1 in Figure 6.1 is on, what voltage is present from Q_2 base to ground?
5. Refer to Figure 6.2 and explain how Q_1 and Q_4 transfer the on condition of Q_2 or Q_3.
6. Refer to Figure 6.3 and explain how a high at S causes A to go high. Why will a high at R cause A to go low?
7. Define *symmetrical triggering*.
8. Refer to Figure 6.4 and explain how the flip-flop is transferred every time a trigger pulse is applied.
9. What is the advantage of symmetrical triggering over RS control?
10. Compare the characteristics of a free-running MV to those of a bistable MV.
11. What is the main purpose of a free-running MV in digital circuits?
12. Refer to Figure 6.7 and explain why the transistors alternately and regularly cut off.
13. In the circuit illustrated in Figure 6.7, what components control the rate or frequency?
14. Refer to Figure 6.9 and explain the operation of the circuit. How does this MV differ from the free-running type?
15. Explain how a trigger pulse at C_2 in Figure 6.9 causes the MV to transfer.
16. Refer to Figure 6.9 and explain how C_1 holds Q_2 off for a limited period of time.
17. Explain how a clocked RS flip-flop differs from a simple RS flip-flop.
18. Refer to Figure 6.10 and explain how the clock pulse controls the response of the flip-flop.
19. Explain how an RS flip-flop is used to debounce a switch.
20. Refer to Figure 6.13 and explain how circuit transfer can occur at any time during the clock pulse.
21. Explain what is meant by *toggling* a JK flip-flop.
22. Define *edge triggering*. What is meant by *negative edge triggering*?
23. Will a JK flip-flop set or reset if the clock pulse is zero? Explain why.
24. Explain why a master-slave JK flip-flop is an improvement over a simple JK flip-flop.
25. Define *register*. Why are registers required in computer circuits?
26. Refer to Figure 6.17 and explain how a D flip-flop differs from an RS flip-flop.
27. Refer to Figure 6.18 and explain how four D flip-flops are used to store a 4-bit word.
28. Explain the purpose of preset and clear functions in register circuits.
29. Define *shift register*. Explain how a series of D flip-flops can be used as a shift register.
30. Name the several functions a shift register can perform.
31. In a shift register such as the one illustrated in Figure 6.20, which register holds the most significant bit?
32. Explain why the parallel entry register is faster than the serial entry register.
33. What is the main function of shift-left and shift-right registers?
34. Describe how a register can be used as a sequence generator.

Experiments

Experiment 6.1

Object

To show the operation of a basic flip-flop circuit.

Circuit

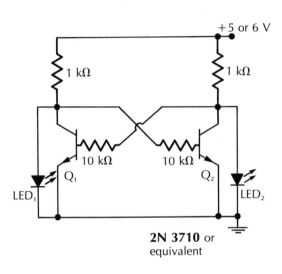

Figure E6.1

Steps

1. Connect the circuit. Observe the LEDs.
2. If LED$_1$ is on, momentarily ground the base of Q$_2$. Observe the LEDs.
3. If LED$_2$ is on, momentarily ground the base of Q$_1$. Observe the LEDs.
4. What determines which LED will be on initially?

Experiment 6.2

Object

To show the operation of an RS flip-flop using NAND gates.

Circuit

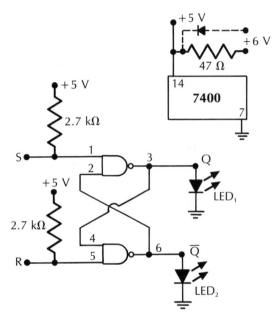

Figure E6.2

Steps

Note: If a 6-V source is used, connect via a 47-Ω resistor or a diode to drop the battery voltage to approximately 5 V.

1. Connect the circuit. Observe LED$_1$ and LED$_2$.
2. If LED$_1$ is on, momentarily short R to ground. Observe the LEDs.
3. If LED$_2$ is on, momentarily short S to ground. Observe the LEDs.
4. With LED$_1$ on, short S to ground. Does the output transfer? Why?

Experiment 6.3

Object

To show the operation of a basic flip-flop trigger circuit.

Circuit

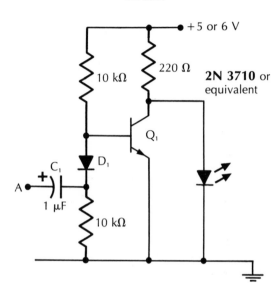

Figure E6.3

Steps

1. Connect the circuit. Observe the LED.
2. Momentarily connect A to +6 V.
3. Connect A to ground and observe the LED.
4. How does the discharge of C_1 cause Q_1 to cut off?
5. Why is D_1 used in the circuit?

Experiment 6.4

Object

To show the operation of a basic clock circuit.

Circuit

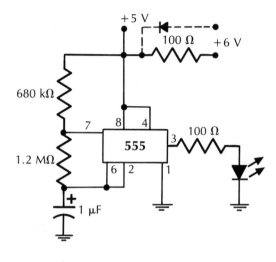

Figure E6.4

Steps

Note: If a 6-V source is used, connect via a 100-Ω resistor or a diode to drop the battery voltage to approximately 5 V.

1. Connect the circuit. Observe the flash rate of the LED.
2. Replace the 1.2-MΩ resistor with a 470-kΩ one, and the 1-μF capacitor with a 0.47-μF one. Observe the change in the LED flash rate.
3. If an oscilloscope is available, observe the waveform at pin 3.

Experiment 6.5

Object

To show the operation of an IC-clocked D flip-flop.

Circuit

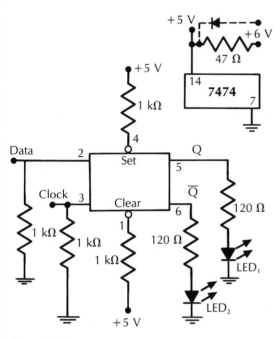

Figure E6.5

Steps

Note: If a 6-V source is used, connect via a 47-Ω resistor or a diode to drop the battery voltage to approximately 5 V.

1. Connect the circuit. Observe the LEDs.
2. If LED₁ is on, momentarily short pin 1 (Clear) to ground. Observe the LEDs.
3. If LED₂ is on, momentarily short pin 4 (Set) to ground. Observe the LEDs.
4. With LED₁ on, momentarily connect the clock input (pin 3) high. Observe the LEDs.
5. With LED₁ off, set the data input high (pin 2). Momentarily connect the clock input high. Observe the LEDs.
6. With LED₁ off, connect the data input high. Momentarily connect the clock input high.

Observe LED₁. Again pulse the clock input high. Observe LED₁.
7. With LED₁ on, set the data input low. Momentarily connect the clock input high. Observe LED₁. Again pulse the clock input high. Observe LED₁.
8. Does the data line condition transfer to the Q output on the positive-going (leading edge) or the negative-going (falling edge) clock pulse?

Experiment 6.6

Object

To show the operation of a bounceless switch.

Circuit

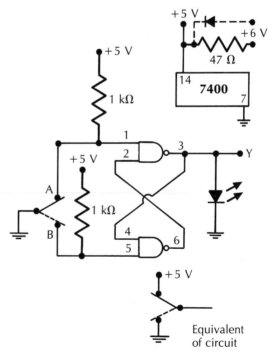

Figure E6.6

Steps

Note: If a 6-V supply is used, connect via a 47-Ω resistor or a diode to drop the battery voltage to approximately 5 V.

1. Connect the circuit.
2. Set switch to A. Observe the LED.
3. Set switch to B. Observe the LED.
4. Why is switch bounce a problem in computer circuits?

Experiment 6.7

Object

To show the operation of a clocked JK flip-flop.

Circuit

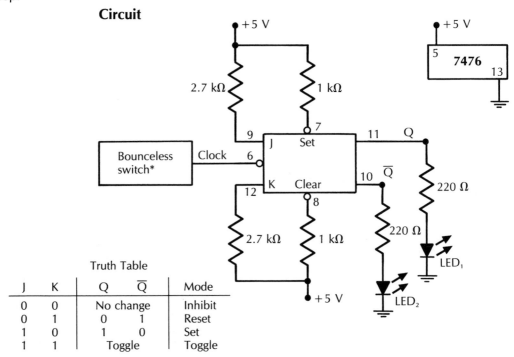

Truth Table

J	K	Q	$\overline{Q}$	Mode
0	0	No change		Inhibit
0	1	0	1	Reset
1	0	1	0	Set
1	1	Toggle		Toggle

*See Experiment 6.6.

Figure E6.7

Steps

1. Connect the circuit to a regulated 5-V source.
2. Alternately short the Clear and Set pins to ground. Observe the LEDs.
3. Operate the bounceless switch several times. Observe the LEDs.
4. Short J to ground. Operate the bounceless switch several times and observe the LEDs.

Remove short from J.
5. Short K to ground. Operate the bounceless switch several times and observe the LEDs.
6. Short both J and K to ground. Operate the bounceless switch several times and observe the LEDs.
7. What do the small circles at pins 6, 7, and 8 indicate?

8. Short the set pin to ground. Operate the bounceless switch several times and observe the LEDs. Remove the short.
9. Short the clear pin to ground. Operate the bounceless switch several times and observe the LEDs.
10. Why are set and clear controls used?

Experiment 6.8

Object
To show the operation of a shift register.

Circuit

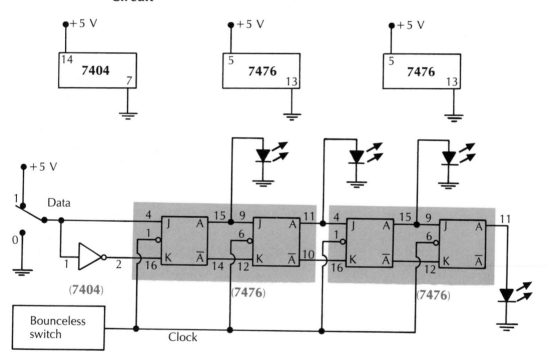

Figure E6.8

Steps
1. Connect the circuit to a regulated 5-V source.
2. Set the data input high. Operate the bounceless switch several times and observe the LEDs.
3. Set the data input low. Operate the bounce-

less switch several times and observe the LEDs.
4. Does the last register hold the most or the least significant binary bit?

CHAPTER 7

Counters

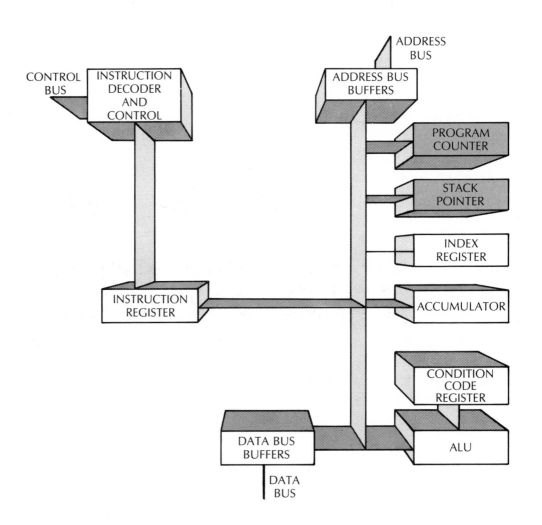

■ INTRODUCTION ■

In this chapter we will study the operation of several basic *counter* circuits. Counters are used throughout digital computer systems to help regulate the sequencing of the various operations. For example, a counter may be used to produce a gating signal allowing the transfer of data into or out of a register. It would count the clock pulses and, after the required number, gate the register output so that its contents can be read.

The sequence in which circuits are enabled (turned on) or disabled (turned off) is usually controlled with an *up counter*, which goes from lower to higher numbers. However, in some cases it is necessary to count down. For example, the initial instruction in a program might be stored in the highest memory location, with all following instructions in lower-numbered lines. In this case a *down counter* is needed to select each instruction in its proper sequence.

Another common device is the *BCD counter*, used to convert from binary data to decimal output.

We will examine all of these basic counters in this chapter.

7.1   Frequency Dividers

The basic counter called a *frequency divider* responds to a clock input and produces a number of output signals of a different frequency (rate of occurrence) than the signals of the clock but exactly tied to it. For example, we might have a counter output of one-half, one-quarter, one-eighth, or one-sixteenth of the clock frequency. More specifically, the counter might produce one output pulse for every four clock pulses. Thus, if we had a register (memory) circuit that had to be read at the end of every

sixteen clock pulses, we would use a frequency divider for this control.

Figure 7.1 shows a basic logic circuit and the timing of pulses for a divide-by-16 counter. First let us check the logic. We are using JK flip-flops. These negative-edge-triggered flip-flops toggle on each clock pulse if both J and K inputs are at binary 1. Notice that the Q (set) output of one stage acts as the "clock input" for the next stage, and that all JK inputs are held high.

The falling edge of the first clock pulse puts stage 1 in the set condition. The trailing edge of the next clock pulse resets stage 1. Thus the Q output of the first stage is at half the pulse rate of the clock.

The following stages respond in exactly the same way. The only difference is that the "clock" input for stage 2 is the signal at the output of stage 1. Every stage becomes a precise, divide-by-two step.

If we look at the pulse chains (signals) at the Q outputs we find that: (1) Q_0 is one-half the clock frequency; (2) Q_1 is one-quarter the clock frequency; (3) Q_2 is one-eighth the clock frequency; (4) Q_3 is one-sixteenth the clock frequency.

There is one more important characteristic of the counter that must be studied. This is the ability of the circuits to produce a running count of every clock pulse entered.

The four Q outputs in Figure 7.1 represent a single 4-bit binary number. The binary condition on these four outputs goes through a binary sequence from 0 to 15. We can examine these outputs at any instant and get a count of the input pulses. Referring to the timing diagram in the figure, we check the Q outputs for any clock pulse. This binary value must correspond to the number of clock pulses entered.

Let us examine the binary data present on the tenth clock pulse. Q_3 is 1, Q_2 is 0, Q_1 is 1, and Q_0 is 0. This yields a 4-bit binary number of $1010_2 = 10_{10}$. We see that the circuit

LOGIC

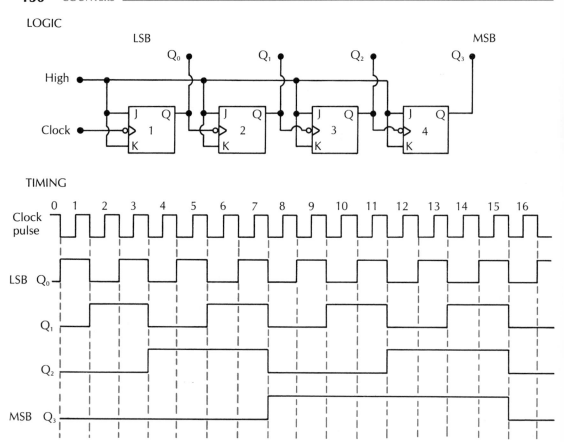

TIMING

Figure 7.1 Four-Stage Ripple Counter

keeps a running count of the pulses it receives. This can be used to trigger an event after a specified number of pulses.

7.2 Ripple and Parallel Counters

The frequency divider and counter we looked at in the previous section is called a *ripple counter*. It gets this name from the pulses that move through the counter like a ripple along the surface of a liquid.

The Zero-to-Seven Counter

The *zero-to-seven counter* is a ripple counter designed to count clock pulses from 0 to 6, then reset or clear. Figure 7.2 shows logic and timing for this device. Though capable, in a sense, of counting to 7 (111), it will recycle after it has counted to 6. This is done by producing a "clear" pulse to all stages when the count attempts to set on 7. That is, when the counter tries to go to 7 (111) all outputs (A, B, and C) will be at 1. Three binary 1s will be fed into the NAND gate and a low condition will be produced at its output. This pulse clears

LOGIC

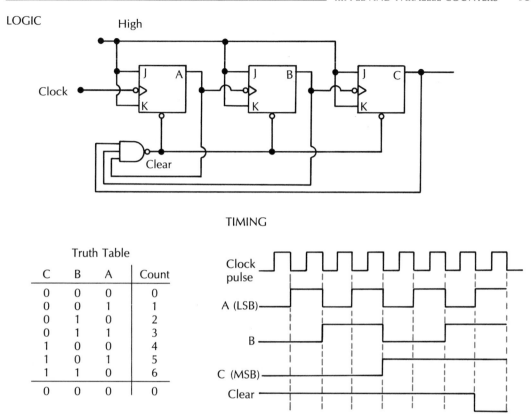

TIMING

Truth Table

C	B	A	Count
0	0	0	0
0	0	1	1
0	1	0	2
0	1	1	3
1	0	0	4
1	0	1	5
1	1	0	6
0	0	0	0

Figure 7.2 Zero-to-Seven Counter (Skip Seven)

all flip-flops and sets the outputs to 0. The counter will once again count from 0 to 6 and recycle.

By properly gating the clear line, we can skip any pulse or combination of pulses in the sequence.

This type of counter is simple but slow. Each stage has its own delay, and the total delay is a function of the number of stages.

The Parallel (Synchronous) Counter

The *parallel* or *synchronous counter* operates like the ripple type, but it is faster. The flip-flop stages are clocked at the same time (syn-

chronously) through gates. Thus, there is no waiting for subsequent stages to be toggled.

Figure 7.3 illustrates the logic and timing for the parallel counter. The cycle begins with all outputs at 0. At the end of this zero clock cycle, stage 1 is toggled to 1 at A. On the next clock pulse, stage 1 toggles A to 0. Simultaneously, stage 2 is toggled by the 1 at the output of AND gate X. This places a 1 at B. This toggling sequence continues for each clock pulse. Stages B and C toggle or remain in their present state depending on the gate inputs.

Take clock cycle 3 as an example. During the positive pulse of clock cycle 3, A is at 1 and B is at 1. C is at 0. The output of gate X is at 1 and the output of gate Y is at 1.

LOGIC

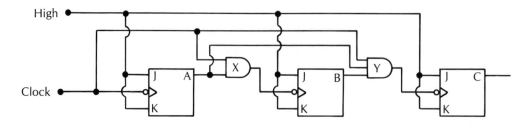

TIMING

Truth Table

C	B	A	Count
0	0	0	0
0	0	1	1
0	1	0	2
0	1	1	3
1	0	0	4
1	0	1	5
1	1	0	6
1	1	1	7
0	0	0	0

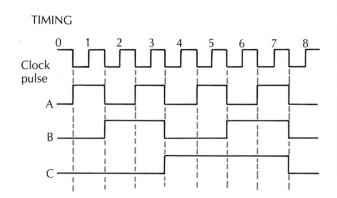

Figure 7.3 Parallel Counter

When the trailing edge of the clock pulse arrives, stages 1, 2, and 3 are all toggled. Their outputs change state. During clock pulse 4, A is at 0, B is at 0, and C is at 1. These changes can be followed for any clock pulse.

The parallel counter can also be gated to make it leave out normal counts. The logic diagram in Figure 7.4 shows a "modulus 5" counter which counts 3, 4, 5, 6, 7 and then recycles. The *modulus* of a counter is the number of states through which it can progress. This counter, as its name implies, simply counts five pulses in order and repeats the count. It produces the following binary numbers in sequence as its count progresses: 011, 100, 101, 110, 111.

These binary numbers need not be of any special significance. However, the waveforms that the counter produces are timed differently than they would be if the count were 0, 1, 2, 3, 4. Figure 7.4 illustrates the difference. We can see from the timing diagram that the two count sequences operating from the same clock provide two different series of pulses. If we pick the time period during the third and the fourth clock cycle we note the following differences: the A outputs are opposite; one B output is on the whole time while the other is off for one cycle and on for the other; and one C output is on for the whole period while the other is on for half and off for half.

The main point is that the two counters operating from the same clock provide a range of waveforms that can be used for gating. Thus,

LOGIC

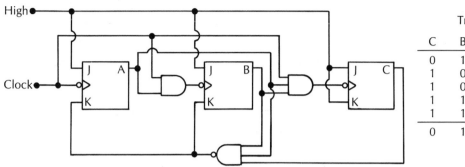

Truth Table

C	B	A	Count
0	1	1	3
1	0	0	4
1	0	1	5
1	1	0	6
1	1	1	7
0	1	1	3

TIMING FOR 3, 4, 5, 6, 7 COUNTER

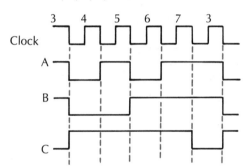

TIMING FOR 0, 1, 2, 3, 4 COUNTER

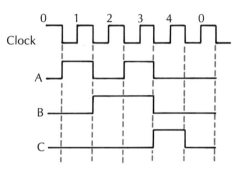

Figure 7.4 Modulus 5 Parallel Counter

control flexibility is increased. We will examine this aspect in more detail when we study computer clocks in Chapter 8.

7.3 Decade Counters

The counters we have examined so far have been used to count the number of clock pulses and to produce output waveforms that are used to gate other circuits. We will now study another common counter circuit used to count numbers 0 to 9. This modulus 10 counter is called a *decade counter*, because it can handle 10 digits. It has the obvious advantage that it

counts in our familiar decimal system. Because of this, it can convert binary numbers into a decimal count which is fed via a decoder into a liquid crystal display (LCD) or an LED.

Figure 7.5 shows a logic arrangement that can be used to count pulses 0 through 9. This set of four flip-flops is connected to 10 four-input AND gates. Each of these produces an output when the correct binary number is present. (Connections are shown here only for the AND gate that produces the 0 digit; for the digits 0 to 9, only the AND gates and the necessary inputs are shown.) For example, the gate that produces an output for the digit 3 requires connections from A, B, $\overline{C}$, and $\overline{D}$. All of these lines are at binary 1 at the end of the third

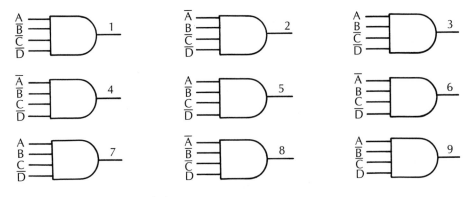

(Zero gate shown in circuit below)

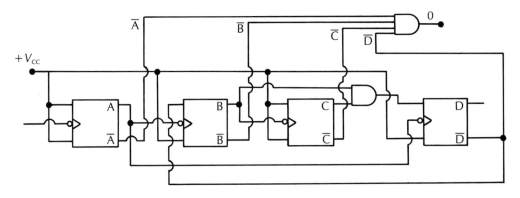

Figure 7.5 Decade Counter

clock pulse. The gate will now produce a binary 1 output, which is used to turn on the digit 3 in the display unit. Finally, we can see from Figure 7.5 that there is a unique set of inputs for each AND gate.

The binary-decade counter can be constructed in various ways; the logic diagram in Figure 7.5 is just one possibility. A standard industrial IC counter is the 7490 chip, which is basically a four-stage master-slave circuit. The 7490 chip is found in many systems.

For counts over 9, more than one counter is used and the counters are cascaded. One counter serves to represent units, the next tens, the next hundreds, and so on. The D output of the counter in Figure 7.5 would be used to toggle the tens counter. The D output of the

tens counter, in turn, would toggle the hundreds counter. With three of the counters shown we could count and display decimal numbers up to 999.

7.4 Up-Down Counters

In the Introduction to this chapter it was mentioned that we often need to count *down* in computers. For example, if we wish to read data in memory line by line in descending order, a *down counter* is used to select each output.

The down counter is really no different from the counters we have already studied. The down

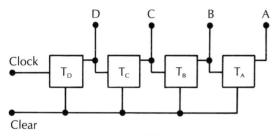

Figure 7.6 4-Bit Ripple Down Counter

Truth Table

Clock Pulse Count	Stage Outputs			
	A	B	C	D
0	0	0	0	0
1	1	1	1	1
2	1	1	1	0
3	1	1	0	1
4	1	1	0	0
5	1	0	1	1
6	1	0	1	0
7	1	0	0	1
8	1	0	0	0
9	0	1	1	1
10	0	1	1	0
11	0	1	0	1
12	0	1	0	0
13	0	0	1	1
14	0	0	1	0
15	0	0	0	1
0	0	0	0	0

counter in Figure 7.6 uses four RST flip-flops which toggle on the leading edge of the clock pulse. The "clear" pulse initially sets all the output lines to 0. When the first clock pulse is applied all the outputs toggle to binary 1, which condition is the equivalent of 15 (1111). On the leading edge of clock pulse 2, flip-flop D toggles to 0. The remaining flip-flops stay set at 1, for they must wait for a leading-edge pulse in order to toggle. On the leading edge of clock pulse 3, D goes back to 1 and C goes to 0. B and A are still "resting" on binary 1. The countdown continues in this fashion until all outputs read 0. The cycle then repeats.

To reduce costs, a single counter can be used to count either up or down. Figure 7.7 shows a simple logic arrangement whereby the count direction can be selected by gating the flip-flop outputs.

The basic counter is the same as the one in Figure 7.6 except that we are using only three flip-flops and that the connections between the stages are different. If the count up line is at binary 1 and the count down at 0, the top AND gates are energized. Therefore the A and B outputs get through to toggle flip-flops B and

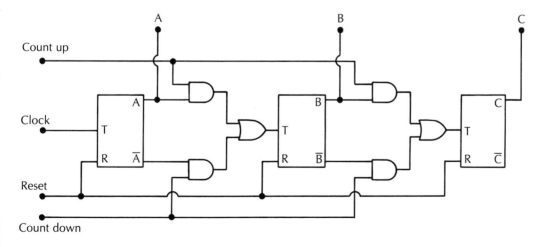

Figure 7.7 Up-Down Ripple Counter

C. When the countdown sequence is selected, the bottom AND gates connect the $\overline{A}$ and $\overline{B}$ outputs to the toggle input of B and C.

7.5 Ring Counters

Another common counter in computer systems is the *shift* or *ring counter*. This device counts input (clock) pulses and recycles, like many other counters we have studied; but it has the advantage that it produces a *direct* count rather than a binary count. This means that decoding gates are normally not required.

Figure 7.8 illustrates the basic characteristics

of a ring counter. We see that the circuit, once preset, will count pulses 0 through 9 and recycle. It will continue to do this as long as the clock pulses are applied. For example, when the circuit is preset, a binary 1 appears at A of the first flip-flop. This output represents 0 in the count sequence. On the next clock pulse, the binary 1 condition shifts to B on the second flip-flop. Binary 1 at this point represents 1 in the 0-to-9 count. We can see how the count progresses. We can also appreciate that the circuit produces a count cycle in a much simpler way than some of the other counters we have seen.

The ring counter is also used as a *waveform generator*. Its output pulses can be used where

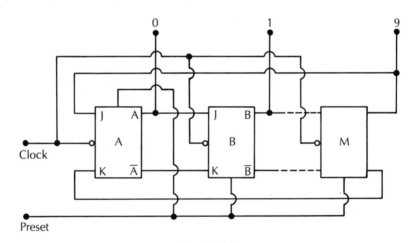

Truth Table

Clock Pulse Count	Stage Outputs									
	A	B	C	D	E	F	G	H	L	M
0	1	0	0	0	0	0	0	0	0	0
1	0	1	0	0	0	0	0	0	0	0
2	0	0	1	0	0	0	0	0	0	0
3	0	0	0	1	0	0	0	0	0	0
4	0	0	0	0	1	0	0	0	0	0
5	0	0	0	0	0	1	0	0	0	0
6	0	0	0	0	0	0	1	0	0	0
7	0	0	0	0	0	0	0	1	0	0
8	0	0	0	0	0	0	0	0	1	0
9	0	0	0	0	0	0	0	0	0	1

Figure 7.8 Ring Counter

a set of gating waveforms are needed. These waveforms appear in sequence and can act like a stepping-switch. Each pulse is like a one-step advance of the switch.

We have discussed a few basic counters that provide a variety of functions in a computer, such as direct counting and division. The division involves producing output signals that are exact sub-multiples of the clock frequency. Counters can also directly measure frequency, by counting the number of input cycles in a fixed period of time. Conversely, a known frequency into the counter can be used as a reference for time measurement. Counters can thus be arranged in circuits as timing devices. The principle of time and frequency measurment can be extended to allow the counter to measure distance and speed. Accordingly, counters have a wide range of application in electronics.

7.6 Decoders

Counters are often used in electronic devices wherein a direct readout is required. Some common examples of such devices are digital clocks, digital voltmeters, and tachometers.

Let us examine the logic diagram and the associated seven-segment display for a digital clock. (The operating principles of the seven-segment display were discussed in Chapter 3.)

The Seven-Segment LED Circuit

In order to drive a seven-segment display properly, counter circuits must have their outputs decoded. First, the binary output must be changed to decimal. Second, the decimal values must be converted to a format that suits the seven-segment display. This decoding can be done for letters as well as numbers. The seven-segment display can quite clearly form the digits 0 through 9 and the letters A, C, E, F, H, I, J, L, O, P, S, U, and Y.

The decoding of decimal digits is done by an IC chip. A common decoder-driver is the 7447 IC chip. Its logic function is illustrated in Figure 7.9.

DECODER

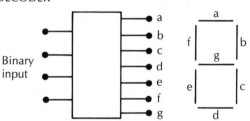

Truth Table

Decimal	BCD Input	Decoder Output						
		a	b	c	d	e	f	g
0	0000	1	1	1	1	1	1	0
1	0001	0	1	1	0	0	0	0
2	0010	1	1	0	1	1	0	1
3	0011	1	1	1	1	0	0	1
4	0100	0	1	1	0	0	1	1
5	0101	1	0	1	1	0	1	1
6	0110	1	0	1	1	1	1	1
7	0111	1	1	1	0	0	0	0
8	1000	1	1	1	1	1	1	1
9	1001	1	1	1	1	0	1	1

Figure 7.9 Binary-to-Seven-Segment Decoder

In circuits where a number of digits are displayed, the logic is simplified by a *multiplexer*. Electronic calculators usually use a multiplexed decoder (see Figure 7.10), which turns the seven-segment displays on in sequence. The displays are recycled fast enough to sustain the illumination. This arrangement allows them to be gated into one decoder, which, in turn, is gated into one set of binary data lines.

We will not go into detail on the internal logic of the multiplexer; with simple counters and combinational logic, the sequencing is easily achieved.

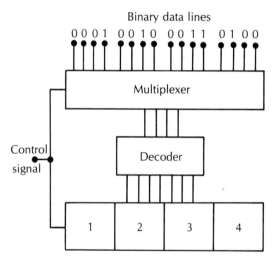

Figure 7.10 Multiplexed Decoder

The Digital Clock

Digital clocks are a common example of counter-decoder combinations. Clocks that operate from domestic AC power lines use that stable 60-Hz source as the clock pulse source. A series of counters acting as frequency dividers are used to time properly the decoder inputs. The decoders are then connected to control the displays. If the clock uses a seconds display, 6 seven-segment units will be used, as shown in Figure 7.11.

The seconds circuit and the minutes circuit normally include a pair of counters each, one a modulus 6 and the other a modulus 10. The mod 10 section recycles the *units* digit and the mod 6 section the *tens* digit. This provides recycling at the end of 60 seconds and 60 minutes.

The hours counter, of course, must reset to 1 when the count tries to advance to 13.

Counters are a vital part of every digital computer. Our study has focussed only on the basic types and a few of their applications. Many types that have not been touched upon and, of course, many applications of the basic counters have not been mentioned. Nevertheless, the reader should have a basic knowledge of counters at this point. The experiments at the end of this chapter should help to further this understanding.

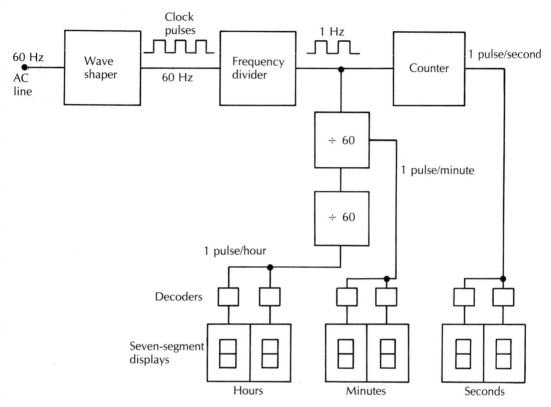

Figure 7.11 Digital Clock Logic

Questions

1. Why are counters needed in computer circuits?

2. Refer to Figure 7.1 and explain how this circuit counts the incoming clock pulses.

3. What symbols are used to indicate negative edge triggering?

4. Refer to Figure 7.2 and explain how this circuit counts from 0 to 6 and repeats.

5. Refer to Figure 7.3 and explain how counting in this circuit differs from counting in Figure 7.2.

6. Explain the meaning of the term *modulus 5 counter*. How are the count progression and recycle point determined in counter circuits?

7. Refer to Figure 7.5 and explain how this circuit converts binary inputs to decimal outputs.

8. Explain what is meant by the term *ripple counter*.

9. Explain the purpose of up-down counters.

10. What is the main advantage of a ring counter? In what way is it simpler than a decade counter?

11. Draw the logic for the binary-to-seven-segment decoder illustrated in Figure 7.9.

12. Explain the function of a multiplexer in binary-to-decimal decoders.

Experiments

Experiment 7.1

Object

To show the operation of a 4-bit binary counter.

Circuit

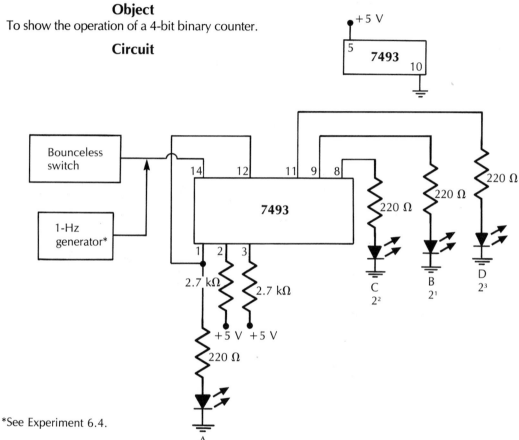

*See Experiment 6.4.

Figure E7.1

Steps

1. Connect the circuit to a regulated 5-V source.
2. Connect a short from pin 2 or 3 to ground.
3. Operate the bounceless switch a number of times and observe the LEDs.
4. Replace the bounceless switch with the 1-Hz generator of Experiment 6.4. Observe the count as it progresses.
5. Does the count proceed on a falling-edge or a leading-edge clock pulse?

Experiment 7.2

Object

To show the operation of a modulus *n* binary counter, where *n* is a given positive integer.

Circuit

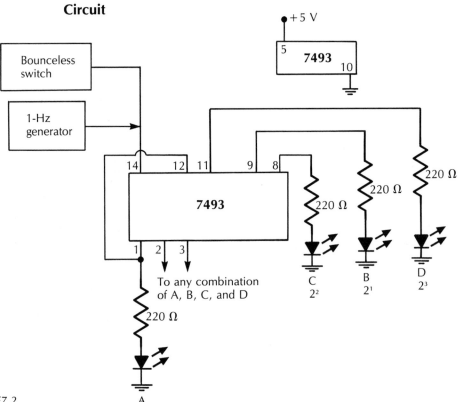

Figure E7.2

Steps

1. Connect the circuit to a regulated 5-V source. Connect pin 2 to 8 and 3 to 9.
2. Connect the 1-Hz generator, or bounceless switch, to pin 14. Observe the progression of the binary count.
3. Connect pin 2 to 11 and 3 to 8. Observe the progression of the binary count.
4. Connect pins 2 and 3 to other combinations of pins 1, 8, 9, and 11. Observe the progression of the binary count.
5. What condition must appear at pins 2 and 3 to reset the circuit?

Experiment 7.3

Object
To show the operation of a decade counter.

Circuit

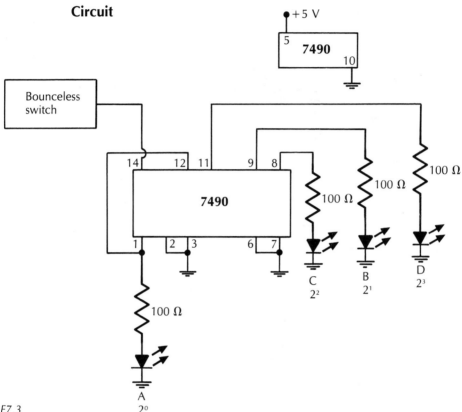

Figure E7.3

Steps
1. Connect the circuit to a regulated 5-V source.
2. Operate the bounceless switch and observe the progression of the count.
3. When does the circuit reset and start from zero?
4. Does the circuit toggle on the negative-going (falling edge) or the positive-going (leading edge) clock pulse?

Experiment 7.4

Object

To show the operation of a ring counter.

Circuit

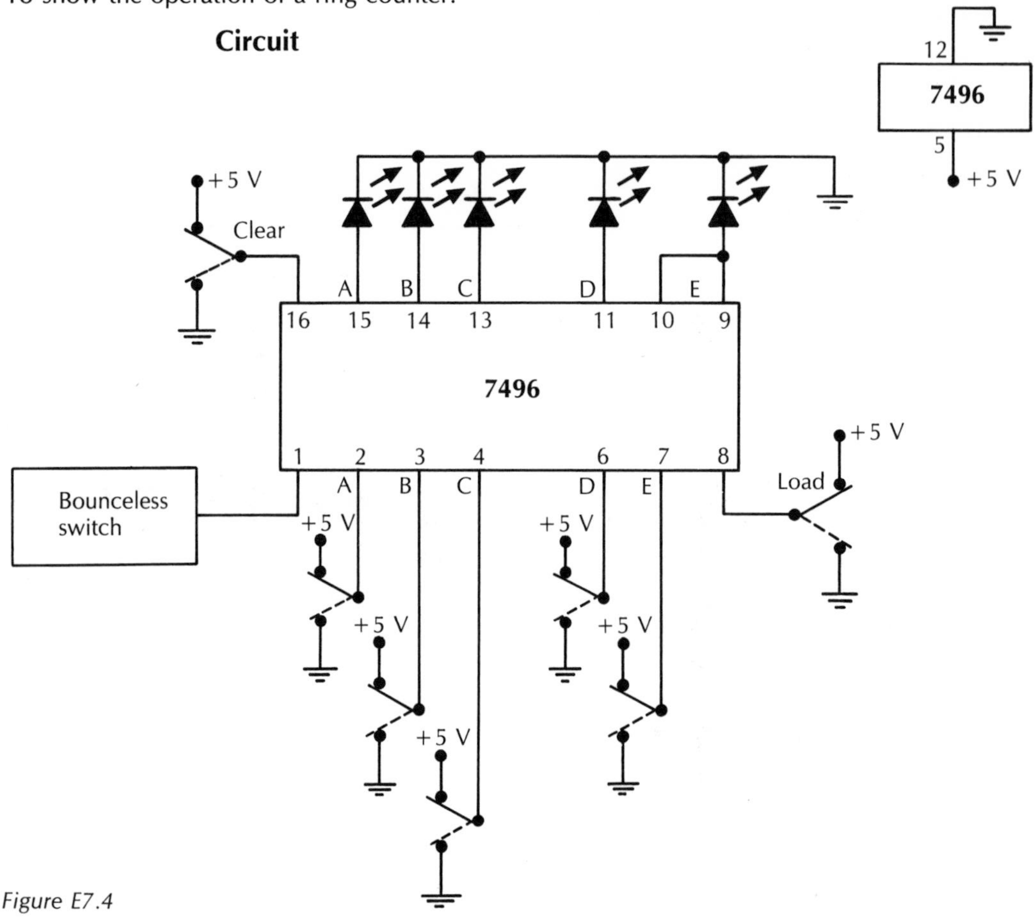

Figure E7.4

Steps

1. Connect the circuit to a regulated 5-V source.
2. Set Clear (pin 16) low. Set Load (pin 8) low.
3. Set A, B, C, D, and E (pins 2, 3, 4, 6, and 7) to load binary 01010.
4. Set pin 16 (Clear) high. Momentarily set pin 8 (Load) high, then return it to ground. Observe the LEDs.
5. Operate the bounceless switch several times and observe the procession of the LEDs.
6. Stop the procession at binary 00101. Momentarily set pin 8 (Load) high, then return it to ground. Observe the LEDs.
7. Does this chip allow lows (binary 0s) to be loaded?
8. Does the data shift right on the positive-going (leading edge) or negative-going (falling edge) clock pulse?

Experiment 7.5

Object

To show the operation of an up-down counter.

Circuit

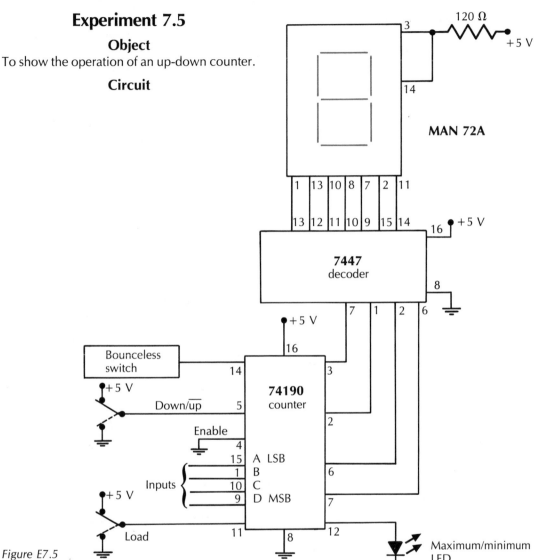

Figure E7.5

Steps

1. Connect the circuit to a regulated 5-V source.
2. Set pin 5 low. Set pin 11 high (Load). Set A, B, C, and D (pins 15, 1, 10, 9) to load binary 0101. (*Note*: Pin 15 (A) is the LSB.) Momentarily connect pin 11 low, then return it to +5 V.
3. Operate the bounceless switch several times. Observe the count progression on the seven-segment display.

4. Connect pin 5 high. Momentarily set pin 11 low, then return it to +5 V. Operate the bounceless switch several times and observe the count progression.
5. When pin 5 is low, at what number does the maximum/minimum LED come on?
6. When pin 5 is high, at what number does the maximum/minimum LED come on?

Experiment 7.6

Object

To show the operation of a latched counter.

Circuit

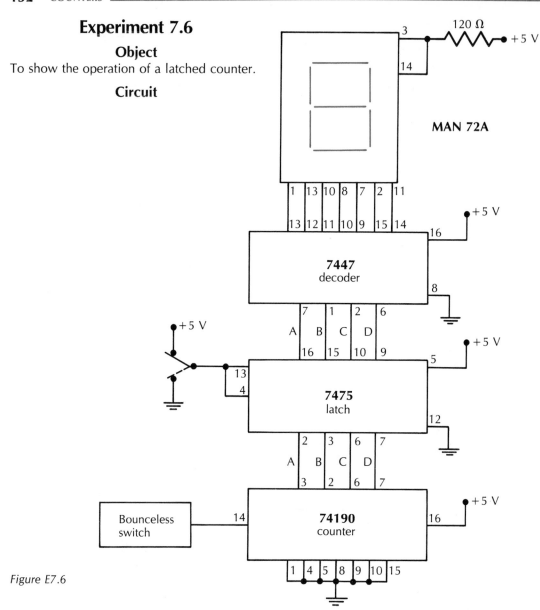

Figure E7.6

Steps

1. Connect the circuit to a regulated 5-V source.
2. Connect pin 13 of the 7475 latch high. Operate the bounceless switch several times and observe the count display.
3. Connect pin 13 of the latch low. Operate the bounceless switch several times and observe the display. Return pin 13 of the latch high. Observe the count on the display.
4. Does the count progress when the display is latched?

CHAPTER 8

Timing

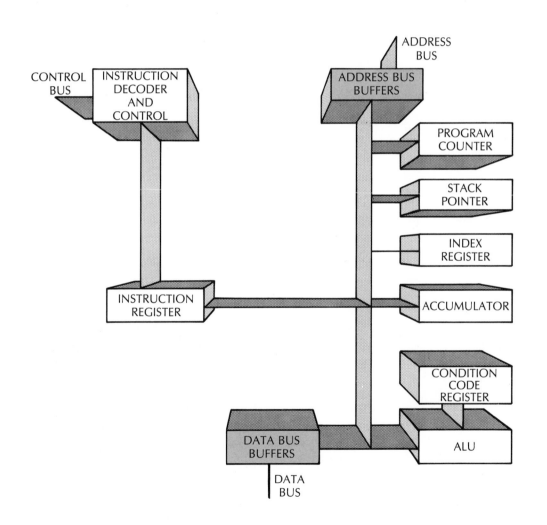

CONTROL BUS

INSTRUCTION DECODER AND CONTROL

ADDRESS BUS

ADDRESS BUS BUFFERS

PROGRAM COUNTER

STACK POINTER

INDEX REGISTER

INSTRUCTION REGISTER

ACCUMULATOR

CONDITION CODE REGISTER

DATA BUS BUFFERS

DATA BUS

ALU

MICROPROCESSOR UNITS

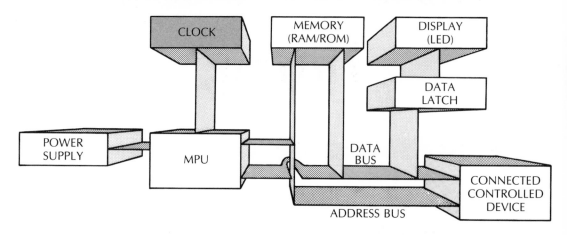

■ COMPUTER SYSTEM ■

■ INTRODUCTION ■

Computer timing is an extremely important aspect of computer system design. Almost every stage of operation in a computer must be timed relative to other occurrences in the system. A simple example of a process that requires accurate timing is the addition of binary numbers. Once the numbers are stored in a register they must be shifted out of the register and into the adder circuit. This must be timed precisely; otherwise, the wrong set of binary digits will be added.

The clock or timing circuit not only synchronizes circuit operation but also determines the amount of time allowed for a certain operation to occur. This makes stability in the clock frequency a must. The computer clock produces the pulse rate for the system. If the system is to be precise and stable the pulse rate must be steady.

Electronic Watch, Internal View
Courtesy of Kurt Schick

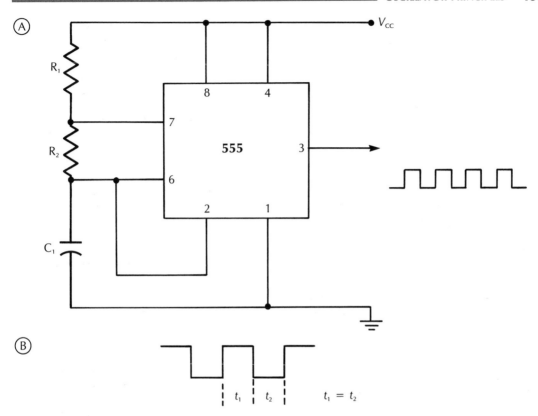

Figure 8.1 555 Timer as a Clock

8.1 Oscillator Principles

Computer clock signals are produced by *oscillators*. An oscillator is simply a signal source. One example of a signal source is the astable or free-running MV we studied in Chapter 6. This circuit, you will recall, runs free when power is applied and produces a series of symmetrical pulses. This circuit can act as a clock if frequency stability is not critical.

Figure 8.1 shows how a common 555 timer IC can be used as a clock. It is connected to run as a free-running MV.

If frequency stability is critical, however — as it is in most synchronous, digital computers — a crystal oscillator is used.

The Piezoelectric Effect

The heart of the *crystal oscillator* is usually a quartz crystal, although other types of crystal can be used. Quartz has a dual property that makes it perfect as an oscillator element. When a voltage is applied, the crystal changes shape minutely. Conversely, when the crystal is deformed by a physical force, a voltage is generated across its surfaces. This is called the *piezoelectric effect*.

When an AC signal is applied, the crystal mechanically vibrates. If we cut the crystal, making it smaller, so that its resonant frequency (its natural vibration rate) is the same as that of the applied signal, it will vibrate vigorously.

The vibration rate of the crystal is controlled by its physical characteristics. Hence, its output frequency is exceptionally accurate and stable. We can compare such a crystal to a string on a musical instrument. The resonant frequency of the string is determined by its physical properties — by its length, thickness, and tension. If the string is vibrating and we keep plucking it so as to sustain its motion, little energy is required.

If we place the crystal in an amplifier circuit, the circuit will keep the crystal vibrating. The steadily vibrating crystal, along with the sustaining energy of the amplifier circuit, creates a precise AC signal.

Figure 8.2 shows a crystal sustained by a MOSFET and by the feedback energy from an *op amp* (operational amplifier). An op amp is basically a direct-coupled, high-gain amplifier to which feedback is added. For our purposes here we can simply consider it an amplifier that sustains the vibrations of the crystal.

The output of the op amp is connected to a *zener diode clipper circuit*. (A zener diode is a reverse-biased diode that conducts at a set reverse-bias potential.) The pair of diodes in this circuit limits (clips) the output waveform to a specified positive and negative level. In the MOSFET circuit the output signal is a sine wave. It has to be sent through a clipper circuit in order to be in a usable form for logic circuit control.

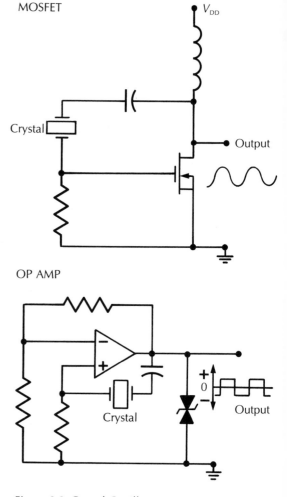

Figure 8.2 Crystal Oscillator

The Schmitt Trigger

A popular wave-shaping circuit is the schmitt trigger. It is connected at the output of the crystal oscillator to change the sine wave into a square wave.

A basic schmitt trigger is a bistable MV that has its state changed by a specified trigger voltage. If the circuit is triggered by a sine wave, the output wave is essentially a square wave at the sine-wave frequency. The key word here is "essentially." The output wave is not exactly a symmetrical square wave. In some digital circuits this squared wave is quite satisfactory.

Figure 8.3 shows a basic schmitt trigger circuit. When the input signal rises to a level that turns Q_1 on, Q_2 cuts off. V_{OUT} goes to V_{CC}. At the opposite extreme, when the input signal drops to a level where Q_1 is cut off, Q_2 turns on. V_{OUT} drops to nearly 0 V.

For a more detailed understanding of this circuit, review the bistable MV in Chapter 6.

CIRCUIT   TRIGGERING

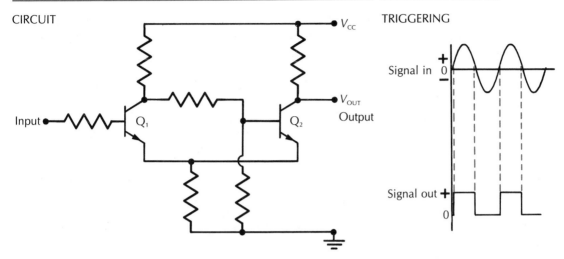

Figure 8.3 Schmitt Trigger

The triggering diagram indicates that the "on" time of the output signal will be shorter than the "off" time.

The Zero-Crossing Detector

An almost perfectly symmetrical square wave can be obtained from the zero-crossing detector. See Figure 8.4. This circuit consists of an op amp working as a regenerative comparator. We will not give a detailed circuit description. It is important, however, to see that the input signal is a varying DC voltage and does not have a 0-V reference point like the signal in Figure 8.3. With this signal input, the upper trigger point and lower trigger point are evenly spaced above and below the centre DC reference of the signal. This feature ensures that

CIRCUIT   WAVEFORM

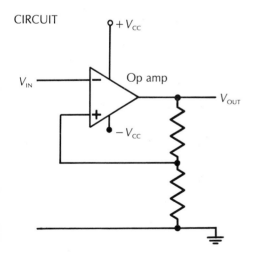
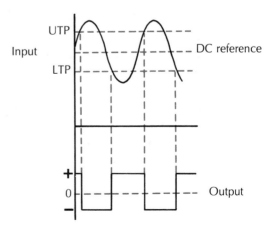

Figure 8.4 Zero-Crossing Detector

the "on" and "off" times of the output square wave will be the same. This charactertistic is important for accurate timing in computer circuits.

8.2 The Computer Clock

As we have seen, the basic oscillator is a simple device. In fact, the whole timing or computer clock system is reasonably simple. The complexity is in trying to visualize how all the circuits work together.

The clock or control generator supplies the waveforms necessary to control all sections of the computer. These timing signals work together with operation control signals from the instruction decoder. They serve to turn the various computer circuits on or off.

Even one simple computer cycle may require several different clock signals. One clock signal might fetch an instruction from memory. Another signal might turn on a decoder circuit to interpret the instruction. Other signals, at

precisely the right time, would be used to shift data out of registers and turn on gates to transfer this data into the arithmetic units. Numerous other steps would occur in this same cycle.

Taken individually, no operation is complex. It is just that so many things are happening at the same time with such speed.

Figure 8.5 shows a basic clock system used to provide four related clock pulses. These output pulse chains are all timed to the crystal oscillator. However, they have different frequency and phase relationships.

The two signals coming from the flip-flop have the same frequency but are opposite (180°) in phase; they are directed to circuits that must be gated oppositely at the same time. A clock that provides such a pair of out-of-phase signals is called a *two-phase clock*.

Microprocessors are usually driven by a two-phase clock. These clock signals must be extremely precise in their relative time and waveform. The falling edge of a wave must reach zero before the rising edge of the next wave begins. Clocks with this kind of precision are designed into IC packages such as the 74163 counter.

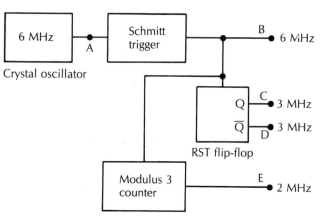

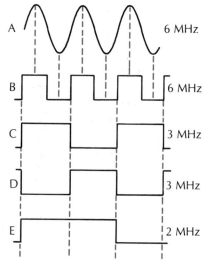

Figure 8.5 Basic Computer Clock System

8.3 Program Execution and Timing

We can see that the computer clock is an integral part of every computer system. Computers and microprocessors must be designed with specific gating speeds and sequences. In order to cover every step in a computer sequence we would have to refer to a specific system and a specific model.

Nevertheless, even though every system has its own clocking requirements, the execution of a basic program involves similar steps. Since our interest at this level of study is more general, we will "construct" a basic computer and discuss the way in which a simple program is handled. The main point of this exercise is to see how the clock controls every circuit action.

Before we go into detail on program steps we should consider some features of Figure 8.6. First, notice that the clock controls every circuit block in the diagram. Though the clock is not shown connected to the instruction decoder, the decoder is linked to the instruction register.

Second, notice that all the circuit blocks except the clock and instruction decoder are interconnected by a *bus*. A bus is simply a set of conductors that joins these blocks together

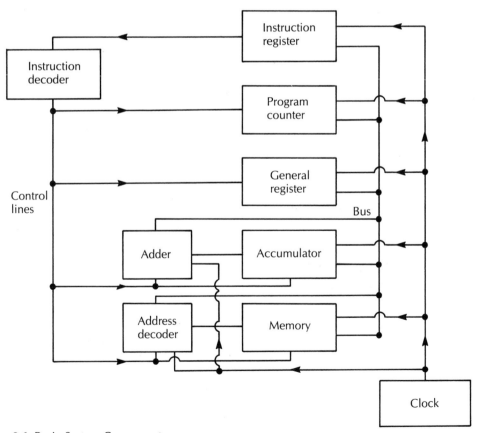

Figure 8.6 Basic System Components

in order to transfer data from one point to the other. This method of interconnection simplifies the circuit design.

The circuits tied to the bus must be designed in such a way that they can be isolated from it. This is necessary because, normally, only two circuits can be active on the bus at a time. For example, if the contents of a certain memory location are to be latched into the instruction register, all the other circuits must be disconnected from the bus. This process might seem very complex. However, it is not. Figure 8.7 illustrates how circuits are switched onto and off of the bus by means of a component called a *buffer*. A buffer is often just a TTL *straight-through* device. This means the output condition is the same as the input. It might seem that such a circuit element would be pointless. However, it is quite useful, as it can both transfer binary signals from its input to its output and act as an open circuit. In Figure

8.7 we can turn buffer A on while B is off. We can also reverse this condition through the direction line and the enable line. This permits two-way transfer of data on the bus. In this example, the buffer is in its straight-through state when its enable line is low.

When buffer A is on, it will transfer its binary input along the bus. B is off during this time and it acts like an open circuit. If the control circuit changes it will turn A off and B on. This will transfer binary data in the opposite direction. This type of bidirectional buffering is needed in situations where data must move into and out of a device by the same path. The memory of a computer is an example of a device calling for the use of such buffering.

The actual operation of a three-state buffer is quite simple. Its logic is similar to that of the totem-pole arrangement discussed in Chapter 4. The basic three-state buffer circuit is shown in Figure 8.8.

The circuit looks involved, but it is really quite straightforward. Let us follow its behaviour step by step.

1. Assume a 0 disable-line condition and a binary 1 input at A. The 0 disable line causes Q_6 to saturate, which in turn cuts off Q_7 and Q_8. With Q_8 cut off, the second emitter of Q_1, and D_1, are *floating* (disconnected).

   The binary 1 at A saturates Q_9, which in turn causes Q_1 to saturate. The saturated Q_1 cuts off Q_2. This cuts off Q_5, leaving Y at binary 1.

2. Assume a 0 at Disable and a 0 at A. The condition of Q_6, Q_7, and Q_8 is the same as in step 1. With a 0 input at A, Q_9 is cut off. This allows Q_1 to turn on Q_2. Q_2 now causes Q_5 to turn on, dropping the output at Y to 0.

3. When the disable line is high, the collector of Q_6 goes high. This turns on Q_7 and Q_8. With Q_8 on, Q_1 is saturated. This cuts off Q_2 and Q_5. With Q_8 on, D_1 conducts and turns off Q_3 and Q_4. We now have both Q_4

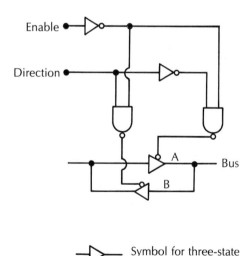

Symbol for three-state buffer (low enable)

Figure 8.7 Bidirectional Three-State Buffer Control

and Q_5 off. This produces an open-circuit condition at Y.

Now we can see the ease with which the buffer can transfer data or isolate a circuit from the bus. Figure 8.9 shows several buffers in their straight-through state used to control the bus access of two computer sections. To get them on the line they are simply clocked in.

Let us now return to the system diagram in Figure 8.6. Assume that the computer is programmed to do the simple task of adding two numbers. An instruction set is keyed into memory. The computer now knows what it is to do

once the two numbers are entered. The memory holds the binary data that tells the instruction register what is to be done. As for the two numbers, they can be either entered into memory (in binary form) before the program is executed or entered as it proceeds. For this example, assume that the program instruction codes and data are already in the memory.

1. Initially, when the program is run, the program counter and address decoder will be clocked onto the bus where the first instruction in memory will be read.

2. The clock disconnects the program counter

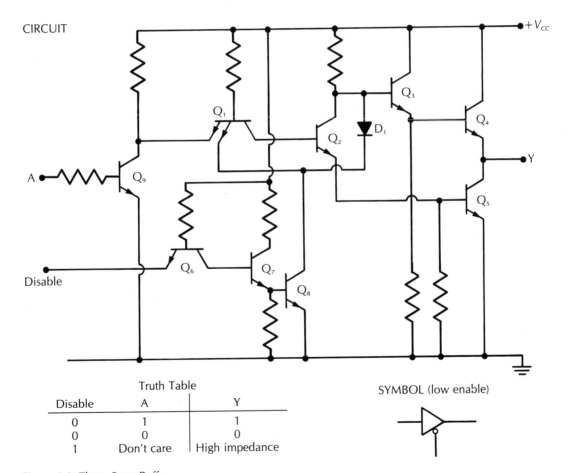

CIRCUIT

Truth Table		
Disable	A	Y
0	1	1
0	0	0
1	Don't care	High impedance

SYMBOL (low enable)

Figure 8.8 Three-State Buffer

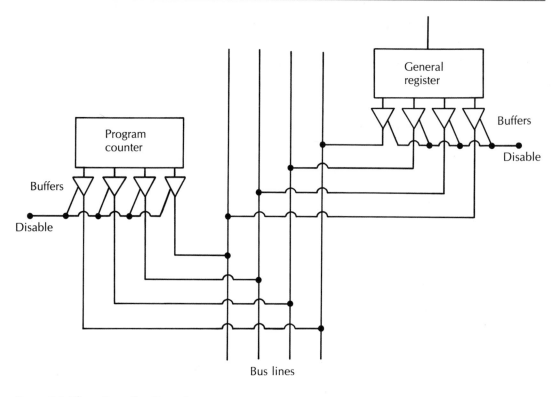

Figure 8.9 Three-State Bus Control

and address decoder from the bus. Now the clock connects the instruction register to the address selected in memory via the bus.

3. Once the binary data in the first memory location is latched into the instruction register, the clock advances the program counter and again connects it to the address decoder via the bus.

The above sequence is processed by the logic circuits in the instruction decoder. The decoder reads the instruction from memory as an

order to load the contents of the next memory location into the general register.

4. The next step of the clock connects the general register to the memory section via the bus. The first of the two numbers to be added is now read from memory and latched into the general register.

5. Next, the instruction decoder reads from memory the order to load the contents of the next memory location into the accumulator.

Now the instruction decoder, along with

the clock, activates the buffers to connect the register to the memory. At the end of this step we have both numbers held in registers.

6. The control lines from the instruction decoder along with the clock now activate the general register, the accumulator, and the adder. The output of the register is sent to the adder via the bus. The two binary numbers are added and stored in the accumulator.

7. Finally, the instruction decoder, along with the clock pulses, connects the output of the accumulator to the memory where the sum of the two numbers is stored.

This description is simplified but it helps us to see how the major components in a computer work together. It also helps us to see how the clock controls the flow of data and instructions in a computer.

Questions

1. Explain the need for accurate timing in computer systems.
2. Define *piezoelectric effect* and explain why crystals are used as signal sources.
3. Explain why computer clock outputs are rectangular or square waves instead of sine waves.
4. Explain how counters and flip-flops can be used as frequency dividers.
5. Explain the need for separating a computer-clock base frequency into several component frequencies.
6. Refer to Figure 8.6 and explain why the clock connects to all the basic system blocks.
7. Explain the need for a three-state buffer in a computer system.
8. Refer to Figure 8.8 and explain how a grounded disable line permits the straight-through transfer of data in the buffer.
9. Refer to Figure 8.8 and explain how a high disable line places the Y output in the floating or high-impedance condition.
10. Refer to Figure 8.9 and indicate whether the buffers are disabled (disconnected) with a low or a high condition on the disable line.

Experiments

Experiment 8.1

Object
To show the operation of a three-state buffer.

Circuit

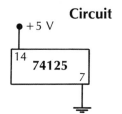

(A) STRAIGHT-THROUGH MODE

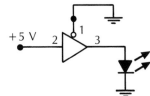

(B) LOW-IMPEDANCE OUTPUT PATH

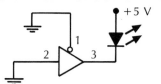

(C) HIGH-IMPEDANCE OUTPUT PATH (FLOATING)

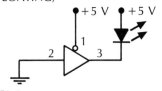

Figure E8.1

Steps

Note: If a 6-V source is used, connect via a 47-Ω resistor or a diode to drop the battery voltage to approximately 5 V.

1. Connect circuit A. Observe the LED. Connect pin 2 low (ground). Observe the LED.
2. Connect circuit B. Observe the LED.
3. Connect circuit C. Observe the LED.
4. Why are buffers required in computer circuits?

CHAPTER 9

Memory

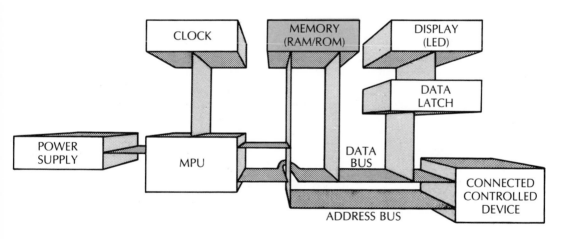

■ INTRODUCTION ■

Computer power is related to computer memory. In order for a computer to execute a large number of instructions it must have a large memory. Memory actually exists in all of the sections of a computer. However, when we speak of computer memory we are normally referring to what is called *main memory*.

The field of computer memory is constantly changing. Scientists are continually searching for cheaper, more efficient, and more stable memory systems. Presently, research and design is active in the area of bubble memory and cryoelectric (low-temperature) memory, but these are not prominent in computers as yet. Today, main memory is most commonly found in two forms: magnetic core and semiconductor. In this chapter we will examine the basics of these two forms.

Magnetic core memory has been used for years. It is extremely reliable and *non-volatile* — i.e., the data is not easily lost when the supply of electric power is interrupted. However, it is bulky and requires relatively large amounts of energy.

Semiconductor storage, on the other hand, is compact and requires small amounts of energy compared to cores. But it has the disadvantage of being very *volatile* — it loses its memory when the power is turned off. Though a non-volatile semiconductor memory exists, it does not have the flexibility required in main memory.

Another important aspect of computer memory is speed. As memory gets larger it is important to be able to get data into or out of it quickly. It is also important to be able to access any data in memory in the same time. Both internal semiconductor storage and core storage have fast *read* and *write* properties. Unfortunately, they have a limited capacity: when enormous quantities of data are to be stored,

a *secondary storage* system is required. This increases access time.

Secondary storage systems, such as floppy discs and tapes, can store huge quantities of data more or less permanently. However, access time is limited by the physical features of the system. Also, severe tolerances are imposed on the mechanical design of these systems.

9.1 Magnetic Memory

Magnetic ferrite cores have been used for main memory devices for over 20 years. These cores are tiny doughnuts of iron oxide that have been formed and baked into rings with an outside diameter of about 1.3 mm and an inside diameter of about 0.75 mm. Binary data are stored in the core by magnetizing it. One direction of magnetization represents a binary 1, and the opposite a binary 0. The binary state of the core is sensed or "read" by magnetizing it in the binary 0 direction. If the core is already magnetized as binary 0, there is a weak sense pulse. If it is at binary 1, there is a strong sense pulse.

Thus, the material selected for the core must have two main magnetic properties: it must be reasonably easy to magnetize and it must retain its magnetism after the magnetizing force is removed. At this point, let us review some of the basics of magnetism.

Magnetization of a material is achieved by the alignment of many of the tiny magnetic domains that exist in the structure of the solid. Some magnetic materials are easy to magnetize. In soft iron, for example, the domains are easily aligned by an external magnetic force. However, they become disordered again when the force is removed. This is generally true of materials easy to magnetize.

Other materials require a strong magnetizing

force to align significant numbers of the magnetic domains. Yet once these domains have been aligned, they tend to stay that way when the external force is removed. Hard steel is an example. The above properties are especially marked when hard steel is alloyed with aluminum and nickel.

The memory cores in use today are mixtures of complex iron oxides and other metallic substances, selected so that the core requires a certain minimum force to change its domain orientation. The graphic description of this force is referred to as a core's *hysteresis loop*. A hysteresis loop is a graph which relates the magnetic field strength in a core to the magnetizing force. In Figure 9.1, *H* represents the magnetizing force and *B*, the magnetic lines

HYSTERESIS LOOP

CORE STRUCTURE

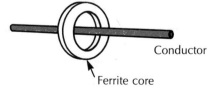

Conductor

Ferrite core

Figure 9.1 Typical Hysteresis Loop for a Memory Core

or flux density in teslas. (The *tesla* is the SI unit of magnetic flux.) Since it is the *current* in the core wires that causes the magnetization, *I* can replace *H*. Similarly, the symbol ϕ for flux can replace *B*.

The term *hysteresis* means "lagging behind." In this case it refers to the fact that the magnetic flux in the core lags behind the force that causes it. For example, assume that the core is demagnetized at first. As the current in the wire is increased, the magnetization of the core increases proportionally. This would produce a straight-line graph from the point of origin to P. If we had started from 0 and increased the current in the opposite direction, the coil flux would have risen from 0 to S. These two states are simply opposite magnetic fields.

Assume that the current has magnetized the core to the level at P. If the current is then dropped to 0, the core stays magnetized at the level shown at Q. The magnetizing force is gone but most of the domains in the core material stay aligned as they were at P.

It must be understood that all points above the x (horizontal) axis represent one field direction in the core and all points below the x axis represent the opposite field direction.

In order to reduce the magnetic field in the core to 0, it is necessary to reverse the current. The magnetic field drops to 0 at R and rises to its final level at S. Now, if the current is reduced to 0 the field in the core will remain at the level indicated by T.

From this point the process simply repeats itself. To demagnetize the core, we must reverse the current once more and increase it. This happens at point U. If we continue to increase the current, the core will return to its previous level of magnetization at P.

If it were not for hysteresis — this "lagging behind" property — the graph of current versus flux in the core would be just the dotted diagonal line on the graph.

CURRENT AND FIELD DIRECTION

Field
Current

LEFT-HAND RULE

Field direction

Current direction

Conductor
(seen end on)   Field

The symbol ⊙ means   The symbol ⊕ means
the current is travelling   the current is travelling
out (toward you)   in (away from you)

Figure 9.2 Fields around a Single Current-
Carrying Conductor

As shown here, it is the current in the conductor that causes the core to become magnetized. A current in a conductor causes a circular magnetic field around the conductor. The strength of this field is proportional to the current in the conductor. The direction of the field around the conductor is related to the direction of the current. Field direction and current direction are interrelated by the *left-hand rule*. Figure 9.2 illustrates these relationships.

To magnetize the iron oxide cores, two wires are used. These are strung through the cores in such a way that their fields combine to change the magnetic state of the core. Also, the currents are selected so that both are necessary to make the coil change state. Figure 9.3 illustrates this arrangement.

HALF-CURRENT EFFECT

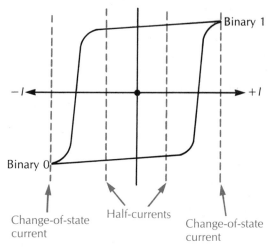

Binary 1

$-I$ $+I$

Binary 0

Change-of-state   Half-currents   Change-of-state
current   current

DIRECTIONALITY OF STATES

State 1 I_Y

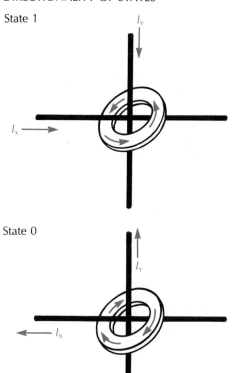

I_X

State 0

I_Y

I_X

Figure 9.3 Two-Current Memory

The graph shows that the individual *half-currents* are not strong enough to cause the core field to change state, but that when the two act together in the correct direction, they are.

When I_X and I_Y are as shown under "State 1," the two half-currents add up to drive the core to its binary 1 state. Notice that the downward current I_Y causes a counterclockwise (often abbreviated CCW) field in the core. Similarly, the left-to-right current I_X also contributes to a counterclockwise field. When the two currents are reversed as shown under "State 0," they again add up, this time to produce a clockwise (CW) field in the core. This field represents a binary 0.

Thus it is possible to write a binary 1 or a binary 0 condition into the core, by sending coincident currents in the proper direction through the X and Y wires. *Write* refers to the magnetization of the magnetic core.

Now, consider the case wherein the core has been set to binary 0. Then, if the currents under "State 0" were to be pulsed through the lines, there would only be a minor change in the field of the core. If, on the other hand, the currents under "State 1" were presented, the core would change state. The 0-state field would vanish and then build up in the opposite direction. In this case there would be a major change in the field of the core.

It is these facts that we take advantage of when we *read* or *sense* the memory.

Read Cycle

In order to read the binary state of the core, a third wire is strung through it. This wire senses the change in the magnetic field during the *read cycle*.

In Figure 9.4 the sense line works by the *generator effect*, which occurs when magnetic flux cuts across a conductor. This cutting action drives electrons along the conductor one way or the other depending on the field direction, creating a pulse.

SENSE LINE

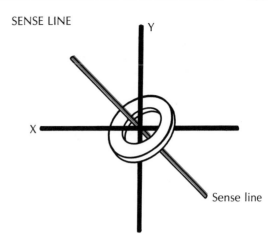

CORE AT BINARY 0 BEFORE READING

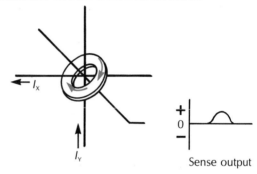

Sense output

CORE AT BINARY 1 BEFORE READING

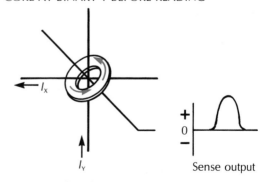

Sense output

Figure 9.4 Core Sensing

The strength of the effect is determined by three things: the field strength, the length of wire affected by the field, and the rate of cutting action. In the case of *memory cores*, the generator action is very weak, because the field in the core is small and the length of wire affected is short. The rate of field change, however, is fast. The field changes in about 0.2 μs (microseconds). As a result, when the core is already at binary 0 and the *read pulse* is applied, only a tiny pulse is generated on the sense line. A read pulse is a pair of coincident currents in the X and Y lines that is required to set the core to binary 0. If the core is at binary 0 when the read currents are applied, the field is not substantially disturbed. As a result, only a tiny pulse is generated on the *sense line*. This pulse is ignored.

But if the core is at binary 1 when the read pulses are applied, the field change is great. It collapses completely from its counterclockwise orientation. Now it builds up to a clockwise field, which represents a binary 0 in this example.

Inhibit

There is still another feature of magnetic cores to be considered. A fourth wire, called the *inhibit line*, is also threaded through the core. This line provides another way of writing in a binary 0 condition. We will see the advantage of it shortly. Figure 9.5 shows how it works. (The figure also shows the *sense line*, which was discussed earlier.)

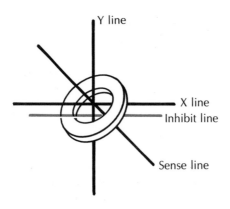

Figure 9.5 Inhibit Line

Assume that the core is in its binary 0 state. The proper direction of I_X and I_Y is needed to switch the core to its binary 1 state. I_X or I_Y alone is not strong enough to make the core switch. Keeping these points in mind we can now see the effect of the inhibit line. If a current is sent down the inhibit line in a direction opposite to the current in the X line, their fields will tend to cancel. If a current is applied to the X and Y lines to cause a binary 1 condition in the core, it will not be effective if an inhibit current is present.

The inhibit line prevents the core from switching from a 0 state to a 1 when it is being told to do so by the X and Y currents. This feature might seem totally useless. However, it is not.

Memory Planes

We know that binary data can be combined into words of various lengths or into 8-bit groups called *bytes*. The data that go into memory are in this form. A large number of cores are arranged on *planes* or *matrixes* in a way that allows entire words to be stored and read.

Let us examine the storage of a 4-bit word. Suppose we wish to store binary 1010 in memory. Let us say that this information is to be stored in the Y_2 column of the memory plane illustrated in Figure 9.6, and that all of these cores are in their binary 0 state. We could store the data without using the inhibit lines as follows:

1. Apply binary 1 currents to X_1 and Y_2. Core A will switch to 1. Cores B, C, and D will only receive half-currents, so their state will not change. Similarly, the other three cores in the top row will only receive half-currents and will be unaffected.
2. Apply binary 0 currents to X_2 and Y_2. These currents simply flow in the direction opposite to that of the binary 1 currents. Since core B is in the 0 state, there will be no

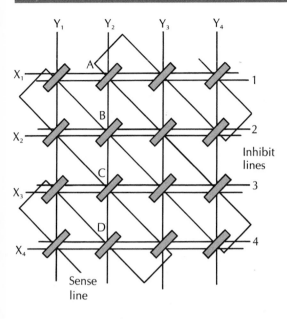

Figure 9.6 Memory Plane

B, C, and D to switch their states to binary 1. If, however, we apply inhibit currents to inhibit lines 2 and 4, cores B and D will be prevented from changing their state.

Here we have stored our data in one operation.

It should be noted that Figure 9.6 is simplified, to make the explanation easier to follow. Actually, the storage described would involve four memory planes. Each row in the diagram would be on a separate plane. A more detailed diagram is shown in the next section.

Non-Destructive Readout

Obviously, there must be provision for a readout that will not destroy the memory in the cores. The reading method described earlier switched all cores to their 0 state. If cores are storing binary 1 data, it will be lost when the core is read by this method. The problem is solved by a *write cycle* that immediately follows every read cycle. For every core read with a binary 1 a pulse is applied to restore the binary 1.

Figure 9.7 shows how this can be done. When a core is read, the X and Y currents going through it drive it to its binary 0 state. If it was in the 1 state, a pulse appears on the sense line. This pulse, along with the read pulse present during this cycle, enables the AND gate. The output

change in it due to the X and Y pulses. Again, the other cores get only half-currents.

3. These steps are repeated for cores C and D.

But there is an easier way to store the number. Consider all of the X lines energized with binary 1 currents. Assume also that line Y_2 has a binary 1 current. This would cause cores A,

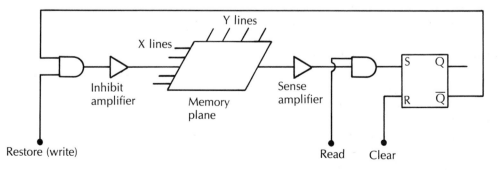

Figure 9.7 Non-Destructive Readout System

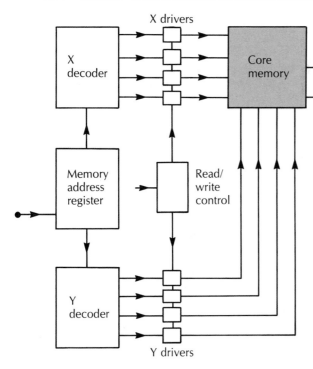

Figure 9.8 Core Memory System

of the AND gate sets the flip-flop. When the flip-flop is set it has a 1 at Q and a 0 at $\overline{Q}$.

Prior to the read-restore cycle all flip-flops are cleared. This places all the Q outputs at 0 and, of course, the $\overline{Q}$ outputs at 1.

The binary 0 at the $\overline{Q}$ output of the set flip-flop is applied to the input of the Restore AND gate. When the "restore" pulse is applied to this gate, its output will be 0 as its input is 0, 1. (This operation is the same as writing data into the core.) The inhibit amplifier will have a 0 output. When the X, Y write currents are now applied, they will reset the core to its binary 1 condition. There is no inhibit current present to prevent it.

When a binary 0 is stored in a core, it produces no significant sense pulse when it is read. Thus the flip-flop will not be reset this time.

When the restore pulse is applied, the inhibit amplifier has a 1 input. An inhibit current now flows and prevents the X, Y currents from switching the core to the binary 1 state.

We have been able to see how these tiny doughnut-shaped cores act as reliable memory devices. Likewise, we have seen how the four tiny wires strung through them allow complete read-write control. Figure 9.8 shows a more detailed diagram of the memory system. The diagram includes the components necessary to select a given set of cores to receive data in memory or to be read for data. The restore cycle components were illustrated in Figure 9.7.

The core memory we have examined can take several forms. For example, some systems use only one wire for both sense and inhibit. This system calls for a more complex control but the tiny cores require only three wires through them.

9.2 Semiconductor Memory

Semiconductor memory is a common feature of the modern computer. It takes many forms and is found both in small pocket calculators and large terminals. It has many advantages over core memory. It also has some disadvantages. Its main advantage is its small size and low power requirements. Thousands of transistor memory cells can be placed on a tiny silicon chip. Research is constantly finding ways to put more memory in less space.

One of the main disadvantages of large-scale semiconductor memory is volatility. When the power is turned off the memory is lost. There are solid state memory circuits which are not volatile, but they lack the flexibility needed for main storage. As we know, main storage must allow us to change data in it and read from it at will.

Figure 9.9 illustrates the circuitry of a popular TTL memory cell. This circuit is basically a simple bistable flip-flop. That is, either Q_1 or Q_2 will conduct and remain in this state, keeping the other transistor cut off. They will hold this state until the transistor that is off is forced to turn on. If Q_1 is conducting with Q_2 off, the cell is understood to store a binary 0. When Q_2 is conducting with Q_1 off, the cell is understood to hold a binary 1.

We put this binary data into the cell for storage via the *write/sense lines*. In order for the flip-flop to be under the control of these lines, the X and the Y select lines must be high (binary 1). Similarly, in order to "read" the cell, the X and the Y select lines must be high.

We select the memory cell to be read or stored by picking the correct pair of X and Y lines. Normally these lines are low (ground or zero). However, when they are used to select a cell they are driven high. A high condition ($+V_{CC}$) on emitters E_2 and E_3 on Q_1 and Q_2 places a reverse bias on them and these emitters are cut off. Then we can control the transistors by their E_1 emitters.

If Q_1 is to be on, we ground its E_1 and keep E_1 on Q_2 high. If we want Q_2 on, we do the opposite.

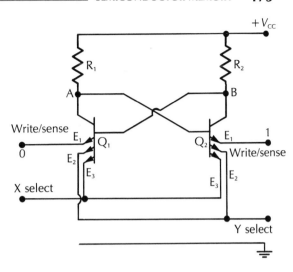

Figure 9.9 Bipolar Memory Cell

Store 0

To store a 0, the correct cell address must be selected and its X and Y lines driven high. While they are high, the write circuit places a low condition on E_1 of Q_1. This turns Q_1 on. With Q_1 on, Q_2 is biased off. When the write pulse is gone, emitter current can continue to flow up through E_1. This keeps Q_1 on.

Once the 0 has been stored, the X and Y select lines drop back to their low state.

With the X and Y lines back at ground (0), emitters E_2 and E_3 on Q_1 provide a path for emitter current. Current flow in Q_1 will now be from the E_2 and E_3 emitters. This is because these emitters go directly to ground. E_1 goes to ground through a resistor in the sense-line amplifier circuit.

Q_1, then, can be held on by E_1 when E_2 and E_3 are high and by E_2 and E_3 when they are low. Further, neither a low nor a high condition on E_2 and E_3 of Q_2 will affect its condition. It will remain off.

Once a digit is stored, it is "locked" into the memory cell. The memory state can only be changed by grounding the *write sense* line on the off transistor. This change can only be made when the select lines are high.

To see why this is true, see Figure 9.10. Part A of the figure shows the unaddressed or isolated condition of a memory cell. Q_1 is on and the cell is storing a 0. The select lines are grounded. Therefore, the current in Q_1 flows up through emitters E_2 and E_3. Q_2 is cut off as its base potential is only about 0.2 V.

The 1.5-V potential on the emitters E_1 comes from the write/sense control circuit. When the X and Y select lines are low, this 1.5 V reverse-biases the E_1 emitters.

When the select lines go high, Q_1 continues to conduct via E_1. Current flows from ground

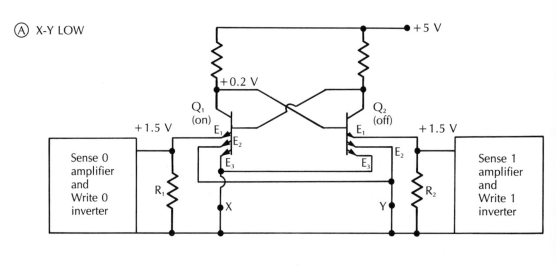

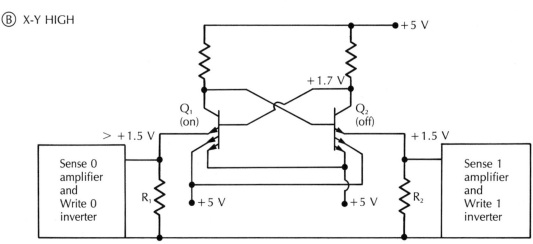

Figure 9.10 Memory Cell Transfer Conditions

up through resistor R_1 and through Q_1, keeping it on. The collector potential of Q_1 is now about 1.7 V to ground. Q_2 is still held off because the 1.5 V on its E_1 maintains a reverse bias on it. Under these conditions the base-emitter voltage would be about 0.2 V. This is far short of the 0.7 V needed to turn Q_2 on.

Store 1

If a 1 is to be stored, the X and Y select lines for the memory address are driven high. Now we must turn Q_2 on and Q_1 off. The control circuit applies a binary 1 to the "write 1" input. The Write 1 Inverter shorts out R_2. This grounds

E_1 of Q_2. The forward bias suddenly turns Q_2 on and the flip-flop action turns Q_1 off. The circuit will remain in this state until a 0 is written in.

Sense

To read the contents of the memory, we simply drive the X and Y select lines high. If Q_1 is on and Q_2 off, Q_1 will conduct through R_1. There will be no Q_2 current in R_2, as Q_2 is cut off.

With Q_1 conducting through R_1, there is a small rise in the voltage across R_1. This increased voltage causes the *sense amplifier* to react and produce a high at its output. This

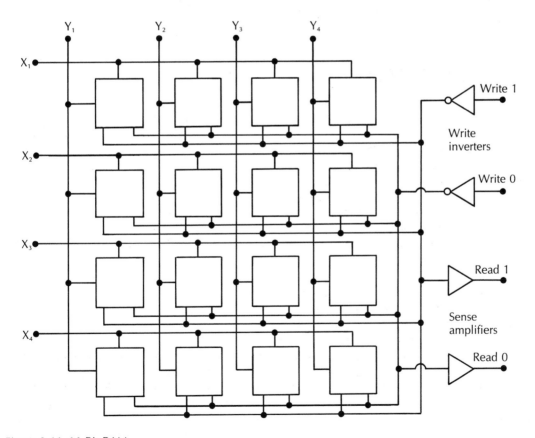

Figure 9.11 16-Bit RAM

indicates the stored data in the memory cell. However, the sense amplifier connected to R_2 will not react because Q_2 is cut off. There will be no rise in the threshold voltage of R_2 and the output of the sense amplifier will remain low.

We have seen that the memory circuit can be addressed and used to store a 1 or a 0. It will hold this datum statically as long as the circuit has power applied to it. We also see that the bipolar memory cell is non-destructive on readout. We can sense its condition — 0 or 1 — over and over again without interfering with its contents.

Figure 9.11 shows the block diagram for a 16-cell memory chip. This is a 16-bit RAM (Random Access Memory). Actually, it could be called *read/write* memory, because we can randomly write into any cell or read out of it.

MOSFET Memory

MOSFET transistors are also popular memory devices. They have the advantage that they expend little energy. Therefore, they can be packed more densely on a chip. They have the disadvantage, however, of capacitance. This means that charge is stored in the device. Because of this it takes longer for it to change state. This feature makes MOSFET memory slower than bipolar memory.

A basic MOSFET memory cell is similar to the bipolar device. Before looking at it, let us review the main features of MOSFETs. Figure 9.12B shows the symbol for a depletion-type MOSFET. This FET has an insulated gate. It allows current flow with 0 bias on the gate. If the channel is N-type (Figure 9.12A), a positive gate will increase channel current. A negative gate will decrease it or even cut it off.

The enhancement MOSFET (part C of the figure) has no channel current flow if there is no gate potential applied. An N-channel enhancement MOSFET will only conduct when its gate is positive.

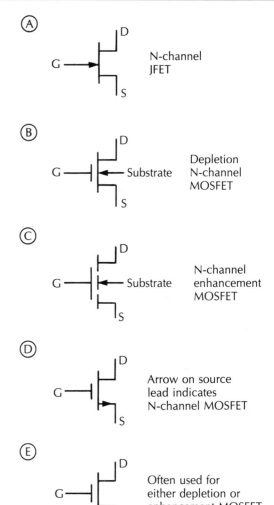

Figure 9.12 FET Symbols

Symbols B and C are sometimes abbreviated. Circuit diagrams commonly use symbols D and E to represent either a depletion or an enhancement MOSFET. In D, the arrow on the source lead identifies it as the N-channel type. If the channel is P-type, the arrow is reversed. Symbol E is commonly used for either type of transistor. The particular type should be specified on the drawing.

Let us now examine the basic MOS RAM memory cell shown in Figure 9.13. The heart of the cell is the bistable flip-flop including Q_1 and Q_2. Their drain load resistors are formed by series MOSFETs represented by the special symbols shown in colour.

Read Memory

Let us go through the steps required to read the data stored in the cell. We will assume that Q_1 is on and Q_2 off. When Q_1 is on a 0 is stored and when Q_2 is on a 1 is stored.

To read the condition of the cell, the X and Y address lines are switched from ground to $+V_{DD}$. The high condition of these lines switches on Q_3, Q_4, Q_5, and Q_6. We can think of these transistors as closed switches. The bit lines are

both at $+V_{DD}$. However, only the line connected to the "on" flip-flop will conduct.

In this case Q_1 is assumed to be on. Current can flow from ground up through Q_1, through Q_3 and Q_5 to the 0 bit line. Current in this line is sensed and amplified. The output is recognized as a stored 0 in memory.

The 1 bit line is also at $+V_{DD}$, but no current flows to it as Q_2 is off.

Write In Memory

To enter a 0 or a 1 into memory we once again select the cell by raising its X and Y address lines to $+V_{DD}$.

If a 1 is to be stored, the 1 bit line is pulsed (switched) to binary 0 or ground while the 0 bit line is held high. The ground condition on the 1 bit line will act as a short across Q_2. This brief low voltage on the drain of Q_2 will cut

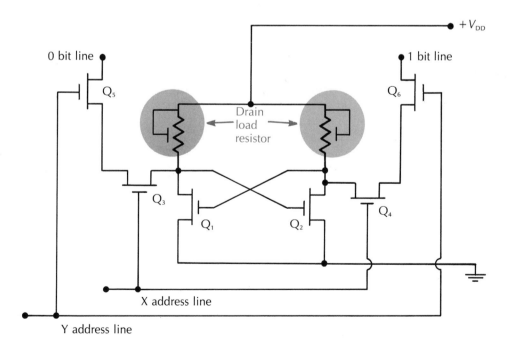

Figure 9.13 MOS RAM Memory Cell

Q_1 off and turn Q_2 on. This is done by the regenerative process of the flip-flop. If Q_2 was already on, the "write 1" pulse would have no effect on the flip-flop.

If a 0 is to be stored, the 0 bit line goes low. At the same time, the X and Y address lines are pulsed high. The low condition on the 0 bit line drives Q_2 off and Q_1 on.

During this write cycle, there is a high pulse on the 1 bit line. This pulse only helps to turn Q_1 on and Q_2 off. This high condition drives the base of Q_1 on. This, through regeneration, drives the base of Q_2 off and the collector of Q_2 high.

Many variations to the basic circuit just discussed are possible. The principle of operation is similar for the whole range of static RAMs.

Dynamic Memory

The static MOS memory cell described above used eight transistors (counting the two used for drain loads). The same memory can be obtained with three MOS transistors if they are operated dynamically. The main advantage, of course, is the packing density on the chip. The disadvantage is that the stored data have to be refreshed constantly. Dynamic memory cells store binary data by a charge on a capacitor in the circuit. The presence of a charge represents binary 1 and the absence of a charge 0. These capacitor charges tend to deteriorate — "leak off" — and have to be built up periodically. In most dynamic memory cells in use today, the capacitors are refreshed about every two milliseconds.

Figure 9.14 shows a basic three-transistor MOSFET dynamic memory cell. Let us examine the read/write sequence for the cell and ignore the refresh cycle for the moment.

The capacitor that we charge to hold the binary 1 or 0 is formed by the gate of Q_1 and its channel. As was noted in Chapter 3, the gate of a MOSFET is a layer of conductive coating separated from the channel by a thin insulator. The gate layer and the channel represent

the plates of the capacitor. The glass layer represents the insulation or the *dielectric*. So Q_1 acts as the storage element in the memory cell.

Write

To store data we use Q_3. To read data we use Q_2.

Assume that we wish to store a binary 1. A positive pulse is applied to the gate of Q_3 to turn it on. At the same time a positive pulse representing a binary 1 is applied to the Write Data line. This charges C to the high voltage on that line.

If a 0 is to be stored, a low or ground condition is applied to the Write Data line, which discharges C.

C is now conditioned by the Write Data line and will hold this charge for later reading.

Read

Data are read from memory via Q_2. A positive pulse on the Read Enable line turns on Q_2. If C is charged, Q_1 will also be turned on. If the Read Data line is connected to $+V_{DD}$ through a resistor, a current will flow. This current indicates the presence of the binary 1 condition

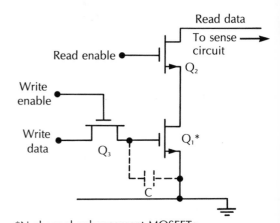

*N-channel enhancement MOSFETs

Figure 9.14 Dynamic Memory Cell

of C. The current in the resistor can be sensed by an amplifier to read the output.

If a binary 0 is stored, C has no charge and Q_1 will be off. Thus, when the Read Data line is energized, there will be no current flow to the sense circuit. As a result the output will be read as a binary 0.

Refresh Cycle

A dynamic memory cell has about four times the density of a static memory cell. However, its memory must be constantly refreshed. There are a variety of ways manufacturers do this. Here, we will look at one basic method used to check and renew cell memory. Figure 9.15 shows such an arrangement.

Capacitors C_1, C_2, and C_3 represent the tiny amounts of capacitance that exist between the conducting elements of the cell. Each capacitor will charge if a voltage is applied across its section of the circuit. It will remain charged for a short period of time, then gradually lose its charge due to leakage. It is the job of the

refresh amplifier to maintain the charge on the memory cell C_1. If C_1 is storing a binary 0, it must be kept at 0; if it is storing a binary 1, it must be kept at 1. The data must be maintained in memory as long as the power is kept on.

The "memory refresh" cycle depends on the computer clock. Clock pulses are used to time correctly the four steps involved.

1. A pulse is applied to Q_4 to turn it on momentarily. This allows C_2 to charge to $+V_{DD}$.
2. A pulse is applied to Q_3 to turn it on momentarily. Q_3 connects C_1 and C_3 in parallel so that C_1 will take on the charge potential of C_3.
3. A pulse is applied to Q_2 to turn it on momentarily. If C_1 is storing a binary 1 (charged), it will be holding Q_1 on. When Q_2 is turned on, it will allow C_2 to discharge through Q_1 and Q_2.

If C_1 is storing a binary 0 (discharged), it will be holding Q_1 off. Thus, C_2 cannot discharge through Q_1 when Q_2 is pulsed on.

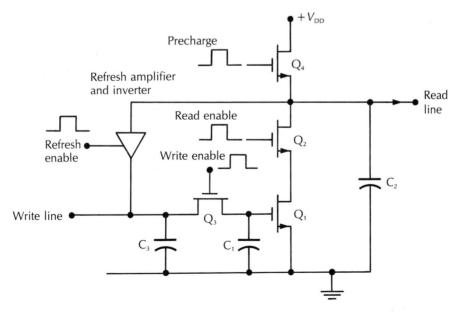

Figure 9.15 MOSFET Memory Refresh

4. A pulse is applied to the refresh amplifier to turn it on momentarily. The charge potential of C_2 is amplified and inverted so as to provide the correct polarity of charge for C_3.

If the memory cell is storing a 1, the refresh amplifier and inverter will repeatedly charge C_3. If the memory is storing a 0, the amplifier will repeatedly hold the charge on C_3 at 0. C_1 finally gets the same charge as C_3.

The refresh cycle we have described is usually carried out by a time-shared refresh amplifier right on the memory chip. Every memory cell is refreshed periodically. Refreshing charges are usually required within two milliseconds for stable storage.

A popular dynamic memory chip is the 1103 MOS/LSI RAM. It has 1024-bit memory and comes in an 18-pin DIP package. Its cycle time is around 600 ns (six hundred nanoseconds or 10^{-9} s).

Read-Only Memory

In computers, many operations are carried out more than once. This fact makes fixed memory useful. A *read-only memory* (ROM) consists of a matrix of addressable cells, just like the random-access type, but these memory cells have been permanently or semipermanently set to either binary 1 or 0. This memory is non-volatile; that is, the contents are not lost when the power is turned off.

Several types of ROM are available. The main

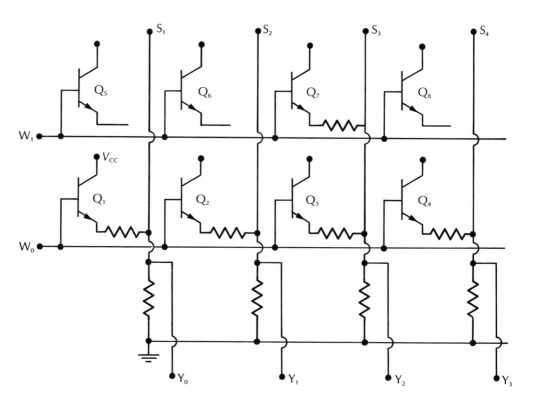

Figure 9.16 Bipolar ROM

ones are: mask-programmed, user-programmed (PROM), erasable user-programmed (EPROM), and electrically alterable (EAROM).

In each of these, binary storage is effected by creating either a conducting or a non-conducting condition at every cell. In the case of the mask-programmed ROM, the storage is set at the time of manufacture. The PROM is either manufactured with its memory in place or it is done in the field with a ROM "burner." The structural features of these two basic ROMs are illustrated in Figure 9.16.

Each memory cell acts as a switch to couple the $+V_{CC}$ potential through to the sense line. Suppose the word line W_0 in the figure is driven high. This would turn on all the transistors connected to it. Current would flow through these transistors, through their emitter resistors, and through the resistors at the bottom of the sense lines. A voltage drop across a sense-line resistor indicates that the active transistor on that line stores a binary 1. The readout on the Y lines in this case would be binary 1111.

If word line W_1 is driven high, these four transistors are allowed to conduct. But Q_5, Q_6, and Q_8 have no emitter resistors. This means that $+V_{CC}$ will not switch through to sense lines S_1, S_2, and S_4. So the binary readout from the sense lines in this case is 0010.

If we wish to store a binary 0, the resistor must be removed from an individual transistor cell such as Q_9.

Bipolar ROMs can be programmed in two ways. During design and manufacture, the emitter resistors can be left out in the required pattern. Alternatively, the ROM can also be field-programmed. This is the process of simply driving a large pulse of current through the emitter resistors to be eliminated. This heats the tiny, deposited resistor layer in the chip and burns it open.

ROM burner kits are available for this purpose. They selectively address the cells and heat the resistors to the melting point so that they open with a pulse of about 30 mA. The kit automatically checks the condition of the cell, and if it is not open after the first pulse the process is repeated.

MOS ROMs

MOS technology is ideal for ROMs due to its high density. Very little heat is generated in a MOSFET. Therefore thousands of them can be packed into the tiny space on a chip.

A MOS memory array is almost the same as the bipolar matrix of Figure 9.16. A typical MOS memory network is shown in Figure 9.17.

A binary 1 or 0 is programmed into each cell by connecting the gate to the word line or leaving it out.

If the Q_5 memory cell is addressed, a positive pulse on word line W_1 will turn it on. Current will flow up through Q_5 and through the FET load to the $+V_{DD}$ line. The voltage drop across the load drops the Y_0 column select line to 0.

If we address the Q_2 cell, a positive on the W_0 word line attempts to turn it on. The gate of Q_2 is not connected, so Q_2 is inactive. There will be no current in the Y_1 line load. Therefore, Y_1 will stay high.

ROMs are in constant use in computers as character generators, bootstrap programs, and look-up tables. They are also used for fixed-function applications such as addition.

A common use of *look-up tables* is in a calculator. Trigonometric functions, logarithms, square roots, and so on are often stored in ROMs. Suppose the decimal equivalent of sin 30° were required. The binary equivalent of sin 30° is stored in memory. Decoders associated with the ROM address the correct memory and extract the data. It is then read out, decoded, and displayed.

The *bootstrap program* is another important job for a ROM. When computers are turned off, the RAM memory is lost if it is not the magnetic-core type. The bootstrap ROMs set up the circuit in a fixed starting state when the power is reapplied. Otherwise memory data would be random at every start-up.

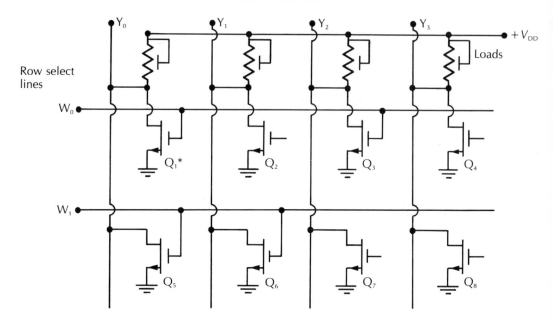

Column select lines

Row select lines

*N-channel enhancement MOSFETs

Figure 9.17 MOS Memory Section

EPROMs

These chips can be programmed, erased, and then reprogrammed. They are excellent for experimental work and for applications where "fixed" data must be replaced from time to time. This memory is fabricated using MOS transistors with floating (open) gates. The gates are charged if the cell is to hold a binary 1 or left uncharged if a 0 is to be stored.

One such EPROM is the INTEL 8702A. It is a 2084-bit memory that can be erased with ultraviolet light. The surface of the chip is covered with a quartz window. To erase the charges on the gates, they are subjected to a UV (ultraviolet) light source for about 20 minutes. New memory data can now be introduced.

9.3 Bulk Memory

Voluminous memory data are usually stored magnetically, on *tape* or on hard or floppy *discs*. Magnetic storage is rather slow as computer speeds go. Tapes are the slowest, though the least expensive. It usually takes seconds or even minutes to locate data on a tape. Discs are faster; access time for discs is on the order of milliseconds, and data transfer from the surface is typically 10 000 to 100 000 bytes per second. But discs are more expensive because the mechanics of the disc drive must be extremely precise. Nevertheless, large, *hard* discs are capable of storing as much as 200 million bytes of data.

Binary data is stored on a tape or a disc by

magnetizing tiny sections of the surface. High-quality tapes are generally made of mylar and are coated with a thin film of iron oxide. The oxide is bound to the mylar in a thin layer about 0.01 mm thick on a tape about 0.025 mm thick. The granular nature of the oxide coating allows about 800 bits of binary data to be inserted in a linear 2.5 cm of surface.

Disc or tape surfaces are magnetized (in the "write data" operation) by a tiny electromagnetic coil on the write head. In the case of floppy discs, these heads are extremely small. In some systems the active width of the read/write head is only 0.2 mm. The erase head is about the same. Binary data can be written by magnetizing a small section N-S (north-south) and another section S-N. For example, we can select the N-S field for 1 and the S-N field for 0. There are other ways to record binary data, such as the common FM system that we will discuss shortly.

In the "read" mode, the process is reversed. Instead of segments of the magnetic surface being magnetized, the magnetized bits are moved past the *read coil*. Their fields generate currents in the coil.

Many systems have been implemented for recording data on magnetic surfaces. Two basic systems are shown in Figure 9.18. In part A of the figure, illustrating the "return-to-zero" (RZ) system, consider an unmagnetized surface moving under a write head. On the pulse from the clock, a pulse of current is sent through the write coil. The field around the coil aligns the magnetic domains in the oxide coating as they pass under the coil. When the current drops to zero there is no further magnetization of the moving surface. On the next clock pulse, another pulse of current is sent to the write coil. This time the current is reversed. Because of this the surface is magnetized in the opposite direction.

We can record with greater density if we go to the "non-return-to-zero" (NRZ) system illustrated in part B. In this system, we clock directly from one record bit to the next with no intervening unmagnetized space.

Read Mode

When we wish to recover the stored data, the magnetized surface is moved under the read

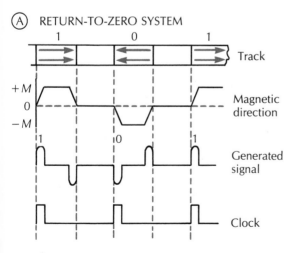

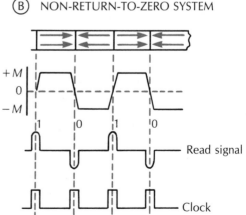

Figure 9.18 Bit Storage Methods

coil. The surface is moving at a fixed rate and while the field is steady there is only a tiny generator action. When the field drops to zero there is an increased cutting action at the coil and a significant voltage pulse is generated. It is like moving a magnet slowly past a coil and then suddenly pulling it away.

Storage Methods

Over the years, various systems have been developed to improve data storage. Some, for example, are less sensitive to noise. Another storage problem is missing bits or areas that have lost their magnetization (also called "dropouts"). Five basic recording systems have been used with tapes and discs: return-to-zero (RZ); non-return-to-zero (NRZ); non-return-to-zero inverted (NRZI); double frequency (DF or FM); and phase encoding (PE). The NRZI system is generally used for tapes and the FM for discs.

In the FM system, the disc storage surface is divided into uniform-sized bit cells. Each bit cell is marked by a clock pulse. If the bit-cell space is to store a 1, a pulse is applied to the record head to magnetize that area. If it is to store a 0, no pulse is applied.

The magnetization of bit cells is illustrated in Figure 9.19. We see that a clock pulse marks the "front" of each bit cell. If the cell contains a 0, there is no further disturbance of the field in this space. If the cell contains a 1, the field is reversed in the middle of the bit space. On the "read" cycle, this field reversal is sensed as a binary 1 pulse. If no pulse is sensed between the clock pulses, it is recognized as a stored 0.

One weakness of the FM system is its zero-storage detection. A stored 0 is recognized by the absence of a pulse between the clock pulses. If a pulse is missing from the disc surface or is dropped out in the transmission of the data, it will not be detected. To overcome this problem, modified FM systems have been devised. PE (phase encoding) is one such system. With PE, every bit cell generates a pulse which indicates its binary storage. If the field changes from $-\phi$ to $+\phi$ at the "front" of the bit cell, it is considered to store a 1. If the field changes from $+\phi$ to $-\phi$, it is considered to store a 0. Figure 9.20 illustrates this property.

The PE system is more complex, because field reversals are necessary to set up the correct field direction if a string of similar pulses are to be stored. For example, bit cell number 1 in the figure stores a 0 as its field goes from $+$ to $-$. Bit cell 2 stores a 1 as it goes from $-$ to $+$. Bit cell 3 also stores a 1, so it must also begin by switching from $-$ to $+$. In order for this to happen, the field must be reversed somewhere in the middle of the bit-cell space. The extra pulses produced on read and required on write demand additional logic in the control circuits.

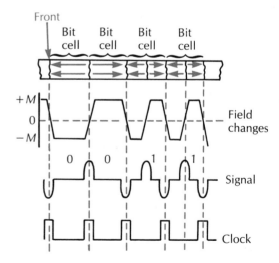

Figure 9.19 Double Frequency (FM) Storage

Bit cells

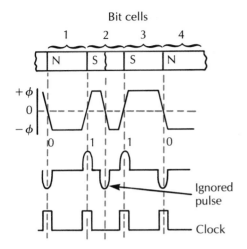

Figure 9.20 Phase-Encoding (PE) Storage

Floppy Discs

Floppy disc storage has become an important part of computer systems. Its low cost and reasonably large storage capacity have made it a companion unit to the microcomputer. There are two basic disc sizes. The standard *floppy disc* is 200 mm × 200 mm; the mini-floppy or *flippy disc* is 133 mm × 133 mm.

Floppy discs are similar to 45-rpm records except that they have no grooves. The disc drive spins it at 360 rpm and the read/write head is pressed against the surface of the disc as it turns.

The binary data stored on the magnetic surface of the disc is precisely organized. How the surface is divided varies from system to system, but the basic organization does not change. The surface is arranged in *tracks* and *sectors* as shown in Figure 9.21. We can think of the tracks as chapters in a book and the sectors as pages. All tracks and sectors which

contain data are identified with codes that tie related program data together. A common arrangement, usually found on the larger and higher density discs, is 77 tracks with 26 sectors each. The recording tracks are only about 0.35 mm wide and are spaced about 0.5 mm apart. This allows approximately 20 tracks per centimetre.

The sectors on many mini-disc systems use a format different from that shown in Figure 9.21. In some systems, the number of sectors per track decreases as the tracks get closer to the centre of the disc.

Some of the mini-discs have only 35 tracks,

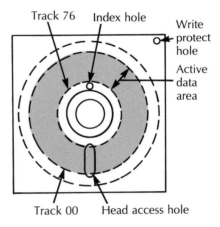

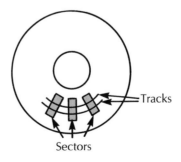

Figure 9.21 Features of the Floppy Disc

with variations in the number of sectors per track. These variations are necessary to allow for the different quality in discs. The number of bits of data stored in a given area is related to the quality of its magnetic surface. A dense film of magnetic particles allows more magnetic regions to be contained in a certain physical space. Similarly, the number of sectors per track is decreased on the inner tracks, as there is less length available.

As has been mentioned, the lengths of the sectors depend on the track chosen. Nevertheless, the data contained in each sector are fixed. When the number of bytes per sector is constant, the rate of data flow in the system is controlled. Otherwise, there would be a higher rate of bits per second moving from the longer, outer sectors. This would be the case because all sectors on a hard-sector disc pass the head in the same period of time.

A standard for many systems is the IBM 3740 format. This format sets each sector at 128 bytes or 1024 bits. Thus a disc with 77 tracks, each containing 26 sectors, would store 256 256 bytes or 2 050 048 bits.

Another system, the Commodore diskette drive 2040, uses a 35-track mini-disc with sectors varying from 17 to 21 per track. This system operates on 256 bytes per sector with a total of 690 sectors on the disc. This gives the disc a total capacity of 176 640 bytes or 1 413 120 bits. This means that for every square centimetre of active disc area, about 15 000 bits of data can be stored.

Obviously, there is a need for exact control of a disc system. If data are to be read from a disc, the machine must be told exactly where they are located. Further, the mechanics of the system must place the read/write head exactly on the track. Otherwise, overlap problems will occur. The control data are recorded on each disc. One track serves as a directory track and another is used as a block availability map (BAM).

The directory track will display on the computer screen such data as disc ID, file number, number of blocks (sectors) used, a pointer to the first block of file, and the number of available free blocks.

The block availability track keeps a record of the used and available space on the disc. If more data are to be stored, the BAM determines if there is space available. Once the data have been added to the disc, the BAM track is updated by the disc control system.

The movement of the recording head is controlled by the head-position motor. This is a "stepper" motor which moves the head from track to track on command from the control unit. Every time the motor receives a pulse from the control unit, it turns the lead screw through a constant angle. This causes the read/write head to move to the next track.

In order to establish a reference for the physical relationship between disc and head, an *index hole* is used. This is a hole in the disc that allows a photosensitive device to correlate the starting point of the tracks with the head.

When the head is stepped from track to track as data is stored or read, the control unit must properly control the flow of data. The time taken for the movement of the head and the time taken for it to settle in place are relatively long periods compared to the read/write data time per track. Depending on the mechanics of the system, it takes the head about 3 to 10 ms to move from one track to an adjacent track, and about 7 to 14 ms is required for the head to come to rest on the disc. Once this is done, it is necessary to enable the read circuit and verify the proper positioning of the head. This is done by having the control unit read the track number in the first field of the first sector read. Every sector contains such data as address, track number, sector number, and data address. We can see that as data is being read from a disc, the control unit is constantly checking on its identification.

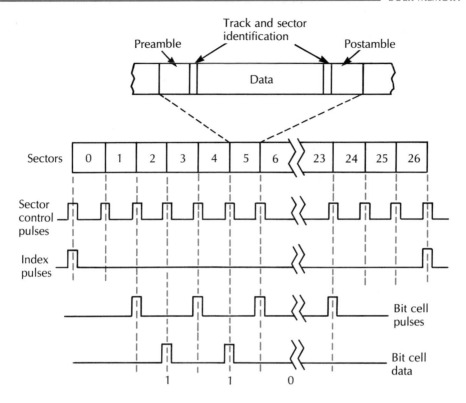

Figure 9.22 Disc Timing Pulses

The disc drive system is mechanically complex and requires constant and precise control. It is, however, remarkably reliable. Figure 9.22 illustrates the overall control of the disc for one revolution. We can see how all aspects of the magnetic surface are controlled. The index pulses occur at the end of each track or revolution. This data is used to step the head position motor. The sector control pulses mark the start of each sector. Finally, each sector has its own identification code.

Questions

1. Explain the distinction between *temporary* and *permanent* memory in a computer.
2. Define *hysteresis loop*. Explain how the idea relates to magnetization in a core.
3. Explain the domain theory of magnetization. How does residual magnetism relate to domain alignment?
4. Explain half-currents in terms of domain alignment.
5. Refer to Figure 9.3 and explain how two currents at right angles can combine to produce one direction of magnetization in a core.
6. Explain the purpose of a sense line in a memory core. How does the "read" process distinguish between a stored 1 and a stored 0?
7. Explain the purpose of the inhibit line in magnetic core memory.
8. Explain the part played by the inhibit line when data is being replaced in the cores on the restore cycle.
9. Is magnetic core memory volatile? Explain.
10. In what way is semiconductor memory superior to core memory? In what way is it inferior?
11. Refer to Figure 9.9 and explain the purpose of the select lines. When the cell is addressed, how is the on transistor sensed?
12. Refer to Figure 9.10 and explain how the stored information in the cell is changed.
13. How many memory cells are contained in a 16 × 4 memory chip?
14. What is the main advantage of MOS memory over TTL memory?
15. Refer to Figure 9.13 and explain how the cell is addressed and its contents read.
16. Explain the advantages and disadvantages of dynamic MOS memory.
17. Refer to Figure 9.14 and explain how data are stored.
18. Refer to Figure 9.15 and explain how the stored data are refreshed.
19. Refer to Figure 9.16 and explain how data are stored in a bipolar ROM chip.
20. Discuss the need for magnetic disc and tape storage.
21. Explain the characteristics of return-to-zero, non-return-to-zero, double frequency, and phase encoding magnetic storage.
22. Explain the advantages of disc storage over tape storage.
23. Describe the organization of data on a floppy disc.

Experiments

Experiment 9.1

Object

To show the operation of a 16-bit TTL random-access memory.

Circuit

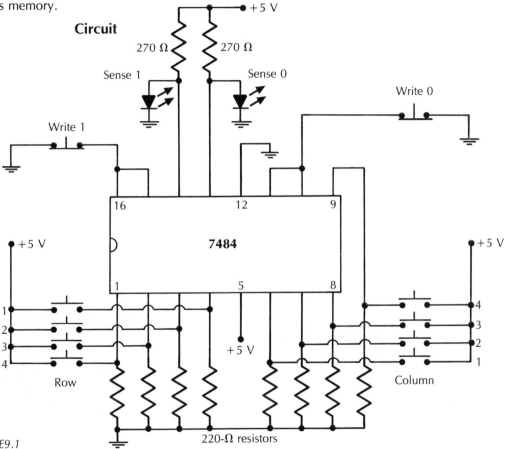

Figure E9.1

Steps

Note: If a 6-V source is used, connect via a 47-Ω resistor or a diode.

1. Connect the circuit. Observe the Sense 1 and Sense 0 LEDs.
2. Simultaneously push one row and one column button. Write in a 1 or a 0.
3. Address the cell selected in step 2. Observe the Sense 1 and Sense 0 LEDs.
4. Address a number of memory cells as in step 2. Write in 0 or 1 data. Record your entries.
5. Readdress the cells selected in step 4. Observe the data sensed.
6. What is the condition of the sense LEDs when no memory cell is addressed?
7. Momentarily disconnect the power to the RAM. Repeat step 5 and record the data stored. Has it changed?

CHAPTER 10

Microprocessors

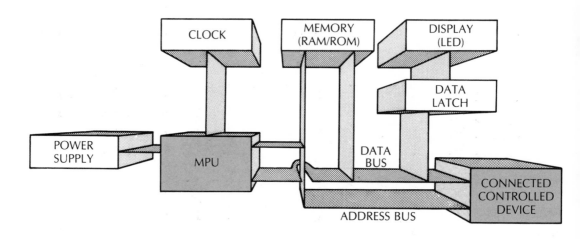

CLOCK

MEMORY (RAM/ROM)

DISPLAY (LED)

DATA LATCH

POWER SUPPLY

MPU

DATA BUS

CONNECTED CONTROLLED DEVICE

ADDRESS BUS

COMPUTER SYSTEM

■ INTRODUCTION ■

Microprocessors are often described as "computers on a chip." This is not a bad definition. Over the past twelve years, technology has enabled the fabrication of more and more elements — of microscopic size — on integrated circuit substrates. This *large-scale integration*, which led to the development of the microprocessor, began in 1971. In that year Integrated Electronics (Intel) of California designed the 4004 chip for a Japanese desk calculator company. This design was put on the market by Intel only three years after the company was formed. It was only one year after the production of the 4004 that Robert Noyce and Gordon Moore, the founders of Intel, designed the 8008 microprocessor. This 8-bit unit led the way to the now-famous 8080 chip.

Microprocessor chips sold rapidly, and several companies designed and put their own units on the market. In 1973 Motorola produced its 6800 microprocessor chip. A short time later Signetics and Rockwell had manufactured their 2650 and PPS8 chips.

Recently, updated versions of the 6800 and 8080 chips have become available. This new generation of microprocessors combines more functions on a single chip. Zilog has produced the Z80, Fairchild and Mostek the F8, and Intel the 8048.

We now find microprocessors almost everywhere — in automobiles, cameras, calculators, electronic games, industrial control circuits, medical apparatus, and of course in computers.

It would take a separate book to cover all the details of microprocessors. In this chapter we will only discuss their general features and relate their internal processes to the circuits we have studied. We will see that the microscopic circuit elements in a microprocessor chip have greatly simplified circuit design. These chips have made circuits smaller, more reliable, and less expensive.

10.1 Microprocessor Basics

A microprocessor is a chip which performs all the functions of a computer's central processing unit. These include:

1. Receiving and storing strings of binary data for processing
2. Performing arithmetic operations such as addition
3. Making logical decisions on the basis of the binary data it receives
4. Delivering processed data to output circuits.

These statements are very general, but they show how complex microprocessors must be.

Figure 10.1 shows in block form most of the basic functions performed by a microprocessor. The diagram makes no attempt to indicate the flow of data and control between the blocks. Before we get to that we will define the general function of each block.

The ALU

The *arithmetic logic unit* (ALU) does what its name implies — all of the arithmetic operations. It also makes logical decisions on the basis of binary data fed into it. It uses combinational logic based on the adder circuits discussed in Chapter 5. The binary input for the ALU is supplied by the data register and the accumulator. The ALU either adds these or uses the data to make a decision.

In order to follow this process in more detail, we must recall the control function involving the system clock discussed in Chapter 8. Suppose the ALU had to perform the simple task of taking two numbers out of memory and adding them. It would carry out the following operations:

Under the control of the clock, the data register is connected to the memory via the data buffers and bus. The binary number is read from memory and stored in the data register. The program steps to the next address in memory and reads the next number. This time it is transferred into the accumulator register, which is clocked on. The clock cycle now shifts these two numbers into the ALU for addition. Then the sum is sent from the ALU to the accumulator register for storage.

The Accumulator

The *accumulator* is a dual-duty circuit section. As we have just seen, it will hold binary numbers. After the numbers have been added in the ALU it will also hold the sum. These numbers can then be transferred into the memory in response to instructions from the instruction decoder.

The Data Register

The *data register* is used for the temporary storage of data coming from the data bus. It can also hold data being sent to the data bus.

The Address Register

The *address register* contains the current addresses of the memory data. It is used to gain access to specific points in memory whenever the central processing unit (CPU) calls for data transfer into or out of memory.

The Program Counter

The *program counter* keeps track of the memory location containing the next program step. Once this program step is executed the counter advances to the next step.

Sometimes the program must break its sequence or jump. When this is done, the binary number stored in the program counter is stored again in another register called a *stack*. The

new number for the repeated or out-of-sequence routine — the *subroutine* — now goes into the program counter and the program proceeds. When the subroutine has been completed, the program number in the stack is returned to the counter.

The Stack Pointer

The *stack pointer* is used to record the last program step (location in memory) just prior to a subroutine. There are two basic systems.

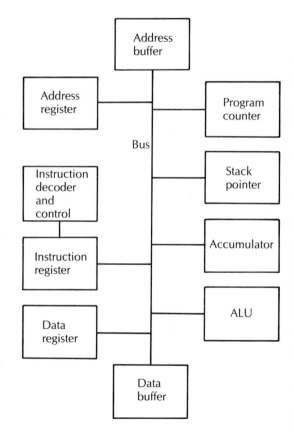

Figure 10.1 Microprocessor Sections

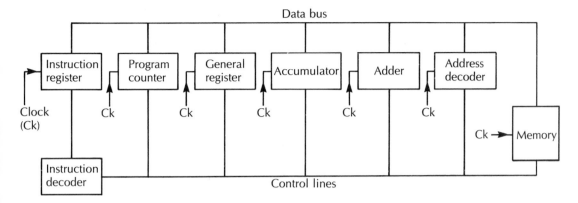

Figure 10.2 Microprocessor Control Blocks

One uses last-in-first-out registers on the chip. This system stores numbers in a register block and outputs the numbers in reverse order. The other method is to store the last program step in memory and use the stack-point counter to indicate the address.

The Instruction Register and the Instruction Decoder

The *instruction register* (IR) stores the binary word fetched from memory during the decoding and execution of the instruction. It tells the *instruction decoder* what is asked of the control circuit. The decoder sets up the logic which controls the entire microprocessor. This involves the state of the control lines, the clock control, and bus access. The entire sequence of events in the processor is controlled from this section of the microprocessor chip.

Figure 10.2 interrelates these block functions in more detail.

Until recently, the memory, the clock, and much of the bus and buffers were external to the microprocessor chip. Now, microprocessor designs include many of these functions on the chip.

10.2 Microprocessor Architecture

The word "architecture" may seem out of place when it is applied to a microprocessor chip. However, the word is used with reference to design or order of arrangement. In the computer field, the word is used to describe the layout features of a chip. These layout features include its bus, register, and pin arrangement, byte size, and overall size.

Why is the architecture of a microprocessor chip important, since it would seem that all the properties of the chip are fixed by its circuit-logic design? The answer is that this knowledge is not sufficient for us to take full advantage of its power. A microprocessor is useless by itself. It gets its power from the program that we present to it. In order to give the microprocessor unit (MPU) instructions intelligently and efficiently, we must understand its architecture.

Buses

One of the main aspects of computer architecture is bus arrangement. As we saw in Chapter 8, a bus is a set of conductors that transfer

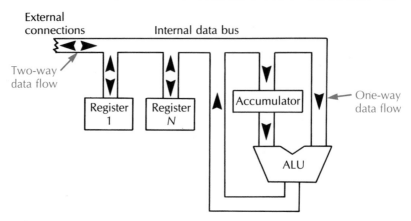

Figure 10.3 Single-Bus Microprocessor

binary data in a system. The bus can be external (a set of flat conductors coupling many circuit blocks) or internal (within the chip).

External buses are called system buses. However, it is the internal chip buses that dictate the architecture of a microprocessor. That is, the bus arrangement in the MPU determines its response time.

The simplest design is the *single-bus* system. By "single bus," we mean that only one set of conductors is used to connect the registers to the ALU section of the chip. There are other main conducting paths, such as the address bus and the control lines, but the main interconnecting bus is the one referred to here. See Figure 10.3.

If the microprocessor illustrated were an 8-bit system, the data bus would consist of eight conductors. Recall also that a common bus can only handle one data condition at a time. Thus, if we were using the bus to transfer data back and forth from the ALU, it would have to be done in steps. For example, if we wished to add the contents of the two registers shown, and to store the sum in register 1, we would have to do it on a time-sharing basis. This design, naturally, slows down the execution of the program. However, the advantage of the single-bus design is space conservation: con-

ducting paths occupy a large percentage of the space on a chip and speed is often sacrificed for room.

Figure 10.4 shows a *triple-bus* design. Here, the problem of time sharing is eliminated. Both bus A and bus B can present input data to the ALU for processing. The output from the ALU can be instantly delivered to the registers. Indeed, bus C can be gated free of the ALU while the A and the B bus are active. This allows simultaneous data transfer on all three buses.

Increasing the number of buses solves one problem, but it creates another. If we use two data buses instead of one, we increase the pin requirements on the chip. One more data line in an 8-bit system calls for eight more pins on the chip. Both the standard 8080 and the standard 6800 have 40 pins. It is difficult to depart from an industrial standard. However, new chips with more pins are coming on the market.

Actual chip architecture is more detailed than that shown in Figure 10.4. Let us go one step further and examine the main features of the 6800 MPU. See Figure 10.5.

Consider the flow of data from the memory to the index register and from the register to the address bus. It has been noted that a 16-line address bus can represent 65 536 address

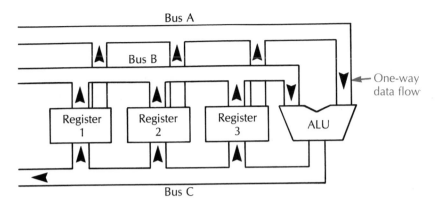

Figure 10.4 Triple-Bus Microprocessor

locations. This range of values includes all possible binary combinations from sixteen 0s to sixteen 1s. Each address stores data in 8-bit groups (bytes). Thus, the memory has 524 288 bits or separate storage cells.

The binary data on the sixteen address lines is sent to the memory via the address bus. There it is presented to the address decoder. The address decoder, which is usually part of the memory chip, selects the correct row in which

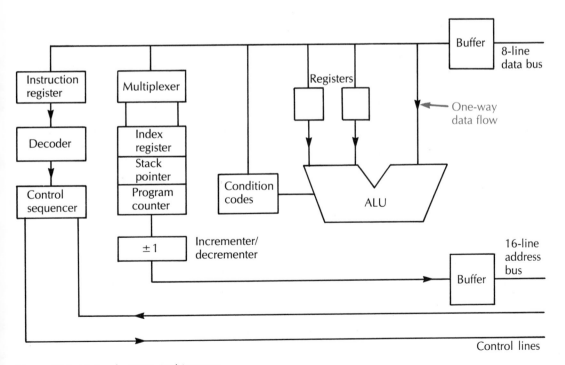

Figure 10.5 Motorola 6800 Architecture

the 8-bit data is stored.

When the 8-bit word is sensed or read out of the memory, it is connected to the data bus. If this byte of data refers to the next address in memory, then the address register must be loaded. In this case the system clock and control lines tie the appropriate circuits to the data bus.

Figure 10.5 shows that there is a multiplexer "block" between the data bus and the address register. This is required in order to store sixteen bits of data from an 8-bit line. The data from the memory is organized in 8-bit bytes. Therefore, it has to be presented to the register in two steps. First, the byte from memory is presented to the *multiplexer*. It switches the data to the appropriate register. Second, the next eight bits of data are switched into the adjacent register. The output from these two "half-registers" constitutes a 16-bit address. These registers are often referred to as *hi-byte* and *lo-byte* memory address registers.

Examining the chip architecture in detail, we gradually become aware of the processes and sequences that can occur in it. Part of this awareness is based on the fact that the bus can handle only one direction of data at a time. We make use of this knowledge when we program the microprocessor.

Before getting involved in the instruction set for the MPU and its various operating codes, we will discuss the execution of a simple instruction.

Instruction Response

Every instruction involves a three-stage sequence. These stages are *fetch, decode,* and *execute.*

Fetch

On the fetch cycle, the contents of the program counter (PC) are switched to the 16-line address bus. This 16-bit binary sequence is read by the address decoder and the correct row in memory is selected.

This address is sensed and the 8-bit binary data stored in this location are presented to the data bus. The instruction register is gated on. The 8-bit data are then latched into the IR.

Decode

The decoder now responds to the data in its register. A specific binary word will represent an instruction. It will condition the *programmable logic array* (PLA) in the decoder. This part of the MPU is a complex network of combinational logic. The sequences that occur in the decoder are implemented by an internal ROM called the "control read-only memory." It is programmed to set up the proper control sequence to match the instruction code entered. Every microprocessor has its own unique internal program. The 6800 MPU responds to a set of 72 *op codes* (operating codes) called its instruction set. The 8080 has an instruction set of 78. The first word of any instruction presented to the decoder is an op code. This code may indicate that there are additional instructions to follow. These additional instructions, called *operands*, are fetched as the op code is executed. By decoding the op code, the control section knows whether it has to go back to the memory to fetch additional bytes of data.

Execute

The instruction from memory is decoded, then executed by the control unit. It is this unit that directs the synchronizing signals which control the ALU, memory, and input-output circuits. This automatic sequencing and timing is kept in sync by the PC. It keeps track of every step in the program. As mentioned earlier in this chapter, if there is a jump or a branch in the program the PC will be forced to a new line number. However, the address from which the branching occurred will be held in the stack register. Because of this, the program can return to where it left off.

Microprocessor Instructions

Every microprocessor is designed to respond to a fixed set of instructions. It was mentioned above that the 6800 MPU responds to 72 op codes and the 8080 to 78. This is only partly true. Op codes that the decoder will recognize and obey actually consist of two parts. One part of such a code indicates the address mode and the other part the op code proper. Generally, two bits of the 8-bit op code are used to indicate the address mode. This leaves six bits for the rest of the code. Thus 8-bit microprocessors are limited to only 64 op codes. This is true where two of eight bits are used to signal the address mode. Manufacturers usually stretch the truth a bit and expand the instruction set figure to include variations due to address-mode possibilities.

Before going further, it is important to note the difference between address mode and op code. The actual op code is simply a set of binary digits (usually six) that form part of the microprocessor instruction set. The programmer enters these instruction codes into memory in the proper sequence. When the program is run, these codes flow from memory to the IR. The register output is decoded and the proper response signals are placed on the control lines.

The address mode, on the other hand, is another part of the op code. It tells the microprocessor how the instruction is to be handled. Multiple address modes add flexibility to program execution. Also, they directly affect the time required to execute.

This whole process might seem very involved. It is, however, a rather simple and logical sequence. We will attempt to make the basic process clear by considering simple program steps in the microprocessor. First we must understand the different modes of addressing.

Modes of Addressing

The op codes are a list of instructions that the MPU can perform. The programmer can use these codes to do a wide range of things in a program. For example, data can be moved from one memory location to another; data held in one register can be transferred to another; the ALU can be instructed to do arithmetic and logical operations; the program sequence can be controlled; and all kinds of input and output functions can be performed.

Instructions that involve addressing memory can be done in any one of several ways. (By memory we refer to both the external memory and the memory on the MPU chip itself. The on-chip memory of the microprocessor itself is its registers or register-pairs. These store data for on-chip instruction execution and for addressing the off-chip memory.)

These are three basic modes in which the microprocessor can produce the 16-bit address on the address bus: inherent, immediate, and direct.

Inherent Mode

This mode of addressing involves the MPU chip itself. Data stored in one or several of the on-chip registers is involved in the execution of this type of instruction. Some of the instructions in the op code involve adding data to or incrementing the count in a register. Sometimes a register pair is instructed to hold an address. Often the op code will call for the transfer of data from one register to another. In these cases the source and destination registers will be identified in the code. Each register on the MP chip has its own code and is identified in the op code. For example, if we wish to transfer data from register A to register

B, this is spelled out in the op code. If A is coded 111 and B is coded 000, the op code might be 01000111. The first two digits from the left indicate the addressing mode, the next three the destination register, and the last three the source register. This byte has all the information required to instruct the decoder. Now the decoder, in conjunction with the clock, goes about executing the transfer.

Immediate Mode

This mode of addressing involves the op code plus an *operand*. The operand is a second byte or perhaps a byte-pair from memory. The operand immediately follows the op code. It may contain eight or sixteen bits of information. The information might be data to be used in the processor or memory address information.

When this mode of addressing is indicated by the op-code byte, the decoder is told how many bytes of data are required for the instruction. If, for example, an instruction called for an address in memory to be accessed, the decoder would "know" that two more bytes of data must be fetched from memory.

Direct Mode

This mode of addressing is used when data is to be transferred from the MPU to memory or vice versa. For example, the instruction can call for the transfer of data from memory to a particular register. It can also select data from a particular register and transfer it to a specified address in memory. The instruction, of course, supplies the exact address to be used. This addressing mode always involves three bytes, as two operand bytes are needed for a 16-bit address.

There are variations on these basic addressing modes. More involved microprocessor programming can employ indexed, relative, and indirect addressing. However, this is beyond the scope of this text.

10.3 Microprocessor Operations

Programming, like most activities, takes practice. Before we can take full advantage of programs, we must have some insight into the internal working of the microprocessor. This is our purpose in this section.

Program execution in a microprocessor follows well-defined steps. The steps involved depend on the addressing mode and, of course, the nature of the instruction. The following are the operations involved in the three basic addressing modes.

Register Addressing Mode

1. *a.* Fetch instruction
   b. Decode instruction
2. Execute instruction

Immediate Addressing Mode

1. *a.* Fetch instruction
   b. Decode instruction
2. *a.* Obtain operand
   b. Execute instruction

Direct Addressing Mode

1. *a.* Fetch instruction
   b. Decode instruction
2. *a.* Obtain address
   b. Decode address
3. *a.* Obtain operand
   b. Execute instruction

In order to get some understanding of the basic addressing modes and the operations related to them, we will analyze two simple programs. These programs use the microprocessor to add two numbers. This is not a very sophisticated or exciting example. However, it will help us to understand some basic operations.

These programs use the op codes for the 6800 MPU. These codes are available on the manufacturer's instruction format sheet.

Example 1

This program instructs the 6800 microprocessor to add two numbers. The op code indicates to the MP that the *immediate* addressing mode is used. This code, listed in hex (hexadecimal), is an 8-bit binary code in memory stored at a particular address. Microprocessor programs are often entered in hex as a timesaver. The input keying is in hex, and is decoded into binary and placed in memory. Therefore, instead of pushing a key eight times to enter a code, we only have to push twice. If we take the first op code 86, it would have a binary equivalent of 1000 0110.

In the immediate addressing mode, the first step is the *fetch* phase. When the op code 1000 0110 is presented to the decoder, it senses that there is an operand to be fetched. The remaining part of the code (000 110) instructs the control circuit to get the data from the next memory location and place it in the accumulator. Of course, the first of the two numbers to be added must be stored in the second memory address. (Keep in mind that this pair of operations is really just one step. That is, the MPU is responding to just one op code.)

The second instruction in the program tells the MPU to add the contents of the next step in memory (step 4) to the present contents of the accumulator.

This instruction is also in the immediate addressing mode. That is, the decoder knows that an operand is part of the two-step instruction and must be fetched. Again, it is necessary that the second number be in the memory. In this program the number would be in program line 4.

The third and final instruction tells the MPU to stop all operations.

Figure 10.6 illustrates the above instruction sequence in more detail.

Op Code	Hex Code	Instruction	Meaning
1000 0110	86	Load accumulator (LDA)	Load the contents of the next memory location into the accumulator.
1000 1011	8B	Add (ADD)	Add the contents of the next memory location to the present contents of the accumulator. Place the sum in the accumulator.
0011 1110	3E	Halt (HLT)	Stop all operations.

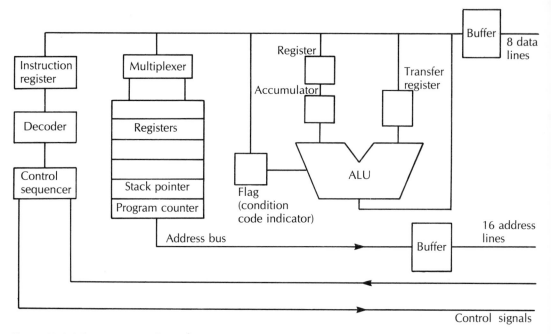

Figure 10.6 Microprocessor Control

The first step of any program is to present the address of the opening instruction to memory. This is known as the first state of the fetch phase. The following events take place:

1. The output of the 16-bit PC is connected to the memory address decoder.
2. The PC is incremented (advanced).
3. The address in memory is sensed. The 8-bit byte is sent from memory along the data bus to the IR. There it will be decoded.
4. The decoder calls for the operand to be fetched. It is in the next address in memory.
5. The PC output is sent to the address decoder.
6. The PC is incremented.
7. The operand stored in memory is sent to the accumulator to be stored.

At this point, the first op code has been completely executed (op code 1000 0110).

8. The PC output is again sent to the address decoder.
9. The PC is incremented.
10. Again the memory output is sensed. The new op code is sent via the data bus to the IR.
11. The decoder senses that an operand is part of the instruction.
12. The number stored in the next memory address is sent to the transfer register.
13. The binary number is added by the ALU to the number stored in the accumulator.
14. The PC output is again sent to the address decoder.
15. The PC is incremented.
16. The memory output is again sensed and sent to the IR.

17. The decoder responds to the halt instruction and the program ends.

The sum of the two numbers stored in memory is now stored in the accumulator. This information could be sent from the accumulator via the data bus to an output. The output, through a decoder or interface, could display the contents of the accumulator — in this case the sum of two numbers. In order to do this, the program would have to be extended.

These steps are just an outline for a simple program. However, we can see from it the repetitive nature of a program in action. This is what microprocessors do. They respond to certain instructions in a logical and direct way. The steps listed are by no means complete, but they do allow us to understand some of the basic MPU operations.

Let us follow another program. Again we will simply add two numbers. This time, however, we will use the direct addressing mode.

This time we will not bother to list all the steps in the MP operation. We will, however, examine the differences in the two programs. First, a note on the address and the op code.

The address is, of course, a 16-bit code which comes from the PC. When it is presented to the address decoder, the eight memory cells at that address are enabled. In our program listing we have numbered the memory addresses 0 to 9 for simplicity.

The main difference in this program is the way in which the operand is treated. The operands are not tied as directly to the op code as they were in program 1. For example, our first instruction begins, as usual, with the op code. The second byte of the instruction is not the operand but the address at which the operand is stored. In this program, a value (N_1) is stored at address 7. This is operand 1.

Address 2 stores the second instruction of the program. It treats the second number to be added in the same way as the first. It is stored

Example 2

Decimal Address	Op Code in Hex	Instruction	Meaning
0	96	LDA	Load accumulator direct with operand 1 which is stored at this address.
1	07		
2	9B	ADD	Add to accumulator direct with operand 2 which is stored at this address.
3	08		
4	97	STA	Store the sum at this address.
5	09		
6	3E	HLT	Stop all operations.
7	N_1		Operand 1
8	N_2		Operand 2
9	00		Reserved for sum.

at address 8. It is true that the numbers to be added are stored in the accumulator as the program progresses, just as in program 1. This time, however, the numbers to be added and their sum are stored at separate addresses.

In programs where operands are acted upon by many different instructions, they are stored separately. This gives the program more flexibility.

Machine Cycles

Timing is critical in a microprocessor. Many circuits share the data bus. They must be connected and disconnected at precise moments. At first glance this might seem an impossible task. However, it is not. The basics of timing will be discussed in this section. (Texts dealing with the timing of a specific MPU are recommended for students who wish to study this aspect in more depth.)

Microprocessor instructions are executed by the control section and timed by a series of machine cycles. These cycles are locked into the system clock discussed in Chapter 8. Machine cycles are subdivided into five parts called *clock periods*. An instruction from memory is executed within one to five machine cycles. Any given set of instructions requires a specific number of clock periods for execution.

Figure 10.7 illustrates this basic timing feature. Look at the time division for the fetch cycle under "Instruction Fetch Cycle." Recall that the microprocessor is allowed five machine cycles to execute an instruction. Within the first three-fifths of the first machine cycle, the PC addresses memory and sends the memory data to the IR. In the next clock period, the instruction is decoded and the PC incremented. Clock period 5 may be idle in the fetch cycle. The actual time involved varies with the microprocessor system. For many systems, the time taken for five clock periods or

one machine cycle is on the order of one or two microseconds.

During period 2 of each machine cycle, an operation decode sequence is activated. It is activated in our sample system by the phase 1 clock pulse and the sync pulse. If these two pulses are inputs to an AND gate, the gate's output will go high only during this period of each machine cycle. The gate is used to activate a system controller circuit which samples the data line at this time. This circuit can be on a separate chip or part of the microprocessor. In either case, it samples the data bus

MACHINE CYCLE SUBDIVISIONS

Machine cycle 1					Machine cycle 2				
1	2	3	4	5					

Clock periods

INSTRUCTION FETCH CYCLE

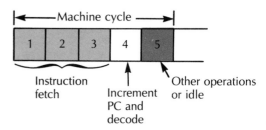

CLOCK CONTROL PULSES

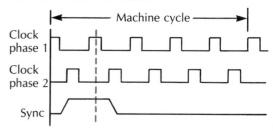

Figure 10.7 MPU Timing

for *status bits* during clock period 2. These bits are placed on the data bus by the microprocessor in response to the instruction codes it receives.

As we might expect, there is a unique code for every instruction decoded in this time period. We must not confuse these instructions with instructions from memory. These decoded instructions or status bits are *microinstructions*. They place an 8-bit code on the data line to be sampled by the system controller. The controller responds to these codes by placing the correct signals on the control bus. These signals command the appropriate devices to become active.

We will now examine how these codes relate to various operations. The status codes for the 8080 will be used as an example. (Actually, these code-condition signals come from the 8212 system controller. The 8212 controller is designed to work in conjunction with the 8080.)

Each microinstruction has its own code. This code sets up the correct 8-bit binary byte on the data line.

Microinstruction	Hex Code
Instruction fetch	A2
Memory read	82
Memory write	00
Stack read	86
Stack write	04
Input read	42
Output write	10
Interrupt acknowledge	23
Halt acknowledge	8A (0A)
Interrupt acknowledge while halted	2B (23)

Consider a microinstruction whereby data is to be read from memory: "Memory read 82." The binary equivalent for this hex value is 1000 0010.

We find that this code places a binary 1 on data lines D_1 and D_7. Line D_1 is a NOT instruction. In this instance the data line will not be

Data Bus Bit	Status Abbreviation	Meaning
D_0	INTA	Acknowledge signal for interrupt request.
D_1	$\overline{WO}$	Data bus used for write operation to either memory or external device.[1]
D_2	STACK	Address bus now holds stack pointer address.
D_3	HLTA	Acknowledge signal for the halt instruction.
D_4	OUT	Address bus indicates output device that should accept data when $\overline{WO}$ is low.
D_5	MI	MPU is in fetch cycle of first byte of an instruction.
D_6	INP	Address bus indicates input device that should put data on bus when DBIN goes high. (DBIN, pin 17 of the microprocessor, when high, readies the data bus to receive data.)
D_7	MEMR	Data bus used for reading from memory.

1. The bar in the symbol $\overline{WO}$ refers to the fact that the write operation occurs when the line is low.

used to write to either memory or an external device. Line D_7 indicates that the data line will be used for reading from memory.

Our discussion of microprocessors could go on and on. Indeed, the microprocessor is a whole field in itself. However, we should know enough about it at this point to dispel some of the mystery. We should also be able to approach its instruction set with a bit of confidence. Well used, the microprocessor is an enormously powerful tool.

10.4 Interfacing

Without *interfacing* — some tangible contact with the "outside world" — the microprocessor is practically useless. It has a certain amount of internal power due to its register memory, but even for simple calculations it requires some form of readable output. If we are using the MPU just to do arithmetic, as in a pocket calculator, we must get the numbers into it and the answers out of it.

When interfacing is added to the microprocessor, its applications are limited only by one's imagination. Every use we can list involves specialized circuitry to deal with input and output signals. Interfacing is so fundamental to microprocessor use that companion apparatus is generally part of the MPU design.

Our basic examination of the MPU has shown us that 8-bit input data gives it its instructions. Once it has the op-code instruction, it decodes it and places an 8-bit status code on the data bus. This code is used to signal the various circuits that must become active to execute the instruction. This may happen several times in response to the one instruction. The data bits that are placed on the data bus by the microprocessor can be decoded and used to control any imaginable device. Basically all that is necessary is a decoder that can read the codes from the data line. The address line as well can send information to circuits tied to the

microprocessor. Thus we can think of interface circuitry and its connection to peripheral equipment as an extension of the microprocessor.

In this section we will look at some of the general features of interfacing. To do more would require an extensive and detailed treatment of interface apparatus. First the basic requirements of interfacing to the MPU must be understood. Then each interface application can be dealt with.

Perhaps the best approach to the topic is to examine several typical interface examples. A common interface is that of a seven-segment display to a microprocessor. Again, the pocket calculator is an example. Normally there would be several displays involved. Here, however, we will restrict our example to one display.

Obviously, we must have control over each of the eight sections in the display — the seven strips and the decimal point. (We will assume that the program contains the necessary instructions to display all hex characters from 0 to F plus the decimal point.) In order to achieve this control, we require an interface circuit between the MPU and the display. This circuit will act as a go-between. It will respond to the data from the MPU and, in turn, decode it and properly activate the various segments of the display. The data lines or address lines cannot do this directly for two main reasons. First, the MPU buses are low-energy circuits. As such, they cannot handle the relatively large currents needed to drive the display. Second, the microprocessor must be isolated from the output apparatus. This is so it can communicate with a variety of circuits, not just one. For example, the MPU would, at one instant, be connected to the memory chips to fetch data or to receive an instruction. At this stage, the display circuit would be electronically disconnected from the data or the address lines, or both. Once the MPU has received its data, it responds to it and delivers the correct data and instructions to the device to be controlled. In

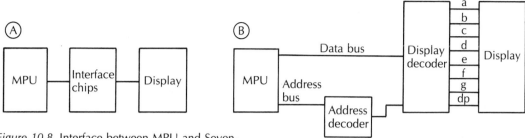

Figure 10.8 Interface between MPU and Seven-
Segment Display

this case the MPU would send out the proper
code to turn on the correct display segment.
It would also send out control data to enable
the decoder at the proper time. This interaction
between the MPU and the decoder is repeated
rapidly so as to present the correct sequence
for a given figure or letter. Figure 10.8 shows
how the interface circuit ties the display to the
microprocessor.

The MPU signals the address decoder via
the address bus. When it receives the correct
binary code, the address decoder supplies the
correct binary condition at its output to enable
the decoder. At the same time, the decoder
senses the data on the data bus, which "tells"
the decoder which display segment is to be
activated. Normally, the address decoder is a
simple chip using a multi-input AND or NAND
gate. If we were dealing with an 8-bit address
bus, an 8-input AND gate would produce a
binary 1 output if all the address lines were
high. On the other hand, an 8-input NAND
gate would produce a binary 1 output if any
of the 8 input lines were high. Actually, any
input combination can be used to produce a
binary 1 output if additional gates are used.
The 7430 TTL chip is commonly used as a
decoder. It is an 8-input NAND gate.

The display decoder can be operated in several ways. One method is to use an 8-bit bistable latch or two 4-bit latches. These latches,
when enabled by the address decoder, lock to
the binary information on the data bus, as shown
in Figure 10.9.

The interface used in Figure 10.9 has full
display flexibility. That is, 256 display patterns
are possible. In the previous figure, on the other
hand, the display combinations are limited by

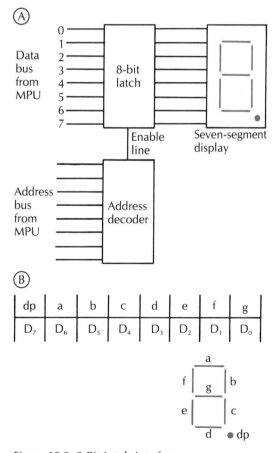

Figure 10.9 8-Bit Latch Interface

the internal logic of the display decoder. The 8-bit latch interface calls for the decoding to be done by the microprocessor in conjunction with its program. In this example the MPU memory would store the correct 8-bit patterns for each of the sixteen hex displays. These sixteen 8-bit patterns would be stored in sixteen consecutive memory locations. These would be called up by the program and presented on the data bus. We can relate this data to the display with the aid of Figure 10.9B. If we wished hexadecimal 7 to be displayed, the microprocessor would convert binary 0111 to the following 8-bit code: 01110000. This code would be called from memory by the MPU and presented on the data bus. At the same

instant the address decoder would be activated by the code on the address bus. The 8-bit latch would be enabled and the stored data would turn on the correct display segments.

This interface is quite simple and straightforward. However, the latch requires at least 19 pins. This makes the chip rather expensive. The 14- and 16-pin designs are less expensive.

The interface can be simplified by the use of serial data input. Instead of eight data lines, the latch has only one. The microprocessor must now send the 8-bit code to the latch, one bit at a time, until the latch is full. This process takes up more MPU time, but it makes the interface less expensive.

We are generally required to interface more

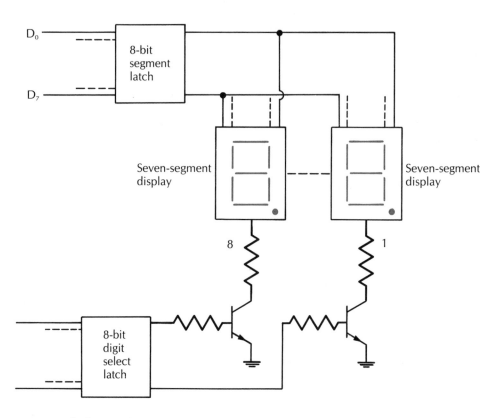

Figure 10.10 Multiplex Interface

than one seven-segment display. In a calculator, for example, there are usually seven or eight digits. An inexpensive method must be found to activate these displays. A common interface used to control a number of seven-segment displays is the *multiplex system*. This uses only two 8-bit latches. One connects to the data bus, as in Figure 10.9 except that its output is connected in parallel to all of the seven-segment displays. The other latch controls each of the displays. Each of the seven-segment displays is turned on sequentially. As each is turned on, it is presented with its segment-control data from the first latch. Various segments light up accordingly. The MPU, under the control of the program, steps from one display to the other and simultaneously sends the 8-bit data to each display. The cycle is repeated rapidly, so that the display appears to be continuous. Figure 10.10 shows the basics of the multiplex interface.

Another arrangement that requires interfacing is keyboard input. Such inputs occur in a wide variety of devices from the simple pocket calculator to the most sophisticated computer. Keyboards can be quite complicated and are often interfaced to the MPU via a *scanning system*. This system generally works on a monitor subroutine wherein the keyboard is scanned. When a key is depressed, its decoded value is stored in an MPU register. The keyboard is scanned rapidly and repeatedly, so that the MPU is in constant contact with all input keys. The scanning method greatly reduces the hardware requirements of the interface circuit.

However, a simple keyboard would not justify scanning and could be interfaced with the simple hardware illustrated in Figure 10.11. In this example, the address decoder must enable the three-state buffer interface before the switches become active. When the switches are depressed, they place a low condition on the data bus. This is transferred to the MPU for processing.

As we have seen in Chapter 6, a problem associated with most mechanical switches is contact bounce: when a switch is activated, the contacts often open and close several times. This is of special concern in fast-acting circuits like those of a microprocessor. To eliminate the effect of the bounce, debouncing circuitry can be placed between the switch and the MPU, as in the circuit used in Experiment 6.6.

Alternatively, the microprocessor itself can be programmed to ignore the effect of the bounce. To do this, a routine is included in the program that calls for a recheck of the switch after a delay of a few milliseconds. If the switch is still in the same state the MPU will respond to the switch condition.

The interface examples we have so far discussed used separate chips to connect to the

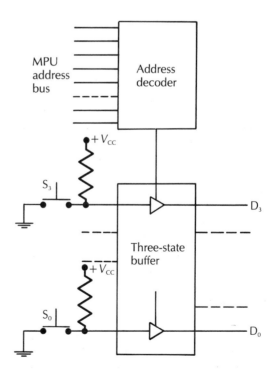

Figure 10.11 Simple Keyboard Interface

MPU. However, any external device — any *peripheral* — can be tied to the MPU using conventional combinational logic. A complex system of peripherals would require many chips, which would complicate the hardware. Therefore, space efficiency and simplicity, with discrete components and wiring kept to an absolute minimum, are the goals of system design. Designers have satisfied these goals by producing chips that contain all or nearly all of the logic required for peripheral interfacing. These chips — known as *peripheral interface adapters* or PIAs — are often designed as companions to a certain microprocessor. One such adapter is the Motorola 6820, which was designed as a support chip for the 6800 MPU. The 6820 is also used in other designs with other MPUs. It is flexible enough to fit in with other systems where there is compatibility between data, address, and control buses. Figure 10.12 shows the basic parts of the 6820 PIA and illustrates how it interfaces between the MPU and the peripheral device.

We see that the PIA ties to the MPU via an 8-bit data bus that can transfer information both ways. The chip is also connected to the MPU's address bus. It uses five of the sixteen address bus lines for its control. It also connects to the MPU control bus where five lines are used.

The PIA has two output sections which are bidirectional. Buffers A and B can act as data output ports or input ports. Thus the PIA offers a high degree of flexibility in tying the MPU to the peripherals. The PIA allows the MPU to deal with its peripherals as if they were simple memory addresses. This frees the MPU from the peripheral. The generally slow data from the peripheral is held in the PIA registers and later transferred to the high-speed MPU when it is ready to accept it.

The A and B sections of the 6820 chips each contain three registers. One is called the control register. It has an address of its own and can be written into, or read directly, by the

MPU. On instructions from the MPU, the control registers set up the chip for the correct direction of data transmission. The other two registers together form the data direction register. As its name implies, this register sets up the data lines either to send data to the peripheral or to receive data from it. We could, for example, program the MPU to call for side A to act as an output while side B acts as an input.

The output registers are used to hold data bytes being transferred to the peripheral data bus. These registers act as temporary storage locations in the PIA chips. Once the chip is *initialized* (set up) for a certain mode of data

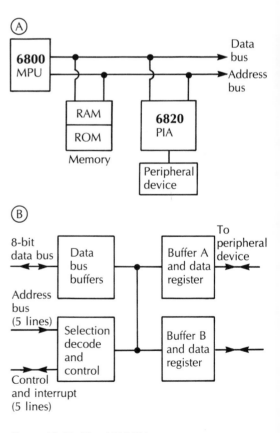

Figure 10.12 The 6820 PIA

transfer, the peripheral data lines can be put in direct contact with the MPU under the control of the program. For example, if side A is set as an output port, the MPU can send an 8-bit byte to it by a store (STAA) instruction. Similarly, if side B is set as an input so as to receive data from a peripheral, the MPU would read from it directly with a load (LDAA) instruction. Figure 10.13 illustrates the internal registers we have been discussing.

In addition to the registers that accommodate the bidirectional flow of data, the chip has an array of control, address, and interrupt lines. The chip is addressed by connecting to

five of the MPU address bus lines. Three of these lines select the PIA. The remaining two select the side A and side B registers that are to be either written into or read by the MPU. Five control lines are used. One is used to set the read/write state of the chip, another is used to enable the chip, and a third to reset the PIA. The remaining pair are interrupt request (IRQ) lines, one for each side of the A-B ports. These lines act to interrupt the MPU and call for service. The MPU can respond to an interrupt request through a software (program) routine. It can also do so on a priority basis under the control of priority circuitry. Simply stated, this

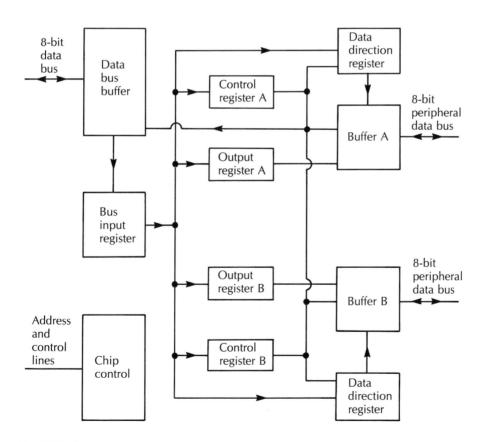

Figure 10.13 PIA Register

means that certain peripherals can be ignored until the MPU completes its handling of more important connected devices.

The PIA must also be synchronized with the MPU. This is achieved through the clock pulses. The system clock is connected to the enable pin of the chip. All internal chip functions are referenced to the clock.

We have looked at the 6820 PIA in a rather general way, with many details left out. We should, however, have an appreciation of both the purpose and the power of this chip. When the PIA is to be used for a specific application, the manufacturer's data sheets must be consulted for its electrical and physical characteristics.

Analog Interfacing

Another important type of interfacing is *analog*. Analog interfaces connect the MPU to peripherals that are non-digital. The detection and measurement of light, temperature, pressure, and vibration often calls for this type of interfacing.

If a computer is to respond to analog signals, the signals must be translated or converted into equivalent digital data. Similarly, if digital data are to be delivered to an analog device they must be converted from their binary form.

There are literally hundreds of situations wherein digital data must be changed to an analog or continuous form. Consider the drive of a pen recorder, where digital data from the computer is translated into a continuous graph on paper. This calls for the position of a stylus to be directly related to the binary data from the MPU.

A more sophisticated example is a robot. Robots are controlled by small servo motors. The positions and torques of the motors are controlled by digital data generated by the program. Such devices get their control currents via a digital-to-analog (D/A) converter. Many chips on the market are designed for this type of interfacing.

The opposite process occurs when analog data must be fed into an MPU. In a temperature monitor, a thermocouple is used to sense the temperature. The device then produces an output voltage that is more or less proportional to the temperature. This voltage is applied to an analog-to-digital (A/D) converter where its intensity is translated into some form of output that can be recognized by the MPU. One possibility is an A/D converter that produces a train of serial data when the temperature (voltage) reaches a certain level. The microprocessor would read and respond to this data, and signal the appropriate action.

Figure 10.14 shows a basic arrangement used to convert digital data from an MPU into analog data at the output of an op amp. This circuit can be programmed to step the output voltage up or down. This can be done in a number of steps determined by the MPU data. When the rise or fall of the output signal is broken down into a large number of steps, its change can appear to be nearly linear. This conversion circuit could be used for any number of devices. One application might be the control of a stylus on a pen recorder.

The D/A converter used in the figure is a 6-bit device. It produces an output current that is proportional to the binary input. Since the digital input has six lines, there are 64 possible steps in the rise or fall of the output current ($2^6 = 64$). The D/A converter can be programmed via the PIA to produce a slow or fast rise or fall under the control of its 6-bit input data. Actually, a whole range of output variations are possible depending on the program. The rate of change, starting value, and direction of change can all be controlled by the program.

It is clear that interfacing is an important and

wide field of study. Indeed, it is practically an endless topic. Thousands of interfacing situations are possible and whole books have been devoted to the subject. Many of these works deal with specific systems and specific PIAs.

We have seen that every interface is different depending on the peripheral and the microprocessor. However, in a way, every interface is basically the same. Whether the application is simple or complex, it still involves communication and control between the MPU and the working peripheral. This is true of both the simple seven-segment display and the most sophisticated robot.

In conclusion, let us cover the basic concepts of one of the most important applications of computer technology: robotics.

Robotics

Robotics — the design of man-like machines — is one of the most significant results of our advanced technology. Microprocessor chips have made "on board" control of robots a practical reality. No longer scientific toys, robots are now important tools of industry. As the technology grows, so do the capabilities of the robots. Robot arms are now in operation

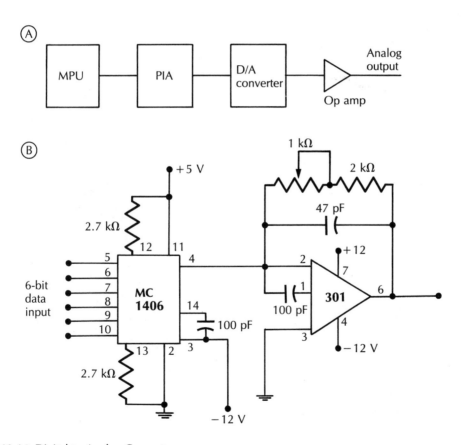

Figure 10.14 Digital-to-Analog Converter

that can handle heavy work such as loading bricks. They also do dangerous work in hostile environments that humans cannot tolerate, such as outer space. As well, today's robots can do precise tasks. With the aid of lasers they scan their work and compare it to a model of the product. If errors are present the control circuit will detect them and reject the piece. They have full-movement accuracy of plus or minus 0.10 mm or better.

As far as the microprocessor is concerned, robots are just interfaces. However, they are complex, because they involve a variety of input and output devices. Motors which control arm movements must be precisely controlled. Similarly, sensors must be connected to feed data back to the microprocessor. They must let it know if the output data has been correctly delivered.

Most robots are designed for specific tasks. The amount of sensing required and the size and accuracy of the control motors and other power apparatus depend on the task. Nevertheless, the basic operating system can be seen as a four-part arrangement: control, sensing, output, and power. The *control* is the microprocessor. In a mobile robot this would be an on-board unit. In stationary robots, such as production-line welders, the microprocessor control could be at a detached centre.

Sensing can take many forms. Distance is often sensed by means of ultrasonics. Sound sensing is sometimes used, whereby a robot is

Courtesy of IBM

designed to respond to voice commands. Miniature radar units are used to detect speed and distance. Force and contact sensing can be done with strain gauges and microswitches. Fibre optics are used where light and colour

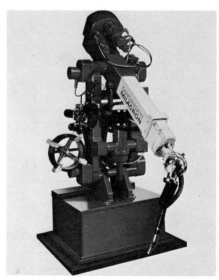

T³-746 Industrial Robot
Courtesy of Cincinnati Milacron, Industrial Robot Division

must be sensed. Servo mechanisms are used to detect position and to control precise movement or rotation. Heat sensors are common in applications such as welding.

Output refers to the way in which the microprocessor data is fed to the robot. Binary

Courtesy of IBM

data from the processor must be converted into a form that is useable by the various control devices. This is usually done through some adaptation of a D/A converter. (The basic principles of such converters were discussed in the previous section.) First the data is converted into an analog form. Then it can be amplified and used to control such devices as motors, relays, stepping switches, hydraulic valves, and pneumatics.

Power refers to the actual motion of the robot or its parts. These requirements vary with application. One example is the robot arm developed by Cincinnati Milacron. It is a general-purpose arm or manipulator that can be used

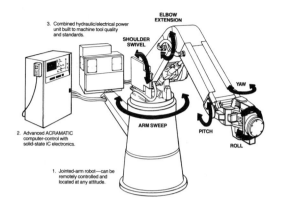

T³-566 Industrial Robot
Courtesy of Cincinnati Milacron, Industrial Robot Division

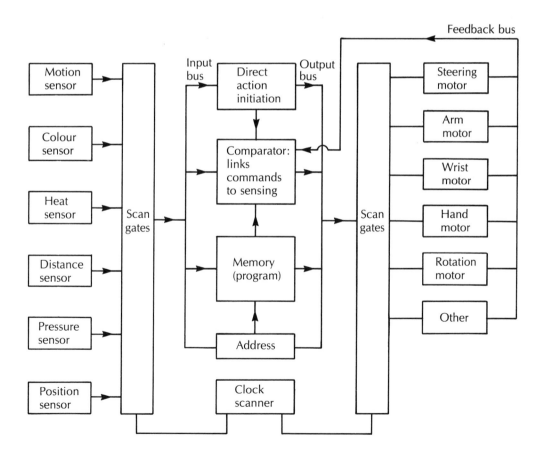

Figure 10.15 Robot "Brain"

for a variety of precise tasks. Loads as heavy as 130 kg can be handled. It has a full range of motion, including horizontal sweep, shoulder and elbow swivel, and wrist pitch, yaw, and roll. The arm uses hydraulic motors and has a microprocessor controller.

It will be appreciated that robot function, accuracy, power, and flexibility depend on a blend of mechanics and electronics. This blend is achieved through sensing and interfacing. Figure 10.15 illustrates a basic arrangement used to interface between a microprocessor and a robot.

This so-called robot "brain" is just the familiar microprocessor interfaced to the power and sensing apparatus of the robot. The microprocessor deals with the robot the same way it would deal with a keyboard and a display or printer. The only difference is in the number of sensors and output devices that must be both controlled and monitored.

Monitoring is done by feedback. For example, if a robot arm is instructed to rotate to a prescribed point, the action must be checked. This verification involves a comparison between the actual position and the position required by the program. A constant flow of sense and feedback data to the microprocessor accomplishes this.

Because of the great variety of apparatus and the many control sequences required, robotics is a major study in itself — and it continues to become more sophisticated. Nevertheless, the field is quickly opening up new opportunities for people trained in digital electronics and microprocessors. Those who understand the basic principles of these disciplines are able to adjust to advances in the technology.

Questions

1. Describe the main functions of the ALU in a microprocessor.
2. Explain the purpose of the PC and stack pointer in a microprocessor.
3. What are the functions of the IR and the instruction decoder in a microprocessor?
4. Explain the meaning of microprocessor architecture.
5. What are the advantages and disadvantages of a single-bus microprocessor?
6. Why is a triple-bus microprocessor faster than the single- or double-bus type?
7. How many address locations can be selected by a 16-line address bus?
8. Why are high- and low-byte memory address registers required in the 6800 microprocessor?
9. What are the advantages and disadvantages of an 8-bit data bus?
10. Describe the fetch, decode, and execute sequence in a microprocessor.
11. Distinguish between op code and address mode in a microprocessor instruction set.
12. If six binary bits are available for op codes, how many codes are possible in the instruction set?
13. Describe the characteristics of inherent mode addressing.
14. Compare immediate mode addressing to inherent mode addressing.
15. How does direct mode addressing differ from inherent mode addressing?
16. Why are op codes generally sent to the microprocessor in hex or some other nonbinary language?
17. Define *machine cycle*. What is the function of the sync pulse during a machine cycle?
18. Define *microinstruction*, relative to the decoder.
19. Why are special circuits called interfaces needed between the microprocessor and connected devices?
20. Explain the need for latches in interface circuits.
21. Refer to Figure 10.10. Explain how the latches turn on each display in sequence.
22. Explain how a microprocessor program can be used to debounce a keyboard.
23. Refer to Figure 10.13 and describe the features of the 6820 PIA.
24. Explain the purpose of a D/A converter.
25. Explain the purpose of an A/D converter.
26. In what way does robotic interfacing differ from other interface situations?
27. Define *robot brain*.
28. Explain the need for feedback in a robot interface.

Appendix A
Chip Data

555 Timer

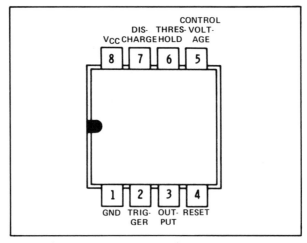

Courtesy of Texas Instruments Incorporated*

functional block diagram

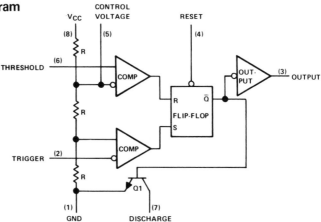

---

recommended operating conditions

	SN52555			SN72555			UNIT
	MIN	NOM	MAX	MIN	NOM	MAX	
Supply voltage, V_{CC}	4.5		18	4.5		16	V
Input voltage, V_I (control voltage, reset, threshold, trigger)			V_{CC}			V_{CC}	V
Output Current, I_O			±200			±200	mA
Operating free-air temperature, T_A	−55		125	0		70	°C

4007 Dual Complementary Pair Plus Inverter

The MC14007UB multi-purpose device consists of three N-channel and three P-channel enhancement mode devices packaged to provide access to each device. These versatile parts are useful in inverter circuits, pulse-shapers, linear amplifiers, high input impedance amplifiers, threshold detectors, transmission gating, and functional gating.

- Quiescent Current = 0.5 nA/package typical @ 5 Vdc
- Noise Immunity = 45% of V_{DD} typical
- Diode Protection on All Inputs
- Supply Voltage Range = 3.0 Vdc to 18 Vdc
- Single Supply Operation = Positive or Negative
- Symmetrical Output Impedance — 200 ohms typical @ 10 Vdc
- Capable of Driving Two Low-power TTL Loads, One Low-power Schottky TTL Load or Two HTL Loads Over the Rated Temperature Range
- Pin-for-Pin Replacement for CD4007A or CD4007UB

MAXIMUM RATINGS (Voltages referenced to V_{SS})

Rating	Symbol	Value	Unit
DC Supply Voltage	V_{DD}	-0.5 to +18	Vdc
Input Voltage All Inputs	V_{in}	-0.5 to V_{DD} + 0.5	Vdc
DC Current Drain per Pin	I	10	mAdc
Operating Temperature Range — AL Device CL/CP Device	T_A	-55 to +125 −40 to +85	°C
Storage Temperature Range	T_{stg}	-65 to +150	°C

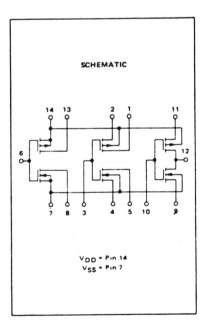

SCHEMATIC

V_{DD} = Pin 14
V_{SS} = Pin 7

Courtesy of Motorola, Inc.

7400 NAND Gate

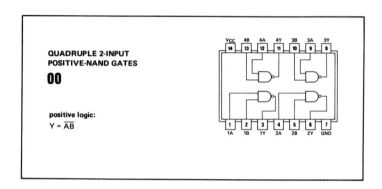

QUADRUPLE 2-INPUT
POSITIVE-NAND GATES

00

positive logic:
$Y = \overline{AB}$

recommended operating conditions

		54 FAMILY 74 FAMILY	SERIES 54 SERIES 74			UNIT
			'00, '04, '10, '20, '30			
			MIN	NOM	MAX	
Supply voltage, V_{CC}		54 Family	4.5	5	5.5	V
		74 Family	4.75	5	5.25	
High-level output current, I_{OH}		54 Family			−400	μA
		74 Family			−400	
Low-level output current, I_{OL}		54 Family			16	mA
		74 Family			16	
Operating free-air temperature, T_A		54 Family	−55		125	°C
		74 Family	0		70	

7402 NOR Gate

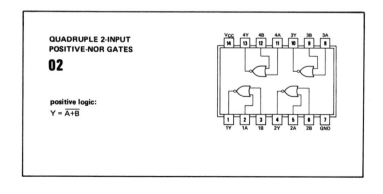

QUADRUPLE 2-INPUT
POSITIVE-NOR GATES

02

positive logic:
$Y = \overline{A+B}$

recommended operating conditions

	54 FAMILY	SERIES 54						UNIT
	74 FAMILY	SERIES 74						
		'02			'25, '27			
		MIN	NOM	MAX	MIN	NOM	MAX	
Supply voltage, V_{CC}	54 Family	4.5	5	5.5	4.5	5	5.5	V
	74 Family	4.75	5	5.25	4.75	5	5.25	
High-level output current, I_{OH}	54 Family			−400			−800	μA
	74 Family			−400			−800	
Low-level output current, I_{OL}	54 Family			16			16	mA
	74 Family			16			16	
Operating free-air temperature, T_A	54 Family	−55		125	−55		125	°C
	74 Family	0		70	0		70	

7404 Inverter

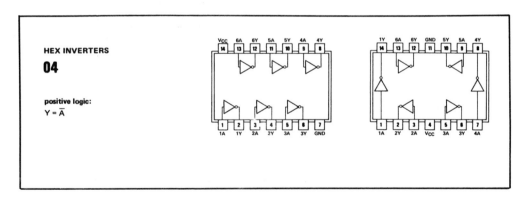

HEX INVERTERS

04

positive logic:

$Y = \overline{A}$

recommended operating conditions

	54 FAMILY	SERIES 54			UNIT
	74 FAMILY	SERIES 74			
		'00, '04, '10, '20, '30			
		MIN	NOM	MAX	
Supply voltage, V_{CC}	54 Family	4.5	5	5.5	V
	74 Family	4.75	5	5.25	
High-level output current, I_{OH}	54 Family			−400	μA
	74 Family			−400	
Low-level output current, I_{OL}	54 Family			16	mA
	74 Family			16	
Operating free-air temperature, T_A	54 Family	−55		125	°C
	74 Family	0		70	

7408 AND Gate

QUADRUPLE 2-INPUT
POSITIVE-AND GATES

08

positive logic:

Y = AB

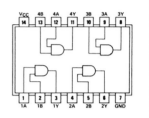

recommended operating conditions

		54 FAMILY	SERIES 54			UNIT
		74 FAMILY	SERIES 74			
			'08,			
			MIN	NOM	MAX	
Supply Voltage, V_{CC}		54 Family	4.5	5	5.5	V
		74 Family	4.75	5	5.25	
High-level output current, I_{OH}					−800	µA
Low-level output current, I_{OL}		54 Family			16	mA
		74 Family			16	
Operating free-air temperature, T_A		54 Family	−55		125	°C
		74 Family	0		70	

7432 OR Gate

QUADRUPLE 2-INPUT
POSITIVE-OR GATES

32

positive logic:

Y = A+B

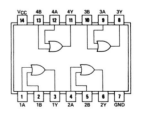

recommended operating conditions

	54 FAMILY 74 FAMILY	SERIES 54 SERIES 74			UNIT
		'32			
		MIN	NOM	MAX	
Supply voltage, V_{CC}	54 Family	4.5	5	5.5	V
	74 Family	4.75	5	5.25	
High-level output current, I_{OH}				−800	μA
Low-level output current, I_{OL}	54 Family			16	mA
	74 Family			16	
Operating free-air temperature, T_A	54 Family	−55		125	°C
	74 Family	0		70	

7447 BCD-to-Seven-Segment
Decoder-Driver

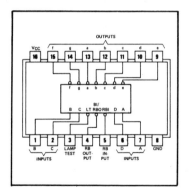

TYPE	DRIVER OUTPUTS				TYPICAL	PACKAGES
	ACTIVE LEVEL	OUTPUT CONFIGURATION	SINK CURRENT	MAX VOLTAGE	POWER DISSIPATION	
SN7446A	low	open-collector	40 mA	30 V	320 mW	J, N
SN7447A	low	open-collector	40 mA	15 V	320 mW	J, N
SN7448	high	2-kΩ pull-up	6.4 mA	5.5 V	265 mW	J, N
SN74L46	low	open-collector	20 mA	30 V	160 mW	J, N
SN74L47	low	open-collector	20 mA	15 V	160 mW	J, N
SN74LS47	low	open-collector	24 mA	15 V	35 mW	J, N
SN74LS48	high	2-kΩ pull-up	6 mA	5.5 V	125 mW	J, N
SN74LS49	high	open-collector	8 mA	5.5 V	40 mW	J, N

7450 AND/OR Inverter

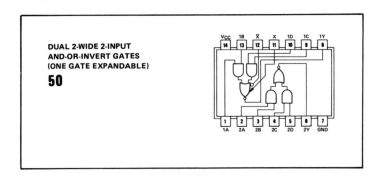

DUAL 2-WIDE 2-INPUT
AND-OR-INVERT GATES
(ONE GATE EXPANDABLE)

50

recommended operating conditions

		54 FAMILY	SERIES 54						UNIT
		74 FAMILY	SERIES 74						
			'23			'50, '53			
			MIN	NOM	MAX	MIN	NOM	MAX	
Supply voltage, V_{CC}		54 Family	4.5	5	5.5	4.5	5	5.5	V
		74 Family	4.75	5	5.25	4.75	5	5.25	
High-level output current, I_{OH}					−800			−400	μA
Low-level output current, I_{OL}		54 Family			16			16	mA
		74 Family			16			16	
Operating free-air temperature range, T_A		54 Family	−55		125	−55		125	°C
		74 Family	0		70	0		70	

7474 D Flip-Flop

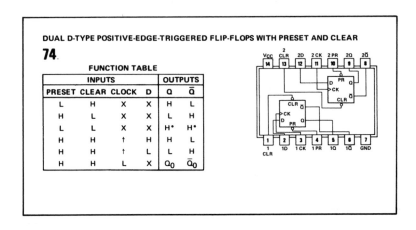

DUAL D-TYPE POSITIVE-EDGE-TRIGGERED FLIP-FLOPS WITH PRESET AND CLEAR

74.

FUNCTION TABLE

INPUTS				OUTPUTS	
PRESET	CLEAR	CLOCK	D	Q	$\bar{Q}$
L	H	X	X	H	L
H	L	X	X	L	H
L	L	X	X	H*	H*
H	H	↑	H	H	L
H	H	↑	L	L	H
H	H	L	X	Q_0	$\bar{Q}_0$

recommended operating conditions

		SERIES 54/74			'70			'72, '73, '76, '107			'74			UNIT
			MIN	NOM	MAX	MIN	NOM	MAX	MIN	NOM	MAX			
Supply voltage, V_{CC}	Series 54		4.5	5	5.5	4.5	5	5.5	4.5	5	5.5			V
	Series 74		4.75	5	5.25	4.75	5	5.25	4.75	5	5.25			
High-level output current, I_{OH}					−400			−400			−400			µA
Low-level output current, I_{OL}					16			16			16			mA
Pulse width, t_W	Clock high				20			20			30			
	Clock low				30			47			37			ns
	Preset or clear low				25			25			30			
Input setup time, t_{su}					20†			0†			20†			ns
Input hold time, t_h					5†			0↓			5†			ns
Operating free-air temperature, T_A	Series 54		−55		125	−55		125	−55		125			°C
	Series 74		0		70	0		70	0		70			

7475 Quad Latch

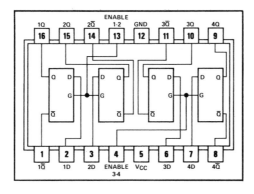

absolute maximum ratings over operating free-air temperature range (unless otherwise noted)

Supply voltage, V_{CC} (see Note 1) . . . . 7 V
Input voltage: '75, 'L75, '77, 'L77 . . . . 5.5 V
                'LS75, 'LS77 . . . . 7 V
Interemitter voltage (see Note 2) . . . . 5.5 V
Operating free-air temperature range: SN54', SN54L', SN54LS' Circuits . . . . −55°C to 125°C
                             SN74', SN74L', SN74LS' Circuits . . . . 0°C to 70°C
Storage temperature range . . . . −65°C to 150°C

NOTES: 1. Voltage values, except interemitter voltage, are with respect to network ground terminal.
          2. This is the voltage between two emitters of a multiple-emitter input transistor and is not applicable to the 'LS75 and 'LS77.

7476 JK Flip-Flop

DUAL J-K FLIP-FLOPS WITH PRESET AND CLEAR

76

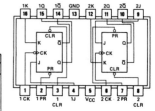

'76, 'H76
FUNCTION TABLE

INPUTS					OUTPUTS	
PRESET	CLEAR	CLOCK	J	K	Q	$\bar{Q}$
L	H	X	X	X	H	L
H	L	X	X	X	L	H
L	L	X	X	X	H*	H*
H	H	⊓	L	L	Q_0	$\bar{Q}_0$
H	H	⊓	H	L	H	L
H	H	⊓	L	H	L	H
H	H	⊓	H	H	TOGGLE	

'LS76A
FUNCTION TABLE

INPUTS					OUTPUTS	
PRESET	CLEAR	CLOCK	J	K	Q	$\bar{Q}$
L	H	X	X	X	H	L
H	L	X	X	X	L	H
L	L	X	X	X	H*	H*
H	H	↓	L	L	Q_0	$\bar{Q}_0$
H	H	↓	H	L	H	L
H	H	↓	L	H	L	H
H	H	↓	H	H	TOGGLE	
H	H	H	X	X	Q_0	$\bar{Q}_0$

recommended operating conditions

		SERIES 54/74	'70			'72, '73, '76, '107			UNIT
			MIN	NOM	MAX	MIN	NOM	MAX	
Supply voltage, V_{CC}		Series 54	4.5	5	5.5	4.5	5	5.5	V
		Series 74	4.75	5	5.25	4.75	5	5.25	
High-level output current, I_{OH}					−400			−400	μA
Low-level output current, I_{OL}					16			16	mA
Pulse width, t_w	Clock high		20			20			ns
	Clock low		30			47			
	Preset or clear low		25			25			
Input setup time, t_{su}			20↑			0↑			ns
Input hold time, t_h			5↑			0↓			ns
Operating free-air temperature, T_A		Series 54	−55		125	−55		125	°C
		Series 74	0		70	0		70	

7483 Full-Adder

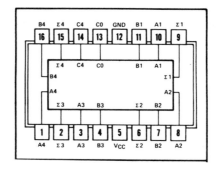

absolute maximum ratings over operating free-air temperature range (unless otherwise noted)

Supply voltage, V_{CC} (see Note 1) . . . . 7 V
Input voltage: '83A . . . . 5.5 V
              'LS83A . . . . 7 V
Interemitter voltage (see Note 2) . . . . 5.5 V
Operating free-air temperature range: SN5483A, SN54LS83A . . . . −55°C to 125°C
                            SN7483A, SN74LS83A . . . . 0°C to 70°C
Storage temperature range . . . . −65°C to 150°C

NOTES: 1. Voltage values, except interemitter voltage, are with respect to network ground terminal.
           2. This is the voltage between two emitters of a multiple-emitter transistor. This rating applies for the '83A only between the following pairs: A1 and B1, A2 and B2, A3 and B3, A4 and B4.

7484 16-Bit RAM

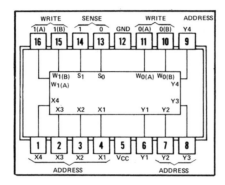

logic diagram

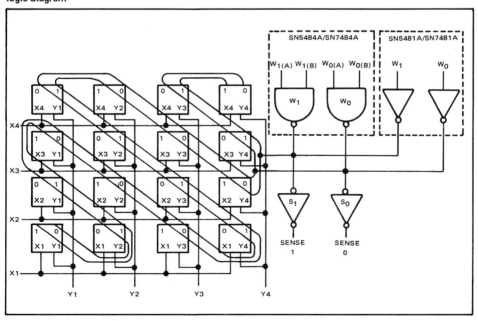

recommended operating conditions

	SN5481A, SN5484A			SN7481A, SN7484A			UNIT
	MIN	NOM	MAX	MIN	NOM	MAX	
Supply voltage, V_{CC}	4.5	5	5.5	4.75	5	5.25	V
High-level output voltage, V_{OH}			5.5			5.5	V
Low-level output current, I_{OL}			20			40	mA
Width of write pulse, $t_{w(write)}$ (see Figure 1)	20			20			ns
Address input setup time, t_{setup} (see Figure 1)	0			0			ns
Operating free-air temperature, T_A	−55		125	0		70	°C

7486 XOR Gate

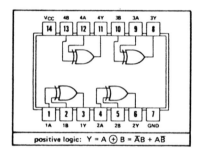

positive logic: $Y = A \oplus B = \overline{A}B + A\overline{B}$

recommended operating conditions

	SN5486			SN7486			UNIT
	MIN	NOM	MAX	MIN	NOM	MAX	
Supply voltage, V_{CC}	4.5	5	5.5	4.75	5	5.25	V
High-level output current, I_{OH}			−800			−800	μA
Low-level output current, I_{OL}			16			16	mA
Operating free-air temperature, T_A	−55		125	0		70	°C

7490 Decade Counter

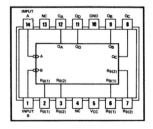

recommended operating conditions

		SN5490A, SN5492A SN5493A			SN7490A, SN7492A SN7493A			UNIT
		MIN	NOM	MAX	MIN	NOM	MAX	
Supply voltage, V_{CC}		4.5	5	5.5	4.75	5	5.25	V
High-level output current, I_{OH}				−800			−800	μA
Low-level output current, I_{OL}				16			16	mA
Count frequency, f_{count} (see Figure 1)	A input	0		32	0		32	MHz
	B input	0		16	0		16	
Pulse width, t_w	A input	15			15			
	B input	30			30			ns
	Reset inputs	15			15			
Reset inactive-state setup time, t_{su}		25			25			ns
Operating free-air temperature, T_A		−55		125	0		70	°C

7493 Binary Counter

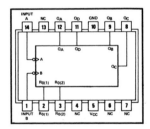

recommended operating conditions

		SN5490A, SN5492A SN5493A			SN7490A, SN7492A SN7493A			UNIT
		MIN	NOM	MAX	MIN	NOM	MAX	
Supply voltage, V_{CC}		4.5	5	5.5	4.75	5	5.25	V
High-level output current, I_{OH}				−800			−800	μA
Low-level output current, I_{OL}				16			16	mA
Count frequency, f_{count} (see Figure 1)	A input	0		32	0		32	MHz
	B input	0		16	0		16	
Pulse width, t_w	A input	15			15			
	B input	30			30			ns
	Reset inputs	15			15			
Reset inactive-state setup time, t_{su}		25			25			ns
Operating free-air temperature, T_A		−55		125	0		70	°C

7496 Shift Register

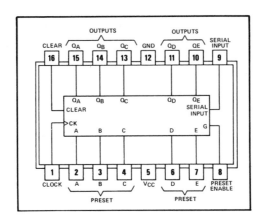

recommended operating conditions

	SN5496			SN7496			UNIT
	MIN	NOM	MAX	MIN	NOM	MAX	
Supply voltage, V_{CC}	4.5	5	5.5	4.75	5	5.25	V
High-level output current, I_{OH}			−400			−400	μA
Low-level output current, I_{OL}			16			16	mA
Clock frequency, f_{clock}	0		10	0		10	MHz
Width of clock input pulse, $t_{w(clock)}$	35			35			ns
Width of preset and clear input pulse, t_w	30			30			ns
Serial input setup time, t_{su} (see Figure 1)	30			30			ns
Serial input hold time, t_h (see Figure 1)	0			0			ns
Operating free-air temperature, T_A	−55		125	0		70	°C

74125 Three-State Buffer
(Low Enable)

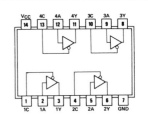

QUADRUPLE BUS BUFFER GATES WITH THREE-STATE OUTPUTS

125

positive logic:

Y = A

Output is off (disabled) when C is high.

recommended operating conditions

	54 FAMILY	SERIES 54			SERIES 54LS			SERIES 54S			
	74 FAMILY	SERIES 74			SERIES 74LS			SERIES 74S			
		'125, '126, '425, '426			'LS125A, 'LS126A			'S134			UNIT
		MIN	NOM	MAX	MIN	NOM	MAX	MIN	NOM	MAX	
Supply voltage, V_{CC}	54 Family	4.5	5	5.5	4.5	5	5.5	4.5	5	5.5	V
	74 Family	4.75	5	5.25	4.75	5	5.25	4.75	5	5.25	
High-level output current, I_{OH}	54 Family			−2			−1			−2	mA
	74 Family			−5.2			−2.6			−6.5	
Low-level output current, I_{OL}	54 Family			16			12			20	mA
	74 Family			16			24			20	
Operating free-air temperature, T_A	54 Family	−55		125	−55		125	−55		125	°C
	74 Family	0		70	0		70	0		70	

74126 Three-State Buffer
(High Enable)

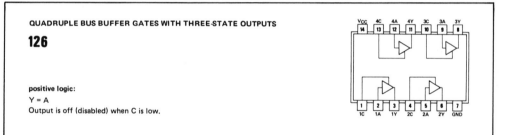

QUADRUPLE BUS BUFFER GATES WITH THREE-STATE OUTPUTS

126

positive logic:
Y = A
Output is off (disabled) when C is low.

(For recommended operating conditions see table for 74125 buffer.)

74190 Decade Up-Down Counter

- Counts 8-4-2-1 BCD or Binary
- Single Down/Up Count Control Line
- Count Enable Control Input
- Ripple Clock Output for Cascading
- Asynchronously Presettable with Load Control
- Parallel Outputs
- Cascadable for n-Bit Applications

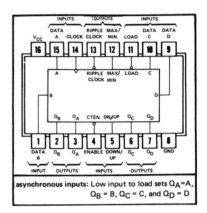

asynchronous inputs: Low input to load sets $Q_A = A$, $Q_B = B$, $Q_C = C$, and $Q_D = D$

TYPE	AVERAGE PROPAGATION DELAY	TYPICAL MAXIMUM CLOCK FREQUENCY	TYPICAL POWER DISSIPATION
'190, '191	20 ns	25 MHz	325 mW
'LS190, 'LS191	20 ns	25 MHz	100 mW

recommended operating conditions

	SN54190, SN54191			SN74190, SN74191			UNIT
	MIN	NOM	MAX	MIN	NOM	MAX	
Supply voltage, V_{CC}	4.5	5	5.5	4.75	5	5.25	V
High-level output current, I_{OH}			−800			−800	μA
Low-level output current, I_{OL}			16			16	mA
Input clock frequency, f_{clock}	0		20	0		20	MHz
Width of clock input pulse, $t_{w(clock)}$	25			25			ns
Width of load input pulse, $t_{w(load)}$	35			35			ns
Data setup time, t_{setup} (See Figures 1 and 2)	20			20			ns
Data hold time, t_{hold}	0			0			ns
Operating free-air temperature, T_A	−55		125	0		70	°C

Appendix B
Common Resistor Colour Code System

COLOUR	NUMBER
BLACK	0
BROWN	1
RED	2
ORANGE	3
YELLOW	4
GREEN	5
BLUE	6
VIOLET	7
GREY	8
WHITE	9
GOLD	÷ 10
SILVER	÷ 100

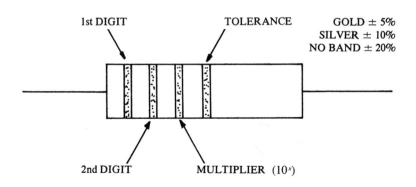

1st DIGIT TOLERANCE GOLD ± 5%
SILVER ± 10%
NO BAND ± 20%

2nd DIGIT MULTIPLIER (10^x)

Appendix C

American Standard Code for Information Interchange (ASCII)

	000	001	010	011	100	101	110	111
0000	NULL	①DC_0		0	@	P		
0001	SOM	DC_1	!	1	A	Q		
0010	EOA	DC_2	''	2	B	R		
0011	EOM	DC_3	#	3	C	S		
0100	EOT	DC_4	$	4	D	T		
0101	WRU	(Stop) ERR	%	5	E	U		
0110	RU	SYNC	&	6	F	V		
0111	BELL	LEM	'	7	G	W		
1000	FE_0	S_0	(	8	H	X	Unassigned	
1001	HT SK	S_1	)	9	I	Y		
1010	LF	S_2	*	:	J	Z		
1011	V_{TAB}	S_3	+	;	K	[		
1100	FF	S_4	,	<	L	\		ACK
1101	CR	S_5	–	=	M	]		②
1110	SO	S_6	*	>	N	↑		ESC
1111	SI	S_7	/	?	O	←		DEL

Glossary

Access time: For a coincident-current memory, the time required for one read/write cycle. In general, access time is the time required to write one word into memory or to read one word from memory.

Accumulator: A register that combines the data from other registers.

A/D conversion: The process of converting an analog input voltage to a number of equivalent digital output levels.

Address: A series of binary digits used to specify the location of a word stored in memory.

Address register: A register that stores the binary data used to select the next address in memory.

Algorithm: A series of operations in which the result of each step is used in the next step.

Alphanumeric information: Information composed of the letters of the alphabet, numerals, and special characters.

Analog interfacing: Intermediate hardware that translates binary data from the MPU into continuously variable (analog) data or vice versa.

AND gate: An all-or-nothing gate: the output is a 1 only when all the inputs are 1s.

And-or network: A group of AND gates whose outputs drive a single OR gate.

American Standard Code for Information Interchange: The most widely used alphanumeric code.

ASCII: See American Standard Code for Information Interchange.

Astable MV: A flip-flop that regularly changes its state with no input control.

Asynchronous system: A system in which logic operations and level changes occur at random times.

Bar matrix: A display using bars or segments. The seven-segment indicator is an example.

Base: The number of digits or basic symbols in a number system. The decimal system has a base of ten because it uses ten digits. (Also called *radix*.)

Barrier potential: The voltage created at the interface of a PN junction due to the diffusion of charge from N to P.

Base ten system: A number system wherein each column has ten times the value of the preceding column as we move from right to left.

Base two system: A number system wherein each column has twice the value of the preceding column as we move from right to left.

BCD: Abbreviation for *binary-coded decimal*.

BCD counter: The binary-coded-decimal counter, which converts binary numbers to their equivalent decimal form.

Binary: Having only two possible alternatives.

Binary coding: A system wherein binary digits are grouped to represent the digits of a number in another base.

Binary number system: A number system using only two digits: 0 and 1.

Bistable MV: A flip-flop that has two stable states.

Bit: An abbreviated form of the term *binary digit*. Instead of saying 10110 has five binary digits, we can say it has five bits.

Boolean algebra: An algebra invented by George Boole. It is the main tool used in analyzing and designing digital circuits. (Also called *symbolic logic*.)

Bootstrap program: A ROM programmed to start up the computer in a specified way so its initial condition is constant.

Buffer register: A group of memory elements, or flip-flops, that can store a binary word.

Bus: A group of wires used as a common transmission path by many registers and other digital circuits.

Byte: Eight bits.

Carry bit: The leftmost bit in the sum when the one's complement method of subtraction is used.

Clock: A circuit that produces a chain of output pulses used to control other circuits.

Clock cycle time: One clock period. The reciprocal of clock frequency.

Complement method of binary subtraction: A method of subtraction done by an addition process.

Covalent bonding: The orderly formation of outer-orbit electrons in pure silicon such that the electrons are not free to contribute to a current flow in the crystal.

D/A conversion: The process of converting a number of digital input signals to one equivalent analog output voltage.

Data: A set of numbers or other information that goes into a computer before calculation begins.

Data register: A register that temporarily stores binary data from the data line.

Decade counter: A counter that counts input pulses from 0 to 9, then recycles and repeats the count.

D flip-flop: A flip-flop that transfers input data to its output under control of a clock pulse.

Digit: A basic symbol used in a number system. The decimal system has ten digits, 0 through 9.

Diode: A device that allows current flow in one direction only.

Doping: A process whereby impurity atoms are added to pure silicon to allow it to act as a conductor.

DRO: Abbreviation for *destructive readout*.

Dynamic memory: A memory whose contents must be restored periodically.

8421 Code: The most popular BCD code. Each decimal digit is changed into its binary equivalent.

End-around carry: A binary 1 carry bit in the sum of one's complement subtraction. This carry bit is added to the first sum to yield the correct binary sum.

EPROM: Abbreviation for *erasable programmable read-only memory*.

Flip-flop circuits: Circuits that switch between two states which represent binary 0 and binary 1.

Floppy: A magnetic-disc storage unit.

Forward bias: The external voltage across a junction such that the barrier potential is overcome.

Frequency divider: A flip-flop system used to convert an input pulse chain at one frequency to sub-multiples of that frequency.

Full-adder: A logic circuit with three inputs and two outputs. The circuit adds three bits at a time, giving a sum and a carry output.

Gate: A device with one output and two or more inputs. It is designed so that there is an output only for certain combinations of input signals.

Half-adder: A logic circuit with two inputs and two outputs.

Half-subtractor: A two-input, two-output logic circuit. It subtracts one binary digit from another.

Hex: *See* Hexadecimal.

Hexadecimal: Refers to the number system with a base of 16. For its digits, the system uses the symbols 0 through 9 and A through F. Often abbreviated *hex*.

Hysteresis: Derived from the Greek word *husterein*, which means to lag behind.

Hysteresis loop: Generally, a plot of magnetic flux, density B versus magnetic force H.

Instruction decoder: A microprocessor logic section that translates binary instructions and directs the operations performed by the microprocessor.

Inverter: A NOT circuit. Also called *complementing* or *negating circuit*.

JK flip-flop: A form of RST flip-flop that toggles or alternates between its two output states when pulses are applied to the clock line and the J and K lines are held at binary 1.

Junction transistor: A three-part silicon crystal with a thin centre section that is doped oppositely to the two end sections.

Karnaugh map: A simplified way of displaying the fundamental products corresponding to a truth table.

Large-scale integration: The family of ICs that contain tens of thousands of components.

Least significant bit: The rightmost bit in a number.

LED: See Light-emitting diode.

Light-emitting diode: A junction diode that emits electromagnetic radiation when a current flows in it.

Liquid crystal: A state of matter between solid and liquid. In the absence of an electric field, the long molecules are aligned and the liquid is transparent. When an electric field is present, the molecules scatter and the liquid appears milky white.

Logic circuit: Any digital circuit that can be analyzed with Boolean algebra.

Look-up table: A ROM programmed with fixed data such as trigonometric functions.

LSB: See Least significant bit.

LSI: See Large-scale integration.

Main memory: Bulk memory external to the computer.

Master-slave flip-flop: A clocked RS (or JK) flip-flop composed of two individual flip-flops wired in such a way as to avoid race-around.

Medium-scale integration: The family of ICs whose complexity is comparable to that of logic circuits with 12 to 100 gates.

Memory cycle: In a coincident-current memory system, a read operation followed by a write operation.

Microprocessor: An integrated circuit that includes the arithmetic and control sections of a computer.

Modulus: The number of states through which a given counter can progress.

Monostable MV: A flip-flop that has one stable state. When it is switched from that state it will automatically return to it.

Most significant bit: The leftmost bit in a number.

MPU: Abbreviation for *microprocessor unit.*

MSB: See Most significant bit.

MSI: See Medium-scale integration.

Multiplexer: An electronic switch that connects its output to one of several inputs on a rotation basis.

MV: Abbreviation for *multivibrator.* See Astable MV; Bistable MV; and Monostable MV.

NAND gate: An AND gate followed by a NOT circuit. Sometimes called *NOT-AND gate.*

NDRO: Abbreviation for *nondestructive readout.*

Negative edge triggering: The control of a flip-flop on the falling edge of the clock pulse.

Nibble: Four bits.

Nine's complement: The number obtained when a given decimal number is subtracted from its next higher power minus 1.

NOR gate: An OR gate followed by a NOT circuit. Sometimes called *NOT-OR gate.*

NOT circuit: A circuit that inverts or complements the input signal; it makes 1s out of 0s, and vice versa.

N-type silicon: A pure silicon crystal to which arsenic atoms have been added.

Octal: Refers to the number system with a base of 8. For its digits, the system normally uses the symbols 0, 1, 2, 3, 4, 5, 6, and 7.

One's complement: The opposite set of digits for a given binary number. All zeros become 1s and all 1s zeros.

Op amp: An operational amplifier — a high-gain differential amplifier that uses voltage feedback to provide a stabilized voltage gain.

OR gate: An any-or-all gate. It has a 1 output if any or all of its inputs are 1s.

Oscillator: A free-running source of electronic pulses.

Overflow: The act of exceeding the capacity of a storage register.

Parallel binary addition: Binary addition which takes place in a circuit that accepts all the digits to be added simultaneously.

Parallel counter: A synchronous counter in which all flip-flops change state simultaneously because all clock inputs are simultaneously driven by the clock.

Parallel entry shift register: A system of flip-flops wherein binary input data is entered into all stages at once.

Parity bit: A bit deliberately attached to a group of bits to make the total number of 1s either even or odd.

Peripheral interface adapter: A companion chip to an MPU, that handles external input and output data from peripheral devices.

PN junction: A silicon crystal with one part doped N and the other part doped P.

Positive edge triggering: The control of a flip-flop on the rising edge of the clock pulse.

Positive Logic: The feature of a circuit wherein 1 stands for the more positive of the two voltage levels.

Program: A set of instructions entered into a computer before the start of a calculation.

Programmable logic array: The logic system of an MPU decoder which translates the instructions on the data bus.

PROM: Abbreviation for *programmable read-only memory*.

Propagation delay: The amount of time it takes for the output to change states after an input is applied.

P-type silicon: A pure silicon crystal to which indium atoms have been added.

Race-around: The inability to determine the output of a gate when the inputs to the gate are making simultaneous transitions.

Radix: See Base.

RAM: Abbreviation for *Random-access memory*.

Recomplementation: The reversing process that returns a number complement to its true value.

Register: A circuit that holds or remembers binary digits.

Register capacity: Determined by the number of flip-flops in the register. There must be one flip-flop for each binary bit.

Resistor-transistor logic: A family of logic circuits that uses resistors and transistors.

Reverse bias: The external voltage across a junction such that the barrier potential is reinforced.

Ring counter: A basic shift register with direct feedback. It is designed so the contents of the register simply circulate around the register when the clock is running.

Ripple counter: An asynchronous counter in which each flip-flop is triggered by the output of the previous flip-flop.

ROM: Abbreviation for *read-only memory*.

RST flip-flop: A flip-flop with three modes of control: it can be set, reset, or toggled. When R and S are at 0, pulses on the T line cause the flip-flop to alternate between its two output states.

RTL: See Resistor-transistor logic.

Schmitt trigger: A form of flip-flop circuit that switches its condition at a specified input trigger voltage.

Shift register: A group of flip-flops connected in such a way that a binary number can be shifted into or out of the flip-flops.

Sign bit: The leftmost binary bit in a number, which is used to indicate the sign of the number. Usually, a sign bit of 1 indicates a negative number and one of 0 a positive number.

Sequence generator: A system of flip-flops that recycles its stored data. The data is presented as an output and is replaced continuously.

Serial binary addition: Addition which takes place in a circuit that accepts the digits to be added one at a time.

Small-scale integration: The family of ICs whose complexity is comparable to that of logic circuits with fewer than 12 gates.

SSI: See Small-scale integration.

Stack: A register used to store the binary data that selects the next address in memory.

Static memory: A memory capable of storing binary information indefinitely.

Switch debouncer: A flip-flop circuit used to make a switch respond to the first closure of a switch only, ignoring multiple contact closure or bounce.

Symmetrical triggering: Binary pulses on a single control line that cause a flip-flop to change its state each time a pulse is applied.

Synchronous system: A system in which logic operations and level changes occur in synchronism with a system clock.

Ten's complement: The number obtained when a given decimal number is subtracted from its next higher power.

Tesla: A unit of magnetic induction, equal to one weber per square metre.

Three-state gate: A logic gate whose output can be low, high, or floating.

Toggle: The action of a flip-flop in triggering into the opposite state.

Totem-pole output: A pair of output transistors often used in the 7400 series ICs to provide a low output impedance in either state.

Transistor-transistor logic: A family of logic circuits that uses multiple-emitter transistors in conjunction with other circuit components.

Truth table: A list of all possible input-output combinations for a given logic circuit.

TTL: *See* Transistor-transistor logic.

Two-phase clock: The timing system using two clock waveforms of the same frequency but 180° out of phase with one another; for example, the 1 and 0 outputs of a flip-flop.

Two's complement: The binary number obtained when a given binary number is changed to its one's complement and binary 1 is added to the result.

Up-down counter: A basic counter, either serial or parallel, which is capable of counting either up or down.

Volatile: A memory unit is *volatile* if it loses its contents when electrical power is cut off.

Voltage comparator: A circuit that detects when an input voltage crosses certain levels.

Weighted code: A code whose bit positions carry a fixed value, usually given by the name of the code. For instance, the 8421 code has weights of 8, 4, 2, and 1 in the corresponding bit positions.

Word: In a digital system, a group of bits moved as a unit.

Word length: A prescribed maximum number of binary digits used in the storage and transfer of data.

Zero-crossing detector: A modified schmitt trigger that ensures an output wave with equal on-off periods and fast rise and fall times.

Index